Dictionary of co
of garden and

C000093735

French-Engli
With a list of plants that rabbits do not eat readily
and list of words used in the garden

Dictionnaire des noms communs des
plantes du jardin et sauvages
Français-Anglais-Latin
Avec liste des plantes que les lapins ne mangent pas,
et liste des mots du jardin

John J. Wells
Mere House Barn, Mereworth, Maidstone, Kent ME18 5NB
Great Britain
2005

Published by John J. Wells in 2005
Mereworth, Maidstone Kent ME18 5NB Great Britain

The Editor and Publisher thank Patricia de Montblanc,
Roselle Andrews and all others who have helped in
the compilation and painstaking correction.

ISBN 0-9551011-0-7
Printed by Anthony Rowe Ltd.
2 Whittle Drive
Eastbourne BN 23 6QT

Dictionary of the common names of plants
French-English language-Latin

All plants have botanical Latin names. Some plants with French common names do not have English common names and vice versa. The Latin names are given in every case for French or English language common names

Many American, Australian and other Enlish language common names are included in the lists of English common names, some are virtually unknown in Britain and some of these have no French equivalents.

Common names apply rather more to wild flowers than to garden varieties. Some of the English language common names are perhaps a bit whimsey and the French tend to use more Latin names, where this is the case the Latin botanical name is given in the French section.

Where common names are given to two or more species, both are listed. Latin names are changed from time to time by botanical experts, but traditonal common names mostly remain unchanged down the centuries.

Dictionnaire des noms communs de plantes et leur appelllation botanique latine
Français-Anglais-Latin

Chaque plante a son nom botanique en latin.Certaines plantes ayant des noms communs en français n'ont pas d'équivalent en anglais et vice-versa. Leur nom en latin botanique est toujours indiqué en regard de leur équivalent en nom commun français et / ou anglais, lorsqu'il existe.

De nombreux noms communs américains, australiens ou provenant d'autre langues anglophones, sont inclus dans la liste des noms communs anglais, certains sont virtuellement inconnus en Grande-Bretagne, d'autres n'ont pas d'équivalent en français.

Les noms communs s'utilisent plus fréquemment pour les fleurs sauvages que pour les variétés du jardin. Quelque noms communs de langue anglaise peuvent être un peu fantaisiste, les français préfèrent alors utiliser le nom latin, dans ce cas particuliers, le nom latin botanique sera renseigné dans la section française. Quand un nom commun correspond a deux espèces ou plus, elles sont toutes répertoriés. Les expert en botanique changent de temps à autre les noms latins mais la plu part des noms communs restent inchangés au travers des siècles.

Contents

Plantes que les lapins ne mangent pas.
Plants that rabbits do not eat.

Acanthus
Acer
Achillea
Agapanthus
Agastache foeniculum
Ajuga
Alcea rosea (Hollyhock)
Alchemilla mollis
Allium
Andromeda
Anemone
Aqilegia
Arbutus
Artemesia
Aster
Astilbe
Aubretia
Aucuba
Azalea
Ballota
Bamboos
Bergenia
Bluebell
Borago
Buddleia
Buxus
Camellia
Cardiocrinum
Cerastium tomentosum
Chionodoxa
Choisya
Chyrsanthemum max.
Chyrsanthemum Parthenium
Cistus

Clematis
Convalaria
Cornus alba
Cortaderia
Cotoneaster
Crambe cordifolia
Crocosmia
Cyclamen
Daffodil
Daphne
Deutzia
Digitalis
Doronicum
Echinops
Echium
Endymion non-scriptus
Erica
Eryngium
Euonymus
Euphorbia
Fatsia
Feverfew
Fragraria
Fritillaria
Fuchsia
Galanthus
Gaultheria shallon
Gentian sino ornata
Geranium
Glaucium flavum
Grape Hyacinth
Gunnera
Gypsophila
Hemerocallis

Hedera
Hellebore
Helianthemum
Helichrysum
Helenium
Hepatica
Hesperis
Heuchera
Hippophae
Honesty
Hosta
Hyacinth
Hydrangea
Hypericum
Ilex
Iris
Kalmia
Kniphofia
Lamium
Levisticum
Lilium pyrenaicum
Lippia
Liriope muscari
Lonicera
Lunaria
Lychnis chalcedonica
Lysimachia
Mahonia
Malva moschata
Meconopsis
Melissa
Mentha
Mimulus
Mirabilis jalapa

5

Montbretia
Muscari
Myosotis
Narcissus
Nepeta
Nicotiana
Olearia
Origanum marjorana
Omphalodes
Onopordon nervosum
Ophiopogon planiscapus
Osteosperpum
Oxalis
Paeonia
Papaver
Pernettya
Philadelphus
Phlox alpinus
Phormium tenax
Physalis
Polygonatum
Polygonum
Potentilla
Primula
Prunus laurocerasus

Prunus spinosa
Pulmonaria
Ranunculus
Rheum
Rhododendron
Rhus
Ribes
Rosa rugosa
Rosemarinus
Rubus
Ruscus
Sagittaria lancifolia
Santolina
Salvia
Sambucus
Santolina
Saxifraga peltara
Scabiosa
Sedum
Sempervivum
Senecio
Silene
Skimmia
Snow in Summer
Solomon's Seal

Spiraea
Solanum
Solidago
Stachys lanata
Symphoricarpos
Symphytum
Tagetes
Tamarix
Taxus
Teucrium fruiticans
Thalictrum
Thymus
Tulipa
Tradescantia
Trillium
Tritonia
Trollius
Verbena
Verbascum
Viburnum
Vinca
Weigela
Yucca
Zinnia

Mots du jardin

Acide	Acid	Grappe	Bunch /Cluster
Aigre	Sour	Greffe	Bud / Graft /Scion
Aiguille de pin	Pine needle	Grimpant	Climbing
Aimant de terre calcaire	Chalk loving	Jardin	Garden
Annuel	Annual	Jardinier / Jardinière	Gardener
Arbre	Tree	Lac	Lake
Arbuste	Shrub	Marcotage	Layering
Argile	Clay	Marcotage aérienne	Aerial layering
Arrosoir	Watering can	Mare	Stagnant pond
Barrière	Fence	Mauvaise herbe	Weed (noun)
Bassin	Pond (artificial)	Râteau	Rake
Bêche	Spade	Panier	Basket with a handle
Biennal	Biennial	Pelle	Child's spade
Binette	Hoe	Pomme de pin	Pine cone
Brouette	Barrow	Porte	Gate
Bourgeon	Bud	Porte-greffe	Stock
Bourgeonner	Buded	Propager	Propagate
Bouture	Cutting	Racine	Root
Bouture de racine	Root cutting	Rampante	Creeping
Cascade	Waterfall	Rameau	Small branch
Chute d'eau	Waterfall	Ruisseau	Stream
Corbeille	Basket	Sable	Sand
Couronne	Crown	Seau	Bucket / Pail
Craie	Chalk	Serre	Greenhouse / Conservatory
Déplantoir	Trowel	Suçoir	Sucker
Désherber	Weed (verb)	Taille	Cutting
Désherbant	Weed killer	Tailler	Prune
Ébourgeonner	Disbud	Taillis	Copse
Ente	Graft scion	Tamis	Sieve
Étang	Pond (natural)	Terre	Soil
Forcerie	Greenhouse	Terreau	Loam
Fourche	Fork	Tige	Stem / stalk
Haie	Hedge	Tuteur	Stake
Gel	Frost	Vivace	Perennial
Graine	Seed	Vrille	Tendril

Words used in the garden

Acid	Acide
Aerial layering	Marcotage aérienne
Annual	Annuel
Barrow	Brouette
Basket	Corbeille
Basket with a handle	Panier
Biennial	Biennal
Bucket	Seau
Bud	Bourgeon
Bud (propagate)	Greffe
Buded	Bourgeonner
Bunch	Grappe
Chalk	Craie
Chalk loving	Aimant de terre calcaire
Clay	Argile
Climbing	Grimpant
Cluster	Grappe
Conservatory	Serre
Copse	Taillis
Creeping	Rampant
Crown	Couronne
Cutting	Bouture / Taille
Disbud	Ébourgeonner
Fence	Barrière
Fork	Fourche
Frost	Gel
Garden	Jardin
Gardener	Jardinier / Jardinière
Gate	Porte
Graft	Greffe
Greenhouse	Serre / Forcerie
Hedge	Haie
Hoe	Binette
Lake	Lac
Layering	Marcotage
Loam	Terreau / Compost
Pail	Seau
Pine cone	Pomme de pin
Pine needle	Aiguille de pin
Pond (natural)	Étang
Pond (artificial)	Bassin
Propagate	Propager
Perennial	Vivace
Prune	Tailler
Rake	Râteau
Root	Racine
Root cutting	Bouture de racine
Sand	Sable
Scion (Grafting)	Greffe / Ente
Seed	Graine
Shrub	Arbuste
Sieve	Tamis
Soil	Terre
Small branch	Rameau
Sour	Aigre
Spade	Bêche
Spade for child	Pelle
Stake	Tuteur
Stem / stalk	Tige
Stock (Grafting)	Porte-greffe
Stream	Ruisseau
Sucker	Suçoir
Tendril	Vrille
Tree	Arbre
Trowel	Déplantoir
Waterfall	Cascade / Chute d'eau
Watering-can	Arrosoir
Weed	Mauvaise herbe

English	Latin	Français
	A	
Aaron's beard	**Hypericum calycinum**	*Millepertuis à grandes fleurs*
Abele	**Populus alba**	*Peuplier blanc*
Abyssinian banana	**Musa arnoldiana**	*Bananier d'Abyssinie*
Abraham.Isaac & Jacob	**Trachystemon orientalis**	*Trachystème d'Orient*
Absinthe	**Artemisia absinthium**	*Absinthe*
Achillea	**Achillea**	*Achillée*
Aconite	**Aconitum**	*Aconit*
Adam's needle	**Yucca filamentosa**	*Yucca filamentosa*
Aeroplane propellor	**Crassula falcata**	*Crassula falcata*
African daisy	**Arctotis stoechadifolia**	*Arctotis stoechadifolia*
African daisy	**Dimorphotheca**	*Souci*
African fountain grass	**Pennisetum setaccum**	*Pennisetum setaccum*
African Hemp	**Sparmannia africana**	*Sparmannia africana*
African lily	**Agapanthus africanus**	*Agapanthe*
African marigold	**Tagetes erecta**	*Rose d'Inde*
African milkbush	**Synadenium grantii**	*Synadenium grantii*
African red alder	**Cunonia capensis**	*Cunonia capensis*
African tulip tree	**Spathodea campanulata**	*Spathodea campanulata*
African violet	**Saintpaulia** *Violette africaine / Violette d'Usambara*	
Agapanthus	**Agapanthus**	*Agapanthe*
Agrimony	**Agrimonia eupatoria**	*Aigremoine eupatoire*
Albany bottlebrush	**Callistemon speciosus**	*Callistemon speciosus*
Alder	**Alnus glutinosa**	*Aulne glutineux / Verne*
Alder buckthorn	**Frangula alnus**	*Bourdaine / Neprun*
Aleppo pine	**Pinus halpensis** *Pin d'Alep / Pin de Jerusalem*	
Alexanders	**Smyrnium olusatrum**	*Maceron cultivé*
Alexandra palm	**Archontophoenix alexandrae**	
		Archontophoenix alexandrae
Alexandrian laurel	**Danae racemosa**	*Laurier d'Alexandrie*
Algerian iris	**Iris unguicularis**	*Iris unguicularis*
Algerian oak	**Quercus canariensi**	*Chêne Zeen*
Algerian winter iris	**Iris unguicularis**	*Iris unguicularis*
Alleghany vine	**Adlumia fungosa**	*Adlumia fungosa*
Allium moly	**Allium moly**	*Ail doré*
Allium neapolitanum	**Allium neapolitanumi**	*Ail blanc*
Almond	**Prunus dulcis**	*Amandier*
Aloe	**Aloe**	*Aloè*
Aloe arborescens	**Aloe arborescens**	*Corne de bélier /*
		Corne de cerf

Alpine anemone	**Pulsatilla alpina**	*Anémone des Alpes*
Alpine avens	**Geum montanum**	*Benoîte des montagnes*
Alpine azalea	**Loiseleuria procumbens**	*Azalée des Alpes /*
		Azalée naine
Alpine bartsia	**Bartsia alpina**	*Bartsie des Alpes*
Alpine buttercup	**Ranunculus alpestris**	*Renoncule des Alpes*
Alpine catchfly	**Lychnis alpina**	*Viscaire des Alpes*
Alpine cinquefoil	**Potentilla crantzii**	*Potentille des Alpes*
Alpine coltsfoot	**Homogyne alpina**	*Homogyne alpina*
Alpine columbine	**Aquelegia alpina**	*Ancolie des Alpes*
Alpine enchanter's nightshade **Circaea intermedia**		*Circée des Alpes*
Alpine fleabane	**Erigeron alpinus**	*Vergerette dea Alpes*
Alpine forget-me-not	**Myosotis alpestris**	*Myosotis des Alpes*
Alpine heath	**Erica carnea**	*Bruyère des neiges*
Alpine lady's mantle	**Alchemilla alpina**	*Alchémille des Alpes*
Alpine meadow rue	**Thalictrum alpinum**	*Pigamon des Alpes /Rue des prés*
Alpine milk-vetch	**Astragalus alpinus**	*Astragale des Alpes*
Alpine mouse ear	**Cerastium alpinum**	*Ceraiste des Alpea*
Alpine pearlwort	**Sagina saginoides**	*Sagine des Alpes*
Alpine penny-cress	**Thlaspi alpinum**	*Thlaspi des Alpes*
Alpine pink	**Dianthus alpinus**	*Œillet des Alpes*
Alpine poppy	**Papaver burseri**	*Pavot des Alpes*
Alpine snowbell	**Soldanella alpina**	*Soldanelle des Alpes*
Alpine sow-thistle	**Cicerbita alpina**	*Laitue des Alpes*
Alpine thistle	**Linaria alpina**	*Linaire des Alpes*
Alpine totara	**Podocarpus nivalis**	*Podocarpus nivalis*
Alpine willow-herb	**Epilobium anagallidifolium**	*Épilobe des Alpes*
Alpine woodsia	**Woodsia alpina**	*Woodsia des Alpes*
Alsike clover	**Trifolium hybridum**	*Trèfle hybride*
Alternate golden saxifrage	**Chrysosplenium alternifolium**	
		Dorine à feuilles alternes
Alternate water-milfoil	**Myriophyllum alternifolium**	
		Myriophylle à feuilles alternes
Alum root	**Heuchera**	*Heuchera*
Aluminium plant	**Pilea cadierei**	*Plante aluminium*
Amaryllis	**Hippeastrum**	*Amaryllis*
American arbor-vitae	**Thuja occidentalis**	*Thuja du Canada*
American arrowhead	**Sagittaria latifolia**	*Flèche d'eau américaine*
American aspen	**Populus tremuloides**	*Peuplier tremble d'Amérique*
American beech	**Fagus grandifolia**	*Hêtre d'Amérique*
American bindweed	**Calystegia silvatica**	*Liseron d'Amérique*
American bittersweet	**Celastrus scandens**	*Bourreau des arbres /*
		Célastre grimpant

10

American chain fern	Woodwardia virginica	Woodwardia virginica
American chestnut	Castanea dentata	Châtaigner d'Amérique
American elder	Sambucus canadensis	Sureau du Canada
American holly	Ilex opaca	Houx d'Améique
American hop hornbeam	Ostrya virginiana	Ostryer de Virginie
American hornbeam	Carpinus caroliniana	Charme d'Amérique
American lady's tresses	Spiranthes romanzoffiana	Spiranthe d'Irlande
American lime	Tilia americana	Tilleul d'Amèrique
American lotus	Nelumbo lutea	Lotus jaune d'Amérique
American mountain ash	Sorbus americana	Sorbier d'Amèrique
American pondweed	Potamogeton epihydrus	Potamot epihydrus
American spatterdock	Nuphar advena	Nuphar advena
American speedwell	Veronica peregrina	Véronique voyageuse
American wall fern	Polypodium virginianum	Polypodium virginianum
American white elm	Ulmus americana	Orme d'Amérique / Célastre grimpant
American white oak	Quercus alba	Chêne blanc d'Amérique
Amphibious bistort	Persicaria amphibium	Renouée amphibe
Amur cork tree	Phellodendron amurense	Phellodendron amurense
Amur grape	Vitis amurensis	Vigne de l'Amour
Amur maple	Acer ginnala	Érable du fleuve Amour
Amur silver grass	Miscanthus saccharifolia	Miscanthus saccharifolia
Anceps bamboo	Arundinaria anceps	Arundinaria anceps
Anemone	Anemone	Anémone
Anemone coronaria	Anemone coronaria	Anémone des fleuristes
Anemone pavonia	Anemone pavonia	Anémone des jardins
Anemone ranunculoides	Anemone ranunculoides	Anémone fausse renoncule
Angelica	Angelica archangelica	Angélique
Angel's fishing rod	Dierama	Dierama
Angel's tears	Billbergia x windii	Billbergia x windii
Angel's tears	Narcissus triandrus	Narcissus triandrus
Angels' trumpets	Datura	Stramoine odorante
Angels' wings	Caladium x hortulanum	Caladium x hortulanum
Angelwing begonia	Begonia coccinea	Begonia coccinea
Angled Solomon's seal	Polygonatum odoratum	Sceau de Salomon odorant
Annual mercury	Mercurialis annua	Mercuriale annuelle
Annual pearlwort	Sagina apetala	Sagine apétale
Annual phlox	Phlox drummondii	Phlox annuel
Annual rock-rose	Tuberaria guttata	Hélianthème a gouttes
Annual sunflower	Helianthus annuus	Soleil annuel / Tournesol
Antarctic beech	Nothofagus antarctica	Hêtre antarctica
Apache plume	Fallugia paradoxa	Fallugia paradoxa

11

Apennine anemone	**Anemone apennina**	*Anémone apennina*
Apple	**Malus**	*Pommier*
Apple mint	**Mentha suavolens**	*Menthe à feuilles rondes*
Apple of Peru	**Nicandra physalodes**	*Nicandra physalodes*
Apricot	**Prunus armeniaca**	*Abricotier*
Aquelegia	**Aquelegia**	*Ancolie*
Arabis	**Arabis caucasica**	*Arabette / Corbeille d'argent*
Arctic birch	**Betula nana**	*Bouleau nain*
Arctic saxifrage	**Saxifraga nivalis**	*Saxifrage arctique*
Arctous alpina	**Arctous alpina**	*Arbousier nain*
Arizona ash	**Fraxinus velutina**	*Frêne de l'Arizona*
Arizona cypress	**Cupressus arizonica**	*Cyprès de l'Arizona*
Armand pine	**Pinus armandii**	*Pin du père Armand David*
Armenian oak	**Quercus pontica**	*Chêne d'Arménie*
Arolla pine	**Pinus cembra**	*Arolle / Pin cembro*
Arrow bamboo	**Pseudosasa japonica**	*Pseudosasa japonica*
Arrow-head	**Sagittaria sagittifolia**	*Sagittaire a feuilles en flèche*
Artemisia	**Artemisia**	*Armoise*
Artemisia arborescens	**Artemisia arborescens**	*Armoise arborescente*
Arum Lily	**Zantedeschia aeothiopica**	*Arum de Éthiopie*
Asrabacca	**Asarum europaeum**	*Asaret d'Europe / Cabaret*
Ash	**Fraxinus**	*Frêne*
Ash-leaved maple	**Acer negundo**	*Érable negundo*
Asparagus	**Asparagus officinalis**	*Asperge officinale*
Aspen	**Populus tremula**	*Tremble*
Asphodel	**Asphodelus aestivus**	*Asphodèle*
Aster amellus	**Aster amellus**	*Œil de Christ*
Atamasco lily	**Zephyranthes atamasco**	*Zephyranthes atamasco*
Atlas cedar	**Cedrus atlantica**	*Cèdre de l'Atlas*
Aubrietia	**Aubrietia**	*Aubriette*
Aucuba japonica	**Aucuba japonica**	*Aucuba de Japon*
August lily	**Hosta plantaginea**	*Hosta plantaginea*
Auricula	**Primula auricula**	*Auricule / Oreille d'ours*
Australian Banyan	**Ficus macrphylla**	*Ficus macrphylla*
Australian brush cherry	**Eugenia myrtifolia**	*Myrte d'Australie*
Australian cabbage palm	**Livistona australis**	*Livistona australis*
Australian firewheel tree	**Stenocarpus sinuatu**	*Stenocarpus sinuatu*
Australian heath	**Epicaris impressa**	*Epicaris impressa*
Australian pea	**Lablab purpureus**	*Dolique d'Égypte*
Australian rosemary	**Westringia fruticosa**	*Westringia fruticosa*
Australian sarsparilla	**Hardenbergia violacea**	*Hardenbergia violac*
Australian sassafras	**Westringia fruticosa**	*Westringia fruticosa*

Australian violet	Viola hederacea	*Viola hederacea*
Austrian pine	Pinus larico nigra	*Pin noir d'Autriche*
Autograph tree	Clusia rosea	*Clusia rosea*
Autumn hawkbit	Leontodon autumnalis	*Liondent d'automne*
Autumn crocus	Colchicum autumnale	*Colchique d'automne*
Autumn crocus	Colchicum autumnale	*Safran bâtard /*
		Tue-chien / Veillote
Autumn crocus	Crocus nudiflorus	*Crocus d'automne*
Autumn lady's tresses	Spiranthes spiralis	*Spiranthe contourné*
Autumn snowflake	Leucojum autumnale	*Nivéole automnale*
Autumn squill	Scilla autumnalis	*Scille d'automne*
Avens	Geum	*Benoîte*
Awlwort	Subularia aquatica	*Subulaire aquatique*
Azalea	Rhododendron	*Azalée*
Azalea ponticum	Rhododendron luteum	*Azalée pontique*
Aztec lily	Sprekelia formosissima	*Amaryllis croix Saint-Jacqes*
Aztec marigold	Tagetes erecta	*Rose d'Inde*

B

Baby blue-eyes	Nemophila menziesii	*Némophile*
Baby rubber plant	Peperomia clusiifolia	*Peperomia clusiifolia*
Baby's tears	Soleirolia	*Soleirolia*
Baby's toes	Fenestraria aurantiaca var. rhopalophylla	
		Fenestraria aurantiaca rhopalophylla
Bald cypress	Taxodium distichum	*Cyprès chauve*
Baldmoney	Meum athamanticum	*Méon*
Balearic box	Buxus balearicus	*Buis de Mahon*
Balkan blue grass	Sesleria heufleriana	*Sesleria heufleriana*
Balm	Melissa officinalis	*Mélisse officinale*
Balm-leaved figwort	Scrophularia scorddonia	
		Scrofulaire à feuilles de germandrée
Balm of Gilead	Populus candicans	*Peuplier euroaméricains*
Baloon flower	Platycodon	*Platycodon*
Baloon vine	Cardiospermum halicacabum	*Pois de cœur*
Balsam	Impatiens balsamina	*Balsamine / Impatiente*
Balsam fir	Abies balsamea	*Sapin Baumier*
Balsam Poplar	Populus balsamifera	*Peuplier baumier*
Bamboo Palm	Rhapis excelsa	*Rhapis excelsa*
Banana	Musa	*Bananier*
Banana passion fruit	Passiflora antioquensis	*Passiflora antioquensis*
Baneberry	Actaea	*Actée en épi / Herbe de St. Christophe*

13

Banksia rose	**Rosa banksiae**	*Rosier de Banks*
Banyan	**Ficus benghalensis**	*Figuier des Banyans*
Barbados gooseberry	**Pereskia aculeata**	*Grosseillier de Barbades*
Barbados pride	**Caesalpinia pulcherrima**	*Flamboyant*
Barbed wire plant	**Tylecodon reticulata**	*Tylecodon reticulata*
Barberry	**Berberis**	*Épine-vinette*
Barberton daisy	**Gerbera jamesonii**	*Gerbera jamesonii*
Barrel cactus	**Ferocactus**	*Ferocactus*
Barren strawberry	**Potentilla sterilis**	*Potentille faux-fraisier*
Barrenwort	**Epimedium alpinum**	*Epimedium alpinum*
Bartram's oak	**Quercus x heterophylla**	*Chêne x heterophylla*
Basket grass	**Opilismenus hirtellus**	*Opilismenus hirtellus*
Basswood	**Tilia americana**	*Tilleul d'Amérique*
Bastard balm	**Melittis**	*Mélitte*
Bastard toadflax	**Thesium humifusum**	*Thésium couché*
Bat flower	**Tacca chantrieri**	*Tacca chantrieri*
Bay laurel	**Laurus nobilis**	*Laurier noble*
Bay tree	**Laurus**	*Laurier*
Bay willow	**Salix pentandra**	*Saule laurier*
Bayonet plant	**Aciphylla squarrosa**	*Aciphylla squarrosa*
Beach pine	**Pinus contorta**	*Pin contorta*
Bead plant	**Nertera grandensis**	*Nertera grandensis*
Bead tree	**Melia azedarach**	*Lilas des Indes*
Beaked hawksbeard	**Crepis vesicaria**	*Crépide à vésicules*
Bearberry	**Arctostaphylos uva-ursi**	*Raisin d'ours / Busserole*
Bear grass	**Dasylirion**	*Dasylirion*
Bearded bellflower	**Campanula barbata**	*Campanule barbue*
Bear's breeches	**Acanthus mollis**	*Acanthe à feuilles molles / Branc-ursine*
Beauty bush	**Kolkwitzia amabilis**	*Kolkwitzia amabilis*
Bedstraw	**Galium**	*Gaillet*
Bee Balm	**Monarda didyma**	*Monarde pourprea*
Beech	**Fagus sylvatica**	*Hêtre*
Beech fern	**Phegopteris connectilis**	*Phegopteris connectilis*
Beefsteak plant	**Iresine herbistii**	*Iresine herbistii*
Bee orchid	**Ophrys apifera**	*Ophrys abeille*
Begonia	**Begonia**	*Bégonia*
Belamcanda	**Belamcanda**	*Fleur de léopard / Iris tigré*
Bell heather	**Erica cinerea**	*Bruyère cendrée*
Belladonna Lily	**Amaryllis belladonna**	*Amaryllis belladonna*
Bellflower	**Campanula**	*Campanule*

English	Botanical	French
Bellflowered cherry	Prunus campanulata	*Prunus campanulata*
Bells of Ireland	Moleccella laevis	*Clochette d'Irlande*
Bellwort	Uvularia grandiflora	*Uvularia grandiflora*
Benjamin	Lindera benzoin	*Laurier benzoin*
Bentham's cornel	Cornus capitata	*Cornus capitata*
Bergamot	Monarda	*Monarde*
Berlin poplar	Populus x berolinensis	*Peuplier de Berlin*
Bermuda buttercup	Oxalis pes-caprae	*Oxalis des Bermudes*
Bermuda lily	Lilium longiflorum	*Lilium longiflorum*
Berry bladder fern	Cystopteris bulbifera	*Cystopteris bulbifera*
Besom heath	Erica scoparia	*Brande / Bruyère à balai*
Betony	Stachys officinalis	*Bétoine*
Bhutan pine	Pinus wallichiana	*Pin pleuereur de l'Himalaya*
Big tree	Sequoiadendron giganteum	*Sequoiadendron giganteum*
Big-cone pine	Pinus coulteri	*Pin coulteri*
Bignonia	Campsis grandiflora	*Bignone de Chine*
Bilberry	Vaccinium myrtillus	*Airelle / Myrtille*
Biota	Thuja orientalis	*Thuya d'Orient*
Birch	Betula	*Bouleau*
Bird cherry	Prunus padus	*Cerisier à grappes*
Bird-catcher tree	Pisonia umbellifera	*Pisonia umbellifera*
Bird-of-paradise flower	Strelitzia	*Oiseau de Paradis*
Bird's eye primrose	Primula farinosa	*Primevère farineuse*
Bird's foot ivy	Hedera helix Pedata	*Hedera helix Pedata*
Bird's foot violet	Viola 'Pedata'	*Violette pied d'oiseau*
Bird's nest bromeliad	Nidularium innocentii	*Nidularium innocentii*
Bird's nest fern	Asplenium nidus	*Asplenium nidus*
Bird's nest orchid	Neottia nidus-avis	*Néottie nid-d'oiseau*
Birthroot	Trillium erectum	*Trillie erectum*
Birthwort	Aristolochia clematitis	*Aristoloche clématite*
Bishop pine	Pinus muricata	*Pin d'Anthony*
Bishop's cap	Astrophytum myriostigma	*Mitre d'évêque*
Bishop's mitre	Astrophytum myriostigma	*Mitre d'évêque*
Bishop's weed (In Scotland)	Aegopodium podagraria	*Aegopode podagraire / Herbe aux goutteux*
Bistort	Polygonum bistorta	*Bistorte*
Bistort	Persicaria bistorta	*Bistorte*
Bithynian vetch	Vicia bithynica	*Vesce de Bithynie*
Biting stonecrop	Sedum acre	*Poivre de muraille*
Bitter cress	Cardamine pratensis	*Cressonnette*
Bitter root	Lewisia rediviva	*Lewisia rediviva*
Bittersweet	Solanum dulcamara	*Douce-amère*

Bitternut hickory	**Carya cordiformis**	*Noyer d'Amérique*
Bitter vetch	**Lathyrus montanus**	*Gesse de montagne*
Bitternut	**Carya cordiformis**	*Noyer des marais*
Black alder	**Alnus glutinosa**	*Aulne glutineux / Verne*
Black bamboo	**Phyllostachys nigra**	*Bambou noir*
Black bean	**Kennedia nigricans**	*Kennedia nigricans*
Black bean tree	**Castanospermum**	*Castanospermum*
Black bearberry	**Arctostaphylos alpinus**	*Raisin des Alpes*
Black bryony	**Tamus communis**	*Tamier commun*
Black cherry	**Prunus serotina**	*Ceridier noir*
Black chokeberry	**Aronia melanocarpa**	*Aronia melanocarpa*
Black cottonwood	**Populus trichocarpa**	*Baumier de l'Ouest*
Black currant	**Ribes nigrum**	*Cassis*
Black false hellebore	**Veratrum nigrum**	*Vératre noir*
Black gum	**Nyssa sylvatica**	*Nyssa sylvatica*
Black horehound	**Ballota nigra**	*Ballote noire*
Black huckleberry	**Gaylussacia baccata**	*Gaylussacia baccata*
Black Italian poplar	**Populus x candicans**	*Peuplier euroaméricains*
Black Jack oak	**Quercus marilandica**	*Jaquier noir*
Black medic	**Medicago lupulina**	*Luzerne lupuline / Minette*
Black mulberry	**Morus nigra**	*Mûrier noir*
Black mustard	**Brassica nigra**	*Moutarde noire*
Black nightshade	**Solanum nigrum**	*Morelle noire*
Black oak	**Quercus velutina**	*Chêne noir /*
		Chêne des teinturiers / Quercitron
Black pine	**Pinus jeffreyi**	*Pin de Jeffrey*
Black pine	**Pinus nigra**	*Pin noir d'Autriche*
Black poplar	**Populus nigra**	*Peuplier noir / Liardier*
Black spruce	**Picea mariana**	*Sapinette noir*
Black tree fern	**Cyathea medullaris**	*Cyathea medullaris*
Black walnut	**Juglans nigra**	*Noyer noir*
Black willow	**Salix 'Melanostachys'**	*Saule noir*
Blackberry	**Rubus**	*Ronce*
Black-eyed Susan	**Rudbeckia hirta**	*Rudbeckie hérissée*
Blackthorn	**Prunus spinosa**	*Epine noire*
Bladder campion	**Cucubalus**	*Cucubale*
Bladder cherry	**Physalis Alkekengi**	*Alkéenege du Pérou /*
		Coqueret du Pérou
Bladder nut	**Staphylea**	*Faux pistachier*
Bladder seed	**Physospermum cornubiense**	
		Physosperme de cornouailles
Bladder senna	**Colutea arborescens**	*Baguenaudier commun*

Blanket flower	Gaillardia	*Gaillardia*
Bleeding heart	**Dicentra spectabilis**	*Cœur de Marie*
Blessed Mary's thistle	**Silybum marianum**	*Chardon Marie*
Blinks	**Montia fontana**	*Montie des fontaines*
Blood flower	**Asclepias curassavica**	*Asclepias curassavica*
Blood flower	**Scadoxus multiflorus katherinae**	
	Scadoxus multiflorus katherinae	
Blood leaf	**Haemanthus coccineus**	*Haemanthus coccineus*
Blood leaf	**Iresine lindenii**	*Iresine lindenii*
Blood lily	**Haemanthus coccineus**	*Haemanthus coccineus*
Bloodroot	**Sanguinaria canadensis**	*Sanguinaria canadensis*
Bloody cranesbill	**Geranium sanguineum**	*Géranium sanguin*
Blue Atlas cedar	**Cedrus atlantica glauca**	*Cèdre de l'Atlas bleu*
Bluebell	**Hyacinthoides non-scripta**	*Jacinthe des bois*
Bluebell (In Scotland)	**Campanula rotundifolia**	*Campanule à feuilles rondes*
Blue candle	**Myrtillocactus geometrizans**	*Myrtillocactus geometrizans*
Blue cupidone	**Catananche**	*Cupidone*
Blue Douglas fir	**Pseudotsuga menzieii 'Glauca'**	
	Douglas bleu / Sapin de Douglas bleu	
Blue-eyed grass	**Sisyrinchium bermudianum**	*Bermudienne*
Blue-eyed Mary	**Omphalodes verna**	*Nombril-de-Vénus / Petite bourache*
Blue fescue	**Festuca glauca**	*Festuca glauca*
Blue flag	**Iris versicolor**	*Iris versicolor*
Blue fleabane	**Erigeron acer**	*Vergerette acre*
Blue grama	**Bouteloua gracilis**	*Bouteloua gracilis*
Blue gum	**Eucalyptus globulus**	*Gommier bleu*
Blue holly	**Ilex x meserveae**	*Houx x meserveae*
Blue lace flower	**Trachymene caerulea**	*Trachymene caerulea*
Blue margueritte	**Felicia amelloides**	*Margueritte du Cap / Pâquerette*
Blue oat grass	**Helictotrichon sempervirens**	
	Helictotrichon sempervirens	
Blue passion flower	**Passiflora caerulea**	
	Fleur de la Passion / Passiflore	
Blue pimpernal	**Anagallis foemina**	*Mouron bleu*
Blue poppy	**Meconopsis grandis**	*Pavot bleu*
Blue potato bush	**Solanum rantonnetii**	*Solanum rantonnetii*
Blue sow-thistle	**Cicerbita macrophylla**	*Laitue à grandes feuilles*
Blue star	**Amsonia**	*Amsonia*
Blue trumpet vine	**Thunbergia grandiflora**	*Thunbergia grandiflora*
Bluebell	**Hyacinthoides**	*Jacinthe des bois*
Bluebell (In Scotland)	**Campanula rotundifloia**	*Campanule à feuilles rondes*

17

Bluebell creeper	**Sollya**	*Sollya*
Blueberry ash	**Elaeocarpus reticulatus**	*Elaeocarpus reticulatus*
Bluebottle	**Centaurea cyanus**	*Barbeau bleu / Bleuet*
Blue flowered torch	**Tillandsia lindenii**	*Tillandsia lindenii*
Blunt-leaved pondweed	**Potamogeton obtusifolius**	
		Potamot à feuilles obtuses
Blushing bromeliad	**Neoregalia carolinae**	*Neoregalia carolinae*
Blushing bromeliad	**Nidularium fulgens**	*Nidularium fulgens*
Blushing philodendron	**Philodendron erubescens**	*Philodendron erubescens*
Bo	**Ficus religiosa**	*Ficus religiosa*
Boabab	**Adansonia**	*Adansonia*
Boat lily	**Tradescantia spathacea**	*Tradescantia spathace*
Bog arum	**Calla palustris**	*Calla palustris*
Bog asphodel	**Narthecium ossifragum**	*Ossifrage / Narthèce*
Bog bean	**Menyanthes trifoliata**	*Trèfle d'eau*
Bog myrtle	**Myrica gale**	*Galé odorante*
Bog orchid	**Hammarbya paludosa**	*Malaxis des marais*
Bog pimpernel	**Anagallis tenella**	*Mouron délicat /*
		Mouron des marécages
Bog pondweed	**Potamogeton polygonifolius**	
		Potamot à feuilles de renouée
Bog sage	**Salvia uliginosa**	*Salvia uliginosa*
Bog rosemary	**Andromeda polifolia**	
		Andromède à feuilles de polium
Bonin Isles juniper	**Juniperus procumbens**	*Juniperus procumbens*
Borage	**Borago officinalis**	*Bourrache*
Bosnian pine	**Pinus leucodermis**	*Pin de Bosnie*
Boston ivy	**Parthenocissus tricuspidata**	*Vigne vierge japonais*
Boston ivy	**Parthenocissus tricuspidata**	*Lierre japonais*
Bottle plant	**Hatiora salicornoides**	*Hatiora salicornoides*
Bottlebrush	**Callistemon**	*Callistemon*
Bottlebrush buckeye	**Aesculus parviflora**	*Marronnier paviflora / Pavier blanc*
Bougainvillea	**Bougainvillea**	*Bougainvillée*
Bower vine	**Actinidia arguta**	*Actinidie denticulée*
Bowles's golden sedge	**Carex elata aurea**	*Carex elata aurea*
Box	**Buxus**	*Buis*
Box elder	**Acer negundo**	*Érable negundo*
Box-leafed holly	**Ilex crenata**	*Houx crenata*
Bracelet honey myrtle	**Melaneuca amarillaris**	*Melaneuca amarillaris*
Bramble	**Rubus fruticosus**	*Ronce commune*
Branched bur reed	**Sparganium erectum**	*Rubanier dressé*
Brandy Bottle	**Nuphar lutea**	*Nénuphar jaune*

English	Scientific	French
Brass buttons	Cotula coronopifolia	Cotule coronopifolia
Brazilian firecracker	Manettia inflata	Manettia inflata
Breath of heaven	Diosma ericoides	Diosma ericoides
Breck speedwell	Veronica praecox	Véronique précoce
Breckland catchfly	Silene otites	Silène à petites fleurs
Breckland mugwort	Artemisia campestris	Armoise champëtre
Brewer's spruce	Picea breweriana	Épicéa de Brewer
Bridal bouquet	Porana panicultata	Porana panicultata
Bridal wreath	Francoa appendiculata	Francoa appendiculata
Bridal wreath	Spiraea 'Arguta'	Spirée "Arguta"
Bridal wreath	Spiraea x vanhouttei	Spirée x vanhouttei
Bristle cone pine	Pinus aristata	Pin aristata
Bristle pointed iris	Iris setosa	Iris setosa
Bristly ox-tongue	Picris echioides	Picride vipérine
Bristly poppy	Papaver hybridum	Pavot hybride
Brittle bladder fern	Cystopteris fragilis	Cystopteris fragile
Broad beech fern	Thelypteris hexagonoptera	Thelypteris hexagonoptera
Broad buckler fern	Dryopteris dilatata	Dryopteris dilatata
Broad dock	Rumex obtusifolius	Patience à feuilles obtuses
Broad helleborine	Cephalanthera damasonium	Céphalanthéra pale
Broadleaf	Griselinia littoralis	Griselinia littoralis
Broad-leaved lime	Tilia platyphyllos	Tilleul à grandes feuilles
Broad-leaved pondweed	Potamogeton natans	Potamot nageant
Broad-leaved willow-herb	Epilobium montanum	Épilobe de montagne
Brompton stock	Matthiola incana	Quarantaine
Bronvaux medlar	+Crataegomespilus dardarii	
		Crataegomespilus dardarii
Brooklime	Veronica beccabunga	Cresson de cheval
Brookweed	Samolus valerandi	Samole de valérand
Broom	Cytisus	Genêt
Broom	Genista	Genêt
Broom	Cytisus scoparius	Genêt à balais
Brush-box tree	Tristania conferta	Tristania conferta
Buckbean	Menyanthes trifoliata	Menyanthes trifoliata
Buckeye	Aesculus	Marronnier
Buckshorn plantain	Plantago coronopus	Pied-de-corbeau /
		Plantain corne-de bœuf
Buckthorn	Rhamnus	Nerprun
Buckwheat	Fagopyrum esculentum	Blé noir / Sarrasin
Buddleia	Buddleia davidii	Arbuste à papillons / Buddleia
Buffalo Berry	Shepherdia argentea	Shepherdia argentea
Buffalo currant	Ribes odoratum	Groseille doré
Bugbane	Cimicifuga	Cimicifuge

19

Bugle	Ajuga reptans	*Bugle rampante*
Bugloss	Anchusa	*Buglosse*
Bulbocodium vernum	Bulbocodium vernum	*Crocus rouge*
Bulbous buttercup	Ranunculus bulbosa	*Renoncule bulbeuse*
Bull bay	Magnolia grandiflora	*Magnolia à grandea fleurs*
Bullock's heart	Annona reticulata	*Annona reticulata*
Bullrush	Scirpus	*Scirpe / Jonquine*
Bunch flowered daffodil	Narcissus tazetta	*Narcisse à bouquets /*
		Narcisse de Constantinople
Bunnies' ears	Stachys byzantina	*Stachys byzantina*
Bunny ears	Opuntia microdasys	*Oreille-de-lapin*
Bur chervil	Anthriscus caucalis	*Anthrisque commun*
Bur medick medick	Medicago minima	*Luzerne naine*
Bur oak	Quercus macrocarpa	*Chêne à gros fruits*
Bur reed	Sparganium	*Rubanier*
Burdock	Arctium minus	*Bardane à petites tëtes*
Burnet	Sanguisorba	*Sanguisorbe / Petite pimpernelle*
Burnet rose	Rosa pimpinellifolia	*Rosier pimpernelle*
Burnet-saxifrage	Pimpinella saxifraga	*Petit boucage*
Burning bush	Dictamnus albus	*Fraxinelle*
Burning bush	Kochia scoparia tricophylla	*Kochia scoparia tricophylla*
Burnt-tip orchid	Orchis ustulata	*Orchis brulé*
Burro's tail	Sedum morganianum	*Sedum morganianum*
Bush groundsel	Baccharis halimifolia	*Séneçon en arbre*
Bush vetch	Vicia sepium	*Vesce des haies*
Bush violet	Browallia speciosa	*Browallia speciosa*
Busy Lizzie	Impatiens	*Balsamine / Impatiente*
Butcher's broom	Ruscus aculeatus	*Fragon piquant /*
		Houx frelon / Petit houx
Butterbur	Petasites hybridus	*Chapeau-du-diable / Pètasite hybride*
Butter dock	Rumex longifolius	*Patience à feuilles longues*
Butter tree	Tylecodon paniculata	*Tylecodon paniculata*
Buttercup	Ranunculus	*Renoncule*
Butterfly bush	Buddleia	*Buddleia / Arbuste aux papillons*
Butterfly flower	Schizanthus	*Schizanthus*
Butterfly iris	Iris spuria	*Iris bâtard*
Butterfly orchid	Oncidium papilio	*Oncidium papillon*
Butterfly orchid	Planthera chlorantha	*Orchis verdante / Double feuille*
Butterfly tree	Bauhinia purpurea	*Bauhinia purpurea*
Butterfly weed	Asclepias tuberosa	*Asclepias tuberosa*
Butternut	Juglans cinera	*Noyer cendré*
Button fern	Pellaea rotundifolia	*Pellaea rotundifolia*
Buttonweed	Cotula coronopifolia	*Cotule à feuilles de senebièr*

C

Caesalpinia	Caesalpinia	*Brésillet*
Caesalpinia gilliesii	Caesalpinia gilliesii	*Oiseau de Paradis*
Calamint	Calamintha	*Clinopode*
Calamondin	Citrofortunella mitis	*Citrofortunella mitis*
Calceolaria	Calceolaria	*Calcéolaire*
Calico bush	Kalmia latifolia	*Laurier américain / Laurier des montagnes*
Calico flower	Aristolochia elegans	*Aristoloche*
California allspice	Calycanthus occidentalis	*Calycanthe occidentalis*
California bluebell	Phacelia campanularia	*Phacelia campanularia*
California buckeye	Aesculus californica	*Marronier de Californie*
California nutmeg	Torreya californica	*Torreya californica*
Californian laurel	Umbellularia californica	*Laurier de Californie*
Californianlilac	Ceanothus	*Céanotte*
Californian live oak	Quercus agrifolia	*Chêne agrifolia*
Californian pepper tree	Schinus molle	*Faux poivrier*
Californian poppy	Romneya coulteri	*Romneya coulteri*
Callery pear	Pyrus calleryana	*Poirier calleryana*
Callous-fruited water dropwort	Oenanthe pimpinelloidesa	*Jeannette*
Calycanthus	Calycanthus	*Calycanthe*
Cambridge parsley	Selinum carvifolia	*Sélinum a feuilles de carvi*
Campanula	Campanula	*Campanule*
Campanula isophylla	Campanula isophylla	*Étoile de Bethléem / Étoile de Marie*
Campanula vidalii	Azorina vidalii	*Campanule vidalii*
Campernelle jonquil	Narcissus x odorus	*Narcisse campernellii*
Campion	Silene	*Silène*
Canada hemlock	Tsuga canadensis	*Pruce / Tsuga du Canada*
Canada lily	Lilium canadense	*Lils canadense*
Canada moonseed	Menispermum canadense	*Menispermum canadense*
Canadian burnet	Sanguisorba canadensis	*Sanguisorba canadensis*
Canadian columbine	Aquilegia canadensis	*Ancolie du Canada*
Canadian fleabane	Conyza canadenis	*Vergerette du Canada*
Canadian golden-rod	Solidago canadensis	*Verge d'or du Canada*
Canadian waterweed	Elodea canadensis	*Élodée du Canada*
Canary bird bush	Crotalaria agatiflora	*Crotalaria agatiflora*
Canary creeper	Tropaeolum peregrinum	*Capucine des Canaris*
Canary Island bellflower	Canarina canariensis	*Canarina canariensis*
Canary Island date palm	Phoenix canariensis	*Dattier des Canaries*
Canary Island Ivy	Hedera canariensis	*Lierre des Canaries*

Candle plant	**Senecio articulans**	*Plante chandelle*
Candytuft	**Iberis**	*Corbeille d'argent*
Canna	**Canna**	*Balisier*
Canoe birch	**Betula papyrifera**	*Bouleau à canots*
Canterbury bell	**Campanula medium**	*Campanule à grosses fleurs /*
		Campanule carillon
Capa de oro	**Solandra maxima**	*Solandra maxima*
Cape blue water lily	**Nymphaea capensis**	*Nénuphar bleu du Cap*
Cape cudweed	**Gnaphalium undulatum**	*Gnaphale ondulé*
Cape dandelion	**Arctotheca calendula**	*Arctotheca calendula*
Cape figwort	**Phygelius capensis**	*Fuchsia du Cap /*
		Scrofulaire du Cap
Cape gooseberry	**Physalis peruviana**	*Alkékenge de Pérou /*
		Coqueret du Perou
Cape grape	**Rhoicissus capensis**	*Rhoicissus capensis*
Cape honeysuckle	**Tecomaria capensis**	*Chèvrefeuille du Cap*
Cape jasmine	**Gardenia jasminoides**	*Jasmin du Cap*
Cape leadwort	**Plumbago auriculata**	*Dentelaire du Cap*
Cape marigold	**Dimorphotheca**	*Dimorphotèque*
Cape myrtle	**Myrsine africana**	*Myrsine africana*
Cape pondweed	**Aponogeton distachyos**	*Aponogeton distachyos*
Cape primrose	**Streptocarpus rexii**	*Streptocarpus rexii*
Cape sundew	**Drosera capensis**	*Rossolis du Cap*
Cappadocian Maple	**Acer cappadocium**	*Érable de Cappadocie*
Caraway	**Carum carvi**	*Cumin des prés*
Caraway thyme	**Thymus herba-barona**	*Thym herba-barona*
Cardinal climber	**Ipomoea x multifidia**	*Ipomoea x mulitfidia*
Cardinal flower	**Lobelia cardinalis**	*Lobelia cardinalis*
Cardinal's guard	**Pachystachys coccinea**	*Pachystachys coccinea*
Cardoon	**Cynara cardunculus**	*Cardon*
Caricature plant	**Graptophyllum pictum**	*Graptophyllum pictum*
Carline thistle	**Carlina vulgaris**	*Carline commune*
Carnation	**Dianthus**	*Œillet*
Carolina allspice	**Calycanthus floridus**	*Arbre aux anémones /*
		Arbre Pompadour
Carolina hemlock	**Tsuga caroliniana**	*Tsuga de Caroline*
Carolina jasmine	**Gelsemium sempervirens**	
	Gelsemium sempervirens	
Caryopteris	**Caryopteris**	*Barbe bleue*
Caspian locust	**Gleditsia caspica**	*Févier caspica*
Cast-iron plant	**Aspidistra elatior**	*Aspidistra elatior*
Castor oil plant	**Ricinus communis**	*Palma Christi /*
		Ricin commun

Catalina ironwood	**Lyonothamnus floribundus**	*Lyonothamnus floribundus*
Catchfly	**Silene**	*Silène*
Catmint	**Nepeta cataria**	*Herbe aux chats / Nepeta aux chats*
Cat's claw	**Macfadyena unguis-cati**	*Macfadyena unguis-cati*
Cat's ears	**Antennaria**	*Antennaria*
Cat's ears	**Calochortus**	*Calochortus*
Cat's valerian	**Valeriana officinalis**	*Valériane Officinalis*
Caucasian elm	**Zelkova carpinifolia**	*Faux orme de Sibérie*
Caucasian fir	**Abies nordmanniana**	*Sapin de Nordmann*
Caucasian lime	**Tillia x euchlora**	*Tilleul de Crimée*
Caucasian oak	**Quercus macranthera**	*Quercus macranthera*
Caucasian spruce	**Picea orientalis**	*Sapinette d'Orient*
Caucasian whortleberry	**Vaccineum arctastaphylos**	*Vaccineum arctastaphylos*
Caucasian wing nut	**Pterocarya frazinifolia**	*Pterocarya frazinifolia*
Ceanothus	**Ceanothus**	*Céanothe*
Cedar	**Cedrus**	*Cèdre*
Cedar of Goa	**Cupressus lusitanica**	*Cyprès de Goa*
Cedar of Lebanon	**Cedrus libani**	*Cèdre du Liban*
Celandine	**Chelidonium**	*Chélidoine / Grande Éclaire / Herbe aux verrues*
Celery leafed buttercup	**Ranunculus sceleratus**	*Renoncule scélérate*
Centaurea montana	**Centaurea montana**	*Bleuet vivace*
Century plant	**Agave americana**	*Agave d'Amérique*
Chain cactus	**Rhipsalis paradoxa**	*Rhipsalis paradoxa*
Chain fern	**Woodwardia radicans**	*Woodwardie*
Chalk milkwort	**Polygala calcaria**	*Polygala des sols calcaires*
Chamomile	**Anthemis**	*Anthemis*
Chamomile	**Chamaemelum nobile**	*Chamomille romaine*
Changing forget-me-not	**Myosotis discolor**	*Myosotis bicolore*
Channel centaury	**Centaurium tenuiflorum**	*Petite centauré à fleurs ténues*
Channelled heath	**Erica canaliculata**	*Erica canaliculata*
Charlock	**Sinapis arvensis**	*Moutarde des champs / Sénevé*
Chastity bush	**Vitex agnus castus**	*Agneau chaste / Arbre au poivre / Gattillier commun*
Chatham Island forget-me-not	**Myosotidium hortensia**	*Myosotidium hortensia*
Cheddar pink	**Dianthus gratianopolitanus**	*Œillet bleuatre*
Cherimoya	**Annona**	*Annona*
Cherry	**Prunus**	*Cerisier*

23

Cherry laurel	Prunus laureocerasus	Laurier cerise
Cherry plum	Prunus cerasifera	Prunier myrobolan
Chestnut	Castanea	Châtaignier
Chestnut leaved oak	Quercus casteifolia	Chêne à feuilles de chàtaigner
Chestnut vine	Tetrastigma voinerianum	Tetrastigma voinerianum
Chickweed	Cerastium	Mouron des oiseaux
Chickweed willow-herb	Epilobium alsinifolium	Épilobe à feuilles d'alsine
Chickweed wintergreen	Trientalis europaea	Trientalis d'Europe
Chicory	Chicorium intybus	Chicorée sauvage
Chile pine	Araucaria araucana	Déspoir des singes
Chilean bamboo	Chusquea culeou	Chusquea culeou
Chilean bellflower	Lapageria rosea	Lapageria rosea
Chilean blue crocus	Tecophilaea cyanocrocus	Crocus du Chili
Chilean firebush	Embothrium coccineum	Embothrium coccineum
Chilean glory flower	Eccremocarpus scaber	Bignone de Chili
Chilean hazel	Gevuina avellana	Noisetierv du Chili
Chilean incense cedar	Austrocedrus chilensis	Austrocedrus chilensis
Chilean jasmine	Mandevilla laxa	Mandevilla laxa
Chilean laurel	Laurelia serrata	Laurelia serrata
Chilean wine palm	Jubaea chilensis	Cocotier du Chili
Chiltern gentian	Gentiana germanica	Gentiane d'Allemagne
Chimney bellflower	Campanula pyramidalis	Campanule pyramidale
China aster	Callistephus	Aster de Chine / Reine-margueritte
Chincherinchee	Ornithogalm thyrsoides	Ornithogale
Chinese anise	Illicium anisatum	Badianier
Chinese arbor-vitae	Thuja orientalis	Thuya d'Orient
Chinese box thorn	Lycium barbarum	Lyciet jasminoïde
Chinese elm	Ulmus parvifolia	Orme de Chine / Orme à petites feuilles
Chinese evergreen	Aglaonema	Aglaonema
Chinese fan palm	Livistona chinensis	Palmier évental de Chine
Chinese fir	Cunninghamia lanceolata	Sapin chinois
Chinese fountain grass	Pennisetum alopecuroides	Pennisetum alopecuroides
Chinese fountain palm	Livistona chinensis	Livistona chinensis
Chinese fringe tree	Chionanthus retusus	Arbre à franges de Chine
Chinese gooseberry	Actinidia chinensis	Kiwi / Souris végétale
Chinese hat plant	Holmskioldia sanguinea	Holmskioldia sanguinea
Chinese horse chestnut	Aesculus chinensis	Marronnier de Chine
Chinese juniper	Juniperus chinensis	Genévrier de Chine
Chinese lantern	Physalis	Coqueret

Chinese lantern lily	Sandersonia aurantiaca	*Sandersonia aurantiac*
Chinese necklace poplar	Populus lasiocarpa	*Populus lasiocarpa*
Chinese parasol tree	Firmiana simplex	*Parasol chinois*
Chinese privet	Ligustrum lucidum	*Troène de Chine*
Chinese tallow tree	Sapium sebiferum	*Sapium sebiferum*
Chinese thuja	Thuja orientalis	*Thuya d'Orient*
Chinese trumpet creeper	Campsis grandiflora	*Bignone de Chine*
Chinese tulip tree	Liriodendron chinense	*Tulipier de Chine*
Chinese walnut	Juglans cathayensis	*Noyer de Chne*
Chinese wing nut	Pterocarya stenoptera	*Pterocarya stenoptera*
Chinese wisteria	Wisteria sinensis	*Glycine de Chine*
Chinese witch hazel	Hamamelis mollis	*Hamamelis velouté*
Chives	Allium schoenoprasum	*Ciboulette sauvage*
Chocolate cosmos	Cosmos atrosanguineus	*Cosmos atrosanguineus*
Chocolate vine	Akebia quinata	*Akebia quinata*
Chokeberry	Aronia	*Aronie*
Christmas begonia	Begonia x cheimantha	*Begonia x cheimantha*
Christmas berry	Heteromeles arbutifolia	*Heteromeles arbutifolia*
Christmas box	Sarcococca	*Sarcococca*
Christmas cactus	Schlumbergera bridgesii	*Schlumbergera bridgesii*
Christmas fern	Polystichum acrostchoides	*Polystic*
Christmas rose	Helleborus niger	*Rose de Noël*
Christ's thorn	Paliurus spina-christi	*Argalon / Épine du Christ*
Chrysanthemum	Chrysanthemum	*Chrysanthème*
Chrysanthemum rubellum	Chrysanthemum rubellum	*Margueritte d'automne*
Chusan palm	Trachycarpus fortunei	*Palmier de Chine*
Cider gum	Eucalyptus gunnii	*Eucalyptus de Gunn*
Cigar flower	Cuphea ignea	*Cuphea ignea*
Cineraria	Senecio x hybridus	*Cinéraire hybrides*
Cinnamon fern	Osmunda cinnamonea	*Osmunda cinnamonea*
Cinnamomum camphora	Cinnamomum camphora	*Camphorier / Camphora vrai*
Cistus ladanifer	Cistus ladanifer	*Ciste à gomme*
Cladanthus arabicus	Cladanthus arabicus	*Anthémis d'Arabie*
Claret ash	Fraxinus oxycarpa	*Frêne oxyphylle*
Clary	Salvia horminoides	*Sauge faux-horminum*
Clary sage	Salvia sclarea	*Sauge sclarée / Orvale*
Clematis	Clematis	*Clématite*
Clematis flammula	Clematis flammula	*Flammule*
Cliff spurry	Spergularia rupicola	*Spergulaire des rochers*
Climbing butcher's broom	Semele andrgyna	*Semele andrgyna*
Climbing corydalis	Corydalis claviculata	*Corydale à vrilles*

25

Climbing dahlia	Hidalgoa	*Hidalgoa*
Climbing fumitory	Adlumia fungosa	*Adlumia fungosa*
Climbing hydrangea	Hydrangea anomala petiolaris	*Hortensia grimpant*
Clog plant	Alloplectus nummularia	*Alloplectus nummularia*
Cloth of gold crocus	Crocus angustifolius	*Crocus angustifolius*
Cloud grass	Aichryson x domesticum varieg.	*Aichryson x domesticum varieg.*
Cloudberry	Rubus chamaemorus	*Ronce des tourbières*
Clover	Trifolium	*Trèfle*
Clove-scented broomrape	Orobanche caryophyllacea	*Orobanche giroflée*
Club rush	Scirpus	*Scirpe*
Cluster pine	Pinus pinaster	*Pin maritime*
Clustered bellflower	Campanula glomerata	*Campanule agglomérée*
Clustered clover	Trifolium glomeratum	*Trèfle aggloméré*
Clustered dock	Rumex conglomeratus	*Patience agglomérée*
Coast redwood	Sequoia sempervirens	*Sequoia sempervirens*
Cobnut	Corylus avellana	*Coudrier / Noisette*
Cobweb houseleek	Sempervivum arachnoideum	*Joubarbe toile d'araigné*
Cock's foot	Dactylis glomerata	*Dactyle aggloméré / Dactyle peltonné*
Cockspur coral-tree	Erythrina crista-galli	*Érythrine crête de coq*
Cockspur thorn	Crataegus crus-galli	*Épine ergot de coq*
Coiled pondweed	Ruppia spiralis	*Ruppia spiralée*
Colombian ball cactus	Wigginsia vorwerkiana	*Wigginsia vorwerkiana*
Colorado spruce	Picea pungens	*Épicéa du Colorado*
Coltsfoot	Tussilago farfara	*pas-d'âne*
Columbine	Aquelegia vulgaris	*Ancolie commune*
Comfrey	Symphytum	*Consoude*
Common birdsfoot	Ornithopus perpusillus	*Ornithope délicat / Pied-d'oiseau*
Common birdsfoot trefoil	Lotus corniculatus	*Lotier corniculé*
Common birdsfoot trefoil	Lotus corniculatus	*Pied-de-poule*
Common buckthorn	Rhamnus cathartica	*Nerprun purgatif*
Common butterwort	Pinguicula vulgaris	*Grassette commune*
Common catsear	Hypochoeris radicata	*Porcelle enracinée*
Common centaury	Centaurium erythraea	*Petite centaurée commune*
Common chamomile	Chamaemelum nobile	*Camomille romaine*
Common chickweed	Stellaria media	*Mouron des oiseaux*
Common comfrey	Symphytum officinale	*Grande consoude*
Common cotton-grass	Eriophorum angustifolium	*Eriophorum angustifolium*

Common cudweed	Filago germanica	*Cuscute du thym*
Common dog violet	Viola riviniana	*Violette de rivin*
Common duckweed	Lemna minor	*Petite lentille d'eau*
Common eel-grass	Zostera marina	*Zostère marine*
Common elm	Ulmus procera	*Grand orme*
Common enchanter's nightshade	Circaea lutetiana	*Circée de Paris*
Common field speedwell	Veronica persica	*Véronique de Perse*
Common figwort	Scrophularia nodosa	*Scrofulaire noueuse*
Common fleabane	Pulicaria dysentericum	*Pulicaire dysentérique*
Common gromwell	Lithospermum officinale	*Grémil officinal / Herbe aux perles*
Common hackberry	Celtis occidentalis	*Micocoulier de Virginie*
Common helleborine	Epipactis helleborine	*Épipactis à feuilles larges*
Common hornbeam	Carpinus betulus	*Charme commun*
Common houseleek	Sempervivum tectorum	*Joubarbe des toits*
Common laburnum	Laburnum anagyroides	*Aubour / Cytise / Faux-ébénier*
Common lady's mantle	Alchemilla vulgaris	*Alchémille commune*
Common mallow	Malva sylvestris	*Grande mauve / Mauve sylvestre*
Common meadow-rue	Thalictrum flavum	*Pigamon jaune*
Common melilot	Melilotus officinalis	*Mélilot officinal*
Common morning glory	Ipomoea purpurea	*Volubilis*
Common mudwort	Limosella aquatatica	*Limoselle aquatique*
Common mullein	Verbascum thapsus	*Bonhomme / Bouillon blanc*
Common milkwort	Polygala vulgaris	*Polygala commun*
Common orache	Atriplex patula	*Arroche étalée*
Common penny-cress	Thlaspi arvense	*Tabouret des champs*
Common pepperwort	Lepidium campestre	*Passerage champêtre*
Common quaking grass	Briza media	*Brize commune*
Common ragwort	Senecio jacobaea	*Séneçon jacobée*
Common rock-rose	Helianthemum nummularium	*Hélianthème commun*
Common scurvey-grass	Cochlearia officinalis	*Cranson officinal*
Common seablite	Suaeda maritima	*Soude maritime*
Common skullcap	Scutellaria galericulata	*Scutellaire casquée / Toque en casque*
Common snapdragon	Antirrhinum majus	*Grand muflier / Guele-de-loup*
Common Solomon's seal	Polygonatum multiflorum	*Sceau de Salomon multiflore*
Common sorrel	Rumex acetosa	*Oseille des prés*

Common spotted orchid	**Dactylorhiza fuchsii**	*Orchis de Fuchs*
Common star of Bethlehem	**Ornithogalum umbellatum**	*Dame-d'onze heures / Étoile de Bethléem*
Common storksbill	**Erodium cicutarium**	*Bec-de-grue commun*
Common Sundew	**Drosera rotundifolia**	*Rossolis à feuilles rondes*
Common toadflax	**Linaria vulgaris**	*Linaire commune*
Common twayblades	**Listera ovata**	*Listère a feuilles ovales*
Common valerian	**Valerian officinalis**	*Herbe aux chats / Valériane officinale*
Common vetch	**Vicia sativa**	*Vesce cultivée*
Common wart cress	**Coronopus squamatus**	*Sénebière corne-de-cerf*
Common water plantain	**Alisma plantago-aquatica**	*Plantain d'eau commun*
Common water starwort	**Callitriche palustris**	*Callitriche des marais*
Common whitlow-grass	**Draba muralis**	*Drave des murs*
Common winter-cress	**Barbarea vulgaris**	*Barbarée commune / Herbe de Sainte-Barbe*
Common wintergreen	**Pyrola minor**	*Petite pyrole*
Compass plant	**Silphium laciniatum**	*Plante boussole*
Common yellow trefoil	**Trifolium dubium**	*Trèfle douteux*
Coneflower	**Echinacea**	*Echinacea*
Coneflower	**Rudbeckia**	*Rudbeckia*
Confederate jasmine	**Trachelospermum jasminoides**	*Jasmin étoilé*
Confederate rose	**Hibiscus mutabilis**	*Hibiscus mutabilis*
Cootmandra wattle	**Acacia baileyana**	*Acacia baileyana*
Copey	**Clusis rosea**	*Clusis rosea*
Copihue	**Lapageria rosea**	*Lapageria rosea*
Copper beech	**Fagus sylvatica purpurea**	*Hêtre pourpre*
Copperleaf	**Acalypha wilkesiana**	*Ricinelle*
Coquito	**Jubaea chilensis**	*Cocotier du Chili*
Coral berry	**Aechmea fulgens**	*Aechmea fulgens*
Coral bush	**Templetonia retusa**	*Templetonia retusa*
Coral cactus	**Rhipsalis cereuscula**	*Rhipsalis cereuscula*
Coral drops	**Bessera elegans**	*Bessera elegans*
Coral gem	**Lotus berthelotii**	*Lotier berthelotii*
Coral honeysuckle	**Lonicera sempervirens**	*Chèvrefeuille de Virginie*
Coral necklace	**Illecebrum verticillatum**	*Illécèbre verticillé*
Coral pea	**Hardenbergia violacea**	*Hardenbergia violacea*
Coral plant	**Berberidopsis coralina**	*Berberidopsis coralina*
Coral plant	**Russelia equisetiformis**	*Plante corail*
Coral root	**Cardamine bulbifera**	*Dentaire bulbifère*
Coral-root orchid	**Corallorhiza trifida**	*Racine-de-corail*
Coral vine	**Antigonon leptopus**	*Antigonon*

Coriander	Coriandrum sativum	*Coriandre cultivée*
Cork bark maple	Acer palmatum 'Senkaki'	*Érable palmatum "Senkaki"*
Cork oak	Quercus suber	*Chêne-liège*
Corkscrew nut	Corylus avellana contorta	*Noisetier tortueux*
Corkscrew rush	Juncus effusus spiralis	*Jonc épars*
Corn buttercup	Ranunculus arvensis	*Renoncule des champs*
Corn chamomile	Anthemis arvensis	*Anthémis des champs / Fausse camomile*
Corn cockle	Agrostemma githago	*Nielle des blés*
Corn marigold	Chrysanthemum segetum	*Chrysanthème de blés / Marguerite dorée*
Corn mignonette	Reseda phyteuma	*Réséda raiponce*
Corn parsley	Petroselinum segetum	*Persil des moissons*
Corn plant	Dracaena fragrans	*Dragonnier odorant*
Corn poppy	Papaver rhoeas	*Coquelicot*
Corn sow-thistle	Sonchus arvensis	*Laiteron des champs*
Cornelian cherry	Cornus mas	*Cornouiller mâle*
Cornflower	Centaurea cyanus	*Bleuet des champs*
Cornish elm	Ulmus angustifoliua cornubiensis	*Orme de Cornouaillea*
Cornish golden elm	Ulmus dicksonii	*Orme doré*
Cornish heath	Erica vagans	*Bruyère vagabonde*
Cornish mallow	Lavatera cretica	*Lavatère de crète*
Cornish moneywort	Sibthorpia europaea	*Sibthorpie d'Europe*
Cornsalad	Valerianella locusta	*Mâche doucette*
Coronilla	Coronilla	*Coronille*
Corsican heath	Erica terminalis	*Bruyère de Corse*
Corsican mint	Mentha requienii	*Menthe de Corse*
Corsican pine	Pinus nigra laricio	*Pin noir de Corse*
Cotton ball	Espostosa lanata	*Espostosa lanata*
Cotton lavender	Santolina chamaecyparissus	*Fausse Sanguenitte / Santoline / Santoline blanche*
Cotton rose	Hibiscus mutabilis	*Hibiscus mutabilis*
Cotton thistle	Onopordum acanthium	*Chardon aux ânes / Chardon d'Écosse*
Cottonweed	Otanthus maritimus	*Otanthe maritime*
Cottonwood	Populus deltoides	*Peuplier noir d'Amérique*
Couch grass	Agrophyrum	*Agropyre*
Coulter pine	Pinus coulteri	*Pin coulteri*
Cowbane	Cicuta virosa	*Ciguë aquatique*
Cowbane	Cicuta virosa	*Cicutaire vireuse*

Cowberry	Vaccinium vitis-idaea	*Airelle rouge / Vigne du Mont Ida*
Cow parsley	Anthriscus sylvestris	*Anthrisque sauvage*
Cowslip	Primula veris	*Coucou / Primevère officinale*
Cow's tail pine	Cephalotaxus harringtonia	*Cephalotaxus harringtonia*
Crab apple	Malus sylvestris	*Pommier sauvage*
Crab cactus	Schlumbergera truncata	*Cactus crabe*
Crack willow	Salix fragilis	*Salix fragilis*
Cradle orchid	Anguloa clowesii	*Anguloa clowesii*
Crambe cordifolia	Crambe cordifolia	*Crambé à feuille en cœur*
Cranberry	Vaccinium oxycoccus	*Canneberge*
Crape myrtle	Lagerstroemia indica	*Lilas d été*
Cream cups	Platystemon californicus	*Platystemon californicus*
Creamy butterbur	Petasites japonicus	*Pétasite du Japon*
Creeping bellflower	Campanula rapunculoides	*Campanule fausse-raiponce*
Creeping blue blossom	Ceanothus thyrsiflorus repens	
		Céanothe thyrsiflorus repens
Creeping bluets	Hedyotis michauxii	*Rubiacées*
Creeping buttercup	Ranunculus repens	*Renoncule rampante*
Creeping Charlie	Pilea nummularifolia	*Pilea nummularifolia*
Creeping cinquefoil	Potentilla reptans	*Potentille rampante*
Creeping dogwood	Cornus canadensis	*Cornouiller canadensis*
Creeping fig	Ficus pumila	*Ficus pumila*
Creeping Jenny	Lysimachia nummularia	*Lysimaque nummulaire*
Creeping juniper	Juniperus horizontalis	*Genévrier rampante*
Creeping lady's tresses	Goodyera repens	*Goodyère rampante*
Creeping phlox	Phlox stolonifera	*Phlox stolonifera*
Creeping soft grass	Holcus mollis	*Holcus mollis*
Creeping spearwort	Ranunculus reptans	*Renoncule à tige rampante*
Creeping thistle	Cirsium arvense	*Cirse des champs*
Creeping willow	Salix repens	*Saule rampant*
Creeping yellow cress	Rorippa sylvestris	*Rorippa des forêts*
Creeping zinnia	Sanvitalia procumbens	*Sanvitalia procumbens*
Creosote bush	Larrea	*Larrée*
Cress	Lapidium sativum	*Cresson alénois*
Crested cow-wheat	Melampyrum cristatum	*Mélampyre des prés*
Cretan brake	Pteris cretica	*Pteris cretica*
Cretan dittany	Origanum dictamnus	*Origan dictamnus*
Cricket bat willow	Salix alba caerulea	*Saule blanc var coerulea*
Crimean lime	Tilia x euchlora	*Tilleul de Crimée*
Crimson clover	Trifolium incarnatum	*Trèfle incarnat / Farouch*
Crimson glory vine	Vitis coignetiae	*Vitis coignetiae /*
		Bignonia capreolata

Cross-leaved heath	**Erica tetralix** *Bruyère tétragone / Caminet / Clarin*	
Croton	**Codiaeum**	*Croton*
Crowberry	**Empetrum nigrum**	*Camarine noire*
Crow garlic	**Allium vineale**	*Ail des vignes*
Crown imperial	**Fritillaria imperialis**	*Couronne impériale*
Crown of thorns	**Euphorbia milii**	*Couronne d'épine*
Cruel plant	**Araujia sericofera**	*Araujia sericofera*
Crusaders' spears	**Urginea maritima**	*Urginea maritima*
Crystal anthurium	**Anthurium crystallinum**	*Anthurium crystallinum*
Cuban royal palm	**Roystonea regia**	*Roi des palmers*
Cuckoo flower	**Cardamine pratensis**	*Cardamine des prés / Cressonnette*
Cuckoo pint	**Arum maculatum**	*Guet maculé*
Cucumber tree	**Magnolia acuminata** *Magnolia à feuilles acuminées*	
Cultivated flax	**Linum usitatissimum**	*Lin cultivé*
Cup and saucer vine	**Cobaea scandens**	*Cobée grimpante*
Cupid flower	**Ipomoea quamoclit**	*Ipomoea quamoclit*
Cupid peperomia	**Peperomia scandens**	*Peperomia scandens*
Curled dock	**Rumex crispus**	*Patience crépue*
Curly pondweed	**Potamogeton crispus**	*Potamot crépu*
Currant	**Ribes**	*Groseillier*
Curry plant	**Helichrysum italicum**	*Helichrysum italicum*
Curtis's mouse-ear	**Cerastium pumilum**	*Céraiste visqueux*
Custard apple	**Annona**	*Anone*
Cut-leaved cranesbill	**Geranium dissectum**	*Géranium découpé*
Cut-leaved dead-nettle	**Lamium hybridum**	*Lamier hybride*
Cut-leaved self-heal	**Prunella laciniata**	*Brunelle laciniée*
Cyclamen	**Cyclamen**	*Cyclamen*
Cypress	**Cupressus**	*Cyprès*
Cyprus turpentine	**Pistacia terebinthus**	*Térébinthe*
Cypress vine	**Ipomoea quamoclit**	*Ipomoea quamoclit*

D

Daffodil	**Narcissus**	*Narcisse*
Dahurian juniper	**Juniperus davurica**	*Junipeus davurica*
Daimio oak	**Quercus dentata**	*Chêne denté*
Daisy	**Bellis**	*Pâquerette*
Daisy bush	**Olearia**	*Oléaire*
Dalmatian iris	**Iris pallida** *Iris de Florence / Iris à parfum*	
Dalmatian laburnum	**Petteria ramantacea**	*Petteria ramantacea*

Dalmatian toadflax	**Linaria genistifolia dalmatica**	*Linaire dalmatica*
Dame's violet	**Hesperis matronalis**	*Julienne des dames*
Dancing doll orchid	**Oncidium flexuosum**	*Oncidium flexuosum*
Dandelion	**Taraxacum officinale**	*Dent de lion / Pissenlit*
Daphne	**Daphne**	*Daphné*
Daphne cneorum	**Daphne cneorum**	*Thymélée des Alpes*
Dark mullein	**Verbascum nigrum**	*Molène noire*
Dark red helleborine	**Epipactis atrorubens**	*Épipactis sanguine*
Darling pea	**Swainsonia galegifolia**	*Swainsonia galegifol*
Darwin's barberry	**Berberis darwinii**	*Vinettier de Darwin*
Date palm	**Phoenix dactyliferra**	*Dattier*
Date plum	**Diospyros lotus**	*Plaqueminier faux lotier*
David's pine	**Pinus armandii**	*Pin armandii*
David's peach	**Prunus davidiana**	*Pécher de David*
Dawn redwood	**Metassequoia glyptostroboides**	*Metassequoia glyptostroboides*
Day flower	**Commelina coelistis**	*Commelina coelistis*
Day Lily	**Hemerocallis**	*Hémérocalle*
Dead nettle	**Lamium**	*Lamier*
Deadly nightshade	**Atropa belladonna**	*Belladone*
Delavay fir	**Abies delavayi**	*Sapin delaveyi*
Delphinium	**Delphinium**	*Dauphinelle / Pied d'alouette*
Delta maidenhair	**Adiantum cuneatum**	*Cappiliaire cunéforme*
Dense-flowered orchid	**Neotinea intacta**	*Habenaria à fleurs denses*
Deodar	**Cedrus deodara**	*Cèdre de l'Himalaya*
Deptford pink	**Dianthus armeria**	*Œillet des bois / Œillet velu*
Desert fan palm	**Washingtonia filifera**	*Washingtonia filifera*
Desert privet	**Peperomia magnoliifolia**	*Peperomia magnoliifolia*
Desert rose	**Adenium**	*Rose du désert*
Devi's bit scabious	**Succisa pratensis**	*Succise des prés*
Devil's club	**Oplopanax horridus**	*échinopanax*
Dewberry	**Rubus caesius**	*Ronce bleuâtre*
Daipensia	**Diapensia lapponica**	*Diapensie*
Dickson's golden elm	**Ulmus dicksonii**	*Orme doré*
Digger speedwell	**Veronica perfoliata**	*Véronique perfoliata*
Disk-leaved hebe	**Hebe pinguifolia**	*Hebe pinguifolia*
Dittander	**Lepidium latifolium**	*Passerage à feuilles large*
Dittany	**Dictamnus**	*Dictame*
Dodecatheon	**Dodecatheon**	*Gyroselle*
Dog fennel	**Anthemis**	*Anthemis*
Dog's mercury	**Mercurialis perennis**	*Mercuriale des bois*

Dog's-tooth violet	**Erythronium dens-canis**	*Dent-de-chien*
Dogwood	**Cornus sanguinea**	*Vernouiller*
Doll's eyes	**Actaea pachypoda**	*Actée pachypoda*
Donkey-tail	**Sedum morganianum**	*Sedum morganianum*
Dorset heath	**Erica ciliaris**	*Bruyère ciliée*
Dotted loosestrife	**Lysimachia punctata**	*Lysimaque ponctuée*
Double Common snowdrop	**Galanthus nivalis 'Flore pleno'**	
		Perce-neige 'Flore pleno'
Double daisy	**Bellis Perennis**	*Pàquerette vivace*
Double meadow buttercup	**Ranunculus acris flore pleno**	*Bouton d'or /*
		Renoncle âcre flore pleno
Double sea campion	**Silene vulgaris maritima flore pleno**	
		Silene vulgaris maritima flore pleno
Douglas fir	**Pseudotsuga menziesii**	*Douglas vert /*
	Sapin de l'Oregon /	*Sapin de Douglas*
Dove tree	**Davidia involucrata**	*Arbre aux mouchoirs /*
		Arbre aux pochettes
Downy birch	**Betula pubescens**	*Bouleau pubescent*
Downy woundwort	**Stachys germanica**	*Épiaire d'Allemagne*
Dragon tree	**Dracunculus vulgaris**	*Serpentaire*
Dragon's claw willow	**Salix matsudana 'Tortuosa'**	*Salix matsudana tortuosa*
Dragon's head	**Dracocephalum**	*Dracoléphale*
Dragon's mouth	**Horminum pyrenaicum**	*Horminum pyrenaicum*
Dragon's teeth	**Tetragonolobus maritimus**	*Tétragonolobe siliqueeux*
Drooping juniper	**Saxifraga cernua**	*Saxifrage penchée*
Dropwort	**Filipendula vulgaris**	*Filipendule à 6 petales*
Drumstick primula	**Primula denticulata**	*Primula denticulata*
Drunkard's dream	**Hatiora salicornoides**	*Hatiora salicornoides*
Duck potato	**Sagittaria latifolia**	*Flèche d'eau américaine*
Duck weed	**Lemna**	*Lenticule*
Duke of Argyll's tea tree	**Lycium barbarum**	*Lyciet jasminoïdes*
Dumb cane	**Dieffenbachia**	*Dieffenbachia*
Dumpling cactus	**Lophophora williamsii**	*Peyote /*
		Plante qui fait les yeux émerveillés
Dune cabbage	**Rhynchosinapis monensis**	*Moutarde giroflée*
Durmast oak	**Quercus petraea**	*Chêne sessile*
Dusky cranesbill	**Geranium phaeum**	*Géranium brun*
Dutch crocus	**Crocus vernus**	*Crocus vernus*
Dutch elm	**Ulmus x Hollandica**	*Ulmus x Hollandica*
Dutchman's breeches	**Dicentra cucullaria**	*Cœur de Jeannette / Cœur de Marie*
Dwarf bearded iris	**Iris pumila**	*Iris pumila*
Dwarf birch	**Betula nana**	*Bouleau nain*

Dwarf chickweed	**Moenchia erecta**	*Moenchia dresé*
Dwarf cornel	**Cornus suecica**	*Cornouiller de Suède*
Dwarf cudweed	**Gnaphalium supinum**	*Gnaphale nain*
Dwarf elder	**Sambucus ebulus**	*Hièble*
Dwarf fan palm	**Chamaerops humilis**	*Chamaerops humilis*
Dwarf mallow	**Malva neglecta**	*Petite mauve*
Dwarf mountain palm	**Chamaedorea elegans**	*Chamaedorea elegans*
Dwarf palmeto	**Sabal minor**	*Palmier nain*
Dwarf pine	**Pinus mugo**	*Pin de montagne*
Dwarf pomegranate	**Punica granatum nana**	*Grenadier nain*
Dwarf Siberian pine	**Pinus pumila**	*Pin pumila*
Dwarf sumach	**Rhus copallina**	*Rhus copallina*
Dwarf thistle	**Cirsium acaulon**	*Cirse acaule*
Dwarf white wood lily	**Trillium nivale**	*Trillie nivale*
Dwarf white stripe bamboo	**Pleioblastus variegatus**	*Pleioblastus variegatus*
Dwarf willow	**Salix herbacea**	*Saule herbacea*
Dyers' alkanet	**Alkanet tinctoria**	*Orcanette*
Dyers' greenweed	**Genista tinctoria**	*Genêt des teinturiers*
Dyers' greenweed	**Genista tinctoria**	*Genestrolle*

E

Early gentian	**Gentiana anglica**	*Gentiane d'Angleterre*
Early marsh orchid	**Dactylorhiza incarnata**	*Orchis incarnat*
Early purple orchid	**Orchis mascula**	*Orchis male*
Early scurvy-grass	**Cochlearia danica**	*Cranson du Danemark*
Easter cactus	**Rhipsalidopsis gaertneri**	*Cactus de Pâques*
Easter lily	**Lilium longiflorum**	*Lis à longues fleurs*
Eastern cottonwood	**Populus deltoides**	*Peuplier noir d'Amérique*
Eastern hemlock	**Tsuga canadensis**	*Pruche /Tsuga du Canada*
Eastern redbud	**Cercis canadensis**	*Gainier du Canada*
Eastern white cedar	**Thuja occidentalis**	*Thuya du Canada*
Eastern white pine	**Pinus strobus**	*Pin Weymouth*
Eau-de-Cologne mint	**Mentha piperita "Citrata"**	*Menthe poivrée*
Eccremocarpus	**Eccremocarpus scaber**	*Bignone de Chili*
Edelweiss	**Leontopodium**	*Edelweiss*
Edible prickly pear	**Opuntia ficus-indica**	*Opuntia ficus-indica*
Eel grass	**Zostera**	*Zostère*
Eglantine	**Rosa eglanteria**	*Églantine /Églantier odorant*
Egyptian star	**Pentas lanceolata**	*Pentas lanceolata*
Eight stamened waterwort	**Elatine hydropiper**	*Elatine poivre d'eau*
Elaeagnus	**Elaeagnus**	*Chalef*

Elder	Sambucus	Sureau
Elecampane	Inula helenium	Grande aunée / Inule aunée
Elegant St. John's wort	Hypericum pulchrum	Millepertuis élégant
Elephant apple	Dillenia indica	Dillenia indica
Elephant apple	Feronia elephantum	Féronier
Elephant bush	Portulacaria afra	Pourprier en arbre
Elephant's ears	Hedera colchica 'Dentata'	Lierre de Perse
Elephant's ears	Philodendron domesticum	Philodendron domesticum
Elephant's foot	Beaucarnea recurvata	Pied-d'éléphant
Elephant's foot	Diosorea elephantpes	Pied-d'éléphant
Elm	Ulmus	Orme
Elodea crispa	Lagarosiphon major	Élodée
Emerald ripple	Peperomia caperata	Peperomia caperata
Englemann spruce	Picea englemannii	Épicéa d'Englemann
English bluebell	Hyacinthoides non-scripta	Hyacinthoides non-scripta
English elm	Ulmus procera	Orme d'Angleterre
English iris	Iris latifolia	Iris d'Angleterre
Engish stonecrop	Sedum anglicum	Orpin d'Angleterre
Epaulette tree	Pterostyrax hispida	Pterostyrax hispida
Eritrichium nanum	Eritrichium nanum	Roi des Alpes
Eryngium alpinum	Eryngium alpinum	Chardon bleu des Alpes
Erythrina	Erythrina	Érythrine
Esthwaite waterweed	Elodea nuttallii	Élodée de Nuttall
Etruscan honeysuckle	Lonicera etrusca	Chèvrefeuille d'Italie
European fan palm	Chamaerops humilis	Chamaerops humilis
European larch	Larix decidua	Mélèze de Europe
European white lime	Tilia tomentosa	Tilleul de Hongrie /Tilleul argenté
Evening primrose	Oenothera	Œnothère / Onagre
Everlasting flower	Helichrysum bracteatum	Immortelle à bractées
Everlasting pea	Lathyrus grandiflorus	Gesse à grandes fleurs
Everlasting pea	Lathyrus latifolius	Pois vivace
Everlasting pea	Lathyrus latifolius	Gesse a larges feuilles
Everlasting pea	Lathyrus sylvestris	Pois vivace
Exeter elm	Ulmus glabra	Orme blanc
Exeter elm	Ulmus glabra Exoniensis	Orme de montagne fastigié
Eyebright	Euphrasia officinalis	Casse-lunettes / Euphraise officinal
Eyelash begonia	Begonia bowerae	Begonia bowerae

F

Fair maids of France	Saxifraga granulata	*Saxifrage granulée*
Fairy bells	**Disporum**	*Disporum*
Fairy duster	**Calliandra eriophylla**	*Calliandra eriophylla*
Fairy flax	**Linum catharticum**	*Lin purgatif*
Fairy fountain	**Celosia cristata**	
		Célosie crête de coq "Fairy fountains"
Fairy fountain	**Celosia cristata**	*Amarante crête-de-coq / Passe-velours*
Fairy foxglove	**Erinus alpinus**	*Érine des Alpes*
Fairy lantern	**Calochortus**	*Calochortus*
Fairy thimbles	**Campanula cochlearifolia**	*Campanule menue*
False acacia	**Robinia pseudoacacia**	*Acacia blanc / Robinier faux-acacia*
False anemone	**Anemonopsis**	*Anemonopsis*
False aralia	**Dizygotheca elegantissima**	*Dizygotheca elegantissima*
False beech	**Nothofagus**	*Nothofagus*
False bulrush	**Typha latifolia**	*Massette à larges feuilles*
False cypress	**Chamaecyparis**	*Faux cyprès*
False heather	**Cuphea hyssopifolia**	*Cuphea hyssopifolia*
False indigo	**Amorpha**	*Faux indigo*
False jasmine	**Gelsemium sempervirens**	*Gelsemium sempervirens*
False oat grass	**Arrhenatherum elatius**	*Avoine élevée / Fenasse / Fromental*
False spikenard	**Smilacina racemosa**	*Smilacina racemosa*
Fanwort	**Cabomba carolianus**	*Cabombe carolianus*
Fastigiate pedunculate oak	**Quercus robur fastigiata**	
		Chêne pédonculé pyramidial
Fat duckweed	**Lemna gibba**	*Lentille d'eau bossue*
Fat hen	**Chenopodium album**	*Chénopode blanc*
Fat pork tree	**Clusia rosea**	*Clusia rosea*
Feather-top	**Pennisetum villosum**	*Pennisetum villosum*
Felwort gentian	**Gentiana amarella**	*Gentiane amère*
Fen bedstraw	**Galium uliginosum**	*Gaillet fangeux*
Fen orchid	**Liparis loeselii**	*Liparis de Loesel*
Fennel	**Foeniculum vulgare**	*Fenouil commun*
Fennel pondweed	**Potamogeton pectinatus**	*Potamot pectiné*
Fenugreek	**Trigonella foenum-graecum**	*Fénugrec / Trigonelle*
Fern-leaf aralia	**Polyscias filicifolia**	*Polyscias filicifolia*
Fetterbush	**Pieris floribunda**	*Pieris floribunda*

Feverfew	**Tanacetum parthenium**	*Grande camomille*
Few flowered leek	**Allium paradoxum**	*Allium paradoxum*
Fiddle dock	**Rumex pulcher**	*Patience élégante*
Fiddle-leaf fig	**Ficus lyrata**	*Ficus lyrata*
Field bindweed	**Convolvulus arvensis**	*Liseron des champs*
Field cow-wheat	**Melampyrum arvense**	*Blé de vache /*
		Mélampyre des champs
Field fleawort	**Senecio integrifolius**	*Séneçon à feuilles entières*
Field garlic	**Allium oleraceum**	*Ail des champs*
Field gentian	**Gentiana campestris**	*Gentiane champêtre*
Field madder	**Sherardia arvensis**	*Rubéole des champs*
Field mouse-ear	**Cerastium arvense**	*Céraiste des champs*
Field pansy	**Viola arvensis**	*Pensée des champs*
Field poppy	**Papaver rhoeas**	*Coquelicot*
Field scabious	**Knautia arvensis**	*Knautie des champs / Oreille d'âne*
Field woundwort	**Stachys arvensis**	*Épiaire des champs*
Fig	**Ficus**	*Figuier*
Fig leafed goosefoot	**Chenopodium ficifolium**	
		Chénopode à feuilles de figuier
Figwort	**Scrophularia**	*Scrofulaire*
Filbert	**Corylus maxima**	*Grand coudrier / Avelinier*
Fine-leafed water dropwort	**Oenanthe aquatica**	*Œnanthe aquatique*
Finger-leafed ivy	**Hedera helix digitata**	*Hedera helix digitata*
Fingered saxifrage	**Saxifraga tridactylites**	*Saxifrage digitée*
Fingered speedwell	**Veronica triphyllos**	*Véronique à feuilles trilobées*
Fire lily	**Lilium bulbiferum**	*Lilium bulbiferum*
Firecracker vine	**Manettia cordifolia**	*Manettia cordifolia*
Firethorn	**Pyracantha coccinea**	*Buisson ardent*
Fish grass	**Cabomba caroliana**	*Cabomba caroliana*
Fishtail fern	**Cyrtomium falcatum**	*Cyrtomium falcatum*
Fishbone cactus	**Epiphyllum anguliger**	*Epiphyllum anguliger*
Fishpole bamboo	**Phyllostachys aurea**	*Bambou doré*
Five fingers	**Pseudopanax arboreus**	*Pseudopanax arboreus*
Five fingers	**Syngonium auritum**	*Syngonium auritum*
Five leaved ivy	**Ampelopsis quinquefolia**	*Vigne vierge vraie*
Five leaved ivy	**Parthenocissus quinquefolia**	*Vigne vierge vraie*
Five-spot baby	**Nemophila maculata**	*Némophile maculata*
Flame azalea	**Rhododendron calendulaceum**	*Rhododendron calendulaceum*
Flame coral tree	**Erythrina coralloides**	*Érythrine coralloides*
Flame creeper	**Tropaeolum speciosum**	*Capucine élégante*
Flame flower	**Pyrostegia venusta**	*Pyrostegia venusta*
Flame nasturtium	**Tropaeolum speciosum**	*Capucine élégante*

Flame-of-the-forest	**Spathodea campanulata**	*Spathodea campanulata*
Flame vine	**Pyrostegia venusta**	*Pyrostegia venusta*
Flame violet	**Episcia cupreata**	*Episcia cupreata*
Flaming Katy	**Kalanchoe blossfeldiana**	*Kalanchoe blossfeldiana*
Flaming sword	**Vriesea splendens**	*Vriesea splendens*
Flaming flower	**Anthurium scherzerianum**	*Anthurium scherzerianum*
Flannel flower	**Fremontodendron**	*Fremontodendron*
Flax	**Linum**	*Lin*
Flax lily	**Dianella**	*Dianella*
Flax-seed	**Radiola linoides**	*Radiole faux-lin*
Fleabane	**Erigeron**	*Vergerette*
Flixweed	**Descurainia sophia**	*Sisymbre sagesse*
Floating bur-reed	**Sparganium angustifolium**	*Rubanie à feuilles étroites*
Floating water plantain	**Luronium natans**	*Fluteau nageant*
Floss flower	**Ageratum**	*Agérate bleue / Eupatoire bleue*
Floss silk tree	**Chorisia speciosa**	*Chorisia speciosa*
Flower of the hour	**Hibiscus trionum**	*Hibiscus trionum*
Flowering banana	**Musa ornata**	*Bananier à fleurs décoratives*
Flowering currant	**Ribes sanguineum**	*Faux-Cassis / Groseillier à fleurs / Groseillier sanguin*
Flowering dogwood	**Cornus florida**	*Cornouiller à fleurs*
Flowering gum	**Eucalyptus ficifolia**	*Eucalyptus ficifolia*
Flowering quince	**Chaenomeles**	*Cognassier du Japon*
Flowering raspberry	**Rubus odoratus**	*Ronce odorante*
Flowering rush	**Butomus umbellatus**	*Butome /Jonc fleuri*
Flowering tobacco	**Nicotiana sylvestris**	*Tabac sylvestris*
Fluellin	**Kickxia**	*Kickxie*
Fly honeysuckle	**Lonicera xylasteum**	*Chèvrefeuille des bois*
Fly orchid	**Ophrys insectifera**	*Ophrys mouche*
Foam of May .	**Spiraea "Arguta"**	*Spirée x arguta*
Foamflower	**Tiarella**	*Tiarelle*
Fool's parsley	**Aethusa cynapium**	*Petite ciguë*
Fool's watercress	**Apium nodiflorum**	*Ache nodiflore*
Forget-me-not	**Myosotis**	*Myosotis*
Fountain flower	**Ceropegia sandersonii**	*Ceropegia sandersonii*
Four o'clock flower	**Mirabilis**	*Belle-de-nuit*
Four-leaved allseed	**Polycarpon tetraphyllum**	*Polycarpon à quatre feuilles*
Foxglove	**Digitalis purpurea**	*Digitale / Digitale pourpre / Gant de Notre-Dame*
Foxglove tree	**Paulownia tomentosa**	*Paulownia impérial*

38

Foxtail barley	**Hordeum jubatum**	*Orge barbue*
Foxtail fern	**Asparagus densiflorus 'Myersii'**	
		Asparagus densiflorus 'Myersii'
Foxtail lily	**Eremurus**	*Eremurus*
Foxtail millet	**Setaria italica**	*Millet à grappes / Millet d'Italie*
Fragrant evening primrose	**Oenothera stricta**	*Onagre odorante*
Fragrant olive	**Osmanthus fragrans**	*Olivier odorant*
Fragrant snowbell	**Styrax obassia**	*Styrax obassia*
Frangipani	**Plumeria rubra**	*Frangipanier*
Frankncense	**Boswellia**	*Boswellie*
Freckle face	**Hypoestes phyllostachya**	*Hypoestes phyllostachya*
French cranesbill	**Geranium endressii**	*Géranium d'endresse*
French hales	**Sorbus latifolia**	*Alisier de Fontainebleau*
French hardhead	**Centaurea jacea**	*Centaurée jacée*
French honeysuckle	**Hedysarum coronarium**	*Sainfoin à bouquets / Sainfoin d'Espagns*
French lavender	**Lavendula dentata**	*Lavande dentata / Lavande stoechas*
French marigold	**Tagetes patula**	*Œillet d'Inde*
French toadflax	**Linaria arenaria**	*Linaire des sables*
Friendship plant	**Pilea involucrata**	*Pilea involucrata*
Friendship tree	**Crassula ovata**	*Crassula ovata*
Fringe tree	**Chionanthus virginicus**	*Arbre à franges / Arbre de neige*
Fringed water lily	**Nymphoides peltata**	*Limnanthème faux-nénuphar*
Fritillary	**Fritillaria meleagris**	*Fritillaire pintade*
Frog-bit	**Hydrocharis morsus-ranae**	*Hydrocharis des Grenouilles*
Frog orchid	**Coeloglossum viride**	*Orchis grenouille*
Frosted orache	**Atriplex laciniata**	*Arroche lacinée*
Fuchsia begonia	**Begonia fuchsiodes**	*Begonia fuchsiodes*
Fuchsia flowered currant	**Ribes speciosum**	*Ribes speciosum*
Fuji cherry	**Prunus incisa**	*Prunus incisa*
Full moon maple	**Acer japonicum**	*Érable du Japon*
Fulvous day lily	**Hemerocallis fulva**	*Hémrocallis fulva*
Fumitory	**Fumaria oficinalis**	*Fumeterre officinale*
Funkia	**Hosta**	*Funkia*
Fyfield pea	**Lathyrus tuberosus**	*Macusson*

G

Galingale	Cyperus longus	*Souchet*
Gallant soldier	**Galinsoga parviflora**	*Galinsoga à petites fleurs*
Gandergoose	**Orchis morio**	*Orchis bouffon*
Garden arabis	**Arabis caucasica**	*Corbeille d'argent*
Garden loosestrife	**Lysimachia punctata**	*Lysimaque punctata*
Garden nasturtium	**Tropaeolum majus**	*Grande capucine*
Gardener's garters	**Phalaris arundinacea picta**	*Phalaris arundinacea picta*
Garland flower	**Helichrysum**	*Immortelle*
Garlic mustard	**Alliaria petiolata**	*Alliare officinale*
Gay feathers	**Liatris**	*Liatride*
Gean	**Prunus avium**	*Merisier des oiseaux*
Gentian	**Gentiana**	*Gentiane*
Geraldton waxflower	**Chamaelaucium uncinatum**	
		Chamaelaucium uncinatum
Geranium	**Pelargonium**	*Géranium*
German ivy	**Senecio mikanioides**	*Senecio mikanioides*
Geum "Lady Stratheden"	**Geum chiloense**	*Benoîte à fleurs jaunes*
Ghost orchid	**Epipogium aphyllum**	*Épipognon sans feuilles*
Ghost tree	**Davidia involucrata**	*Arbre aux pochettes*
Giant bellflower	**Campanula latifolia**	*Campanule à feuilles larges*
Giant buttercup	**Ranunculus lyallii**	*Renoncule lyallii*
Giant butterwort	**Pinguicula grandiflora**	*Grassette à grandes fleurs*
Giant cowslip	**Primula florindae**	*Primevère florindae*
Giant elephant's ear	**Alocasia macrorrhiza**	*Grande tayove / Taro*
Giant fennel	**Ferula**	*Férule*
Giant fir	**Abies grandis**	*Sapin de Vancouver*
Giant granadilla	**Passiflora quadrangularis**	*Barbadine*
Giant hogweed	**Heracleum mantegazzianum**	*Berce du Cauccase*
Giant holly fern	**Polystichum munitum**	*Polystic munitum*
Giant larkspur	**Consolida ambigua**	*Pied-d'alouette des jardins*
Giant lily	**Cardiocrinum giganteum**	*Cardiocrinum giganteum*
Giant pineapple flower	**Eucomis pallidiflora**	*Eucomis pallidiflora*
Giant pineapple lily	**Eucomis pallidiflora**	*Eucomis pallidiflora*
Giant redwood	**Sequoiadendron giganteum**	*Sequoiadendron giganteum*
Giant reed	**Arundo donax**	*Canne de Provence*
Giant scabious	**Cephalaria gigantes**	*Cephalaria gigantes*
Giant Spaniard	**Aciphylla scott-thomsonii**	*Aciphylla scott-thomsonii*
Giant valerian	**Valeriana pyrenaica**	*Valériane des Pyrénées*
Giant wood fern	**Dryopteris goldiana**	*Fougère goldiana*
Ginger lily	**Hedychium**	*Gandasuli / Hedychium*

Gingham golf ball	Euphorbia obesa	Euphorbia obesa
Gippsland fountain palm	Livistona australis	Livistona australis
Gipsywort	Lycopus europaeus	Chanvre d'eau / Lycope d'Europe
Gladiolus	Gladiolus	Glaïeul
Gladiolus illyricus	Gladiolus illyricus	Glaïeul d'Illurie
Gladwin	Iris foetidissima	Iris fétide
Gland bellflower	Adenophora	Adenophora
Glasswort	Salicornia europaea	Salicorne d'Europe
Glastonberry thorn	Crataegus mongyna biflora	Aubépine
Globe amaranth	Gomphrena globosa	Amarantoïde
Globe artichoke	Cynara scolymus	Artichaut commun
Globe flower	Trollius europaeus	Boule d'or / Trolle
Globe lily	Calochortus albus	Calochoretus albus
Globe thistle	Echinops spaerocephalus	Echinops à tête ronde
Globularia	Globularia	Globulaire
Glory bush	Tibouchina urvelleana	Tibouchina urvelleana
Glory vine	Eccremocarpus scaber	Bignone du Chili
Glory-of-the-snow	Chionodoxa	Gloire de niege
Glory-of-the-sun	Leucocoryne ixiodes	Leucocoryne ixiodes
Gloxinia	Sinningia speciosa	Gloxinia
Glyceria	Glyceria maxima	Glycérie aquatique
Goat willow	Salix caprea	Saule marsault
Goat's beard	Aruncus dioicus	Barbe -de-bouc / Reine des bois
Goat's beard	Tragopogon pratensis	Barbe-du-bouc / Salsifis des prés
Goat's rue	Galega officinalis	Galéga officinal / Lilas d'Espagne / Rue de chèvre
Goat weed	Aegopodium	Égopode / Herbe aux goutteux
Gold dust	Aurinia saxatilis	Corbeille d'or
Gold of pleasure	Camelina sativa	Caméline cultivée
Golden arum lily	Zantedeschia elliotiana	Zantedeschia elliotiana
Golden ball cactus	Notocactus leninghausii	Notocactus leninghausii
Golden bamboo	Phyllostachys aurea	Bambou doré
Golden barrel cactus	Echinocactus grusonii	Echinocactus grusonii
Golden chain	Laburnum anagryoides	Aubour
Golden chervil	Chaerophyllum aureum	Cerfeuil doré
Golden club	Orontium aquaticum	Oronce
Golden dock	Rumex maritimus	Patience maritime
Golden elder	Sambucus nigra aurea	Sureau noir aurea
Golden fairy lantern	Calochortus amabilis	Calochortus amabilis

Golden flax	**Linum flavum**	*Lin jaune*
Golden foxtail	**Alopecurus pratensis aureomarginata**	
		Alopecurus pratensis aureomarginata
Golden globe tulip	**Calochortus amabilis**	*Tulipe de mormons*
Golden larch	**Pseudolarix amabilis**	*Mélèze doré*
Golden bartonia	**Mentzelia lindleyi**	*Bartonia dorée*
Golden oak of Cyprus	**Quercus alnifolia**	*Chêne alnifolia*
Golden oats	**Stipa gigantea**	*Stipa gigantea*
Golden rod	**Solidago virgaurea**	*Verge d'or*
Golden samphire	**Inula crithmoides**	*Inule faux-crithmum*
Golden saxifrage	**Chrysosplenium oppositifolium**	*Cresson doré /*
		Dorine à feuilles opposées
Golden shower	**Cassia fistula**	*Averse dorée*
Golden shower	**Pyrostegia venusta**	*Pyrostegia venusta*
Golden Spaniard	**Aciphylla aurea**	*Aciphylla aurea*
Golden spider lily	**Lycoris aurea**	*Lycoris aurea*
Golden top	**Lamarckia aurea**	*Lamarckie aurea*
Golden trumpet	**Allamanda cathartica**	*Allamanda cathartica*
Golden trumpet tree	**Tabebuia chrysotricha**	*Tabebuia chrysotricha*
Golden weeping willow	**Salix crysocoma**	*Salix chrysocoma*
Golden willow	**Salix alba vitellina**	*Salix alba vitellina*
Golden wonder	**Cassia didymobotrya**	*Senné didymobotrya*
Golden chalice tree	**Solandra maxima**	*Solandra maxima*
Golden-eyed grass	**Sisyrinchium californicum**	*Sisyrinchium californicum*
Golden-feather palm	**Chrysalidocarpus lutescens**	*Chrysalidocarpus lutescens*
Golden-groove bamboo	**Phyllostachys aureosulcata**	*Bambou aureosulcata*
Golden melilot	**Melilotus altissima**	*Mélilot élevé*
Golden-rain tree	**Koelreuteria paniculata**	*Savonnier*
Golden-rayed lily of Japan	**Lilium auratum**	*Lis doré du Japon*
Golden-rod	**Solidago virgaurea**	*Verge d'or*
Goldfish plant	**Columnea gloriosa**	*Columnea gloriosa*
Goldilocks	**Ranunculus auricomus**	*Renoncle à tête d'or*
Good King Henry	**Chenopodium bonus-henricus**	*Bon-Henri /*
		Épinard sauvage
Good-luck plant	**Cordyline fruticosa**	*Cordyline fruticosa*
Goodyer's elm	**Ulmus angustifolia**	*Ulmus angustifolia*
Gooseberry currant	**Ribes uva-crispa**	*Groseillier à*
		maquereau
Goosegrass	**Galium aparine**	*Gaillet gratteron*
Gorgon's head	**Euphorbia gorgonensis**	*Euphorbia gorgonensis*
Gorse	**Ulex europaeus**	*Ajonc d'Europe*
Grand fir	**Abies grandis**	*Sapin de Vancouver*

Granite bottlebrush	Melaleuca elliptica	*Melaleuca elliptica*
Granny's bonnets	Aquelegia vulgaris	*Ancolie*
Grape hyacinth	Muscari neglectum	*Muscari à grappes*
Grape ivy	Cissus rhombifolia	*Cissus rhombifolia*
Grape vine	Vitis vinifera	*Vigne vrai*
Grass of Parnassus	Parnassia palustris	*Herbe de Parnasse*
Great broomrape	Orobanche rapum-genistae	*Orobanche des genêts*
Grass burnet	Sanguisorba officinalis	*Grande Pimpernelle /*
		Sanguisorbe officinale
Grass leaved daylily	Hemerocallis minor	*Hemerocallis minor*
Grass leaved orache	Atriplex littoralis	*Arroche du littoral*
Grass of Parnassus	Parnassia palustris	*Parnassie des marais*
Grass tree	Xanthorrhoea	*Xanthorrhoée*
Grass vetchling	Lathyrus nissolia	*Gesse sans vrille*
Grass widow	Sisyrinchium douglasii	*Sisyrinchium douglasii*
Great bindweed	Calystegia sepium	*Liseron des haies*
Great burdock	Arctium lappa	*Grande bardane*
Great hound's tongue	Cynoglossum germanicum	
	Cynoglosse d'Allemagne / Langue de chien	
Great sea stock	Matthiola sinuata	*Giroflée des dunes*
Great Solomon's seal	Polygonatum commutatum	*Sceau-de-Salomon*
Great sundew	Drosera anglica	*Rossolis d' Angleterre*
Great water dock	Rumex hydrolapathum	*Patience d'eau*
Great white cherry	Prunus "Tai Haku"	*Prunus "Tai Haku"*
Great willow-herb	Epilobium hirsutum	*Épilobe hirsute*
Great yellow gentian	Gentiana lutea	*Gentiana jaune /*
		Grande gentiane
Greater bladderwort	Utricularis vulgaris	*Utriculaire commune*
Greater burnet-saxifrage	Pimpinella major	*Grand boucage*
Greater celandine	Chelidonium majus	*Grande chélidoine / Éclaire*
Greater chickweed	Stellaria neglecta	*Stellaire négligé*
Greater dodder	Cuscuta europaea	*Cuscute d'Europe*
Greater hawkbit	Leontodon hispidus	*Liondent hispide*
Greater knapweed	Centaurea scabiosa	*Centaurée scabieuse*
Greater periwinkle	Vinca major	*Grande pervenche*
Greater pond sedge	Carex riparia	*Carex riparia*
Greater prickly lettuce	Lactuca virosa	*Laitue vireuse*
Greater quaking grass	Briza maxima	*Amourette / Grande Brize*
Greater sea spurrey	Spergularia media	*Spergulaire marginée*
Greater spearwort	Ranunculus lingua	*Grande douve*
Greater stitchwort	Stellaria holostea	*Stellaire holostée*
Greater water parsnip	Sium Latifolium	*Berle à larges feuilles*

Greater wintergreen	**Pyrola media**	*Pyrole moyenne*
Greater woodrush	**Luzula sylvatica**	*Luzule sylvatica*
Greater yellow cress	**Rorippa amphibia**	*Rorippa amphibie*
Greater yellow rattle	**Rhinanthus crista-galli**	*Cocriste*
Grecian strawberry tree	**Arbutus andrachne**	*Arbousier andrachne*
Greek fir	**Abies cephalonica**	*Sapin de Céphalonie*
Greek sand spurrey	**Spergularia bocconi**	*Spergulaire bocconei*
Green alkanet	**Pentaglottis sempervirens**	*Buglosse vivace*
Green ash	**Fraxinus pennsylvanica**	*Frêne vert*
Green earth star	**Cryptanthus acaulis**	*Cryptanthus acaulis*
Green field speedwell	**Veronica agrestis**	*Véronique agreste*
Green-flowered helleborine	**Epipactis phyllanthes**	*Épipactis à fleurs vertes*
Green hellebore	**Helleborus viridis**	*Ellébore vert / Here à la bosse*
Green nightshade	**Solanum physalifolium**	*Morelle verte*
Green veined orchid	**Orchis morio**	*Orchis bouffon*
Green-winged orchid	**Orchis morio**	*Orchis bouffon*
Grey alder	**Alnus incana**	*Aulne blanc*
Grey field speedwell	**Veronica polita**	*Véronique luisante*
Grey mouse-ear	**Cerastium brachypetalum**	*Céraiste à courts pétales*
Grey poplar	**Populus canescens**	*Grisard / Peuplier grisard*
Gromwell	**Lithospermum**	*Grémil*
Ground elder	**Aegopodium podagraria**	*Aegopode podagraire / Herbe aux goutteux*
Ground ivy	**Glechoma hederacea**	*Lierre terrestre*
Ground-pine	**Ajuga chamaepitys**	*Bugle jaune*
Guelder rose	**Viburnum opulus**	*Viorne obier*
Guernsey centaury	**Exaculum pusillum**	*Cicendia fluette*
Guernsey lily	**Nerine sarniensis**	*Amaryllis de Guernsey / Lis de Guernsey*
Gum tree	**Eucalyptus**	*Eucalyptus*
Gutta-percha tree	**Eucommia ulnoides**	*Eucommia ulnoides*
Gypsophila	**Gypsophila**	*Gypsophile*

H

Hackberry	**Celtis occidentalis**	*Micocoulier de Virginie*
Hairlike pondweed	**Potamogeton trichoides**	*Potamot capillaire*
Hairy brome grass	**Bromus ramosus**	*Brome rameux*
Hairy buttercup	**Ranunculus sardous**	*Renoncule sarde*
Hairy greenweed	**Genista pilosa**	*Arnigo / Genêt poilu*
Hairy pea	**Lathyrus hirsutus**	*Gesse hérissée*
Hairy rock-cress	**Arabis hirsuta**	*Arabette poilu*

Hairy rocket	**Erucastrum gallicum**	*Fausse roquette de France*
Hairy St. John's wort	**Hypericum hirsutum**	*Millepertuis velu*
Hairy tare	**Vicia hirsuta**	*Vesce hérissée*
Hairy violet	**Viola hirta**	*Violette hérissée*
Hampshire purslane	**Ludwigia palustris**	*Ludwigia des marais*
Hard fern	**Blechnum spicant**	*Blechne / Fougère pectinée*
Hardhead	**Centaurea nigra**	*Centaurée noire*
Hard shield fern	**Polystichum aculeatum**	*Polystic aculeatum*
Hardy age	**Eupatorium rugosum**	*Eupatoire rugeua*
Harebell	**Campanula rotundifolia**	*Campanule a feuilles rondes*
Harebell poppy	**Meconopsis quintuplinervia**	*Pavot grande*
Hare's foot clover	**Trifolium arvense**	*Trèfle des champs /*
		Trèfle-pied-de-lièvre
Hare's foot fern	**Davallia canariensis**	*Davallia canariensis*
Hare's tail grass	**Lagurus ovatus**	*Gros minet / Queue de lièvre*
Harlequin flower	**Sparaxis**	*Sparaxis*
Hart's tongue fern	**Phyllitis scolopendrium**	*Langue de bœuf /*
		Langue de cerf / Scolopendre
Hartwort	**Tordylium maximum**	*Tordyle majeur*
Hawkweed	**Hieracium**	*Épervière*
Hawkweed ox-tongue	**Picris hieracioides**	*Picride épervière*
Hawthorn	**Crataegus monogyna**	*Aubépine*
Hawthorn maple	**Acer crataegifolium**	*Érable à feuilles d'aubépine*
Hazel	**Corylus avellana**	*Coudrier / Noisettier*
Heart leaf	**Philodendron cordatum**	*Philodendron cordatum*
Heart of flame	**Bromelia balansae**	*Bromelia balansae*
Heart pea	**Cardiospermum halicacabum**	*Pois de cœur*
Heart seed	**Cardiospermum grandiflorum**	*Pois de cœur*
Heart vine	**Ceropegia woodii**	*Ceropegia woodii*
Hearts-and-honey vine	**Ipomoea x multifida**	*Ipomoea x multifida*
Heartsease	**Viola tricolor**	*Pensée sauvage*
Heath banksia	**Banksia ericifolia**	*Banksia ericifolia*
Heath bedstraw	**Galium saxatile**	*Gaillet des rochers*
Heath cudweed	**Gnaphalium sylvaticum**	*Gnaphale des forêts*
Heath dog violet	**Viola canina**	*Violette des chiens*
Heath groundsel	**Senecio sylvaticus**	*Séneçon des bois*
Heath lobelia	**Lobelia urens**	*Lobélie brûlante*
Heath milkwort	**Polygala serpyllifolia**	*Polygala à fieuilles de serpolet*
Heath pearlwort	**Sagina subulata**	*Sagine subulée*
Heath spotted orchid	**Dactylorhiza maculata**	*Orchis a tubercules digités*
Heavenly bamboo	**Nandina domestica**	*Nandina domestica*
Hedge bedstraw	**Galium mollugo**	*Gaillet commun*

45

Hedge mustard	Sisymbrium officinale	*Herbe aux chantres*
Hedge parsley	Torilis japonica *Grattau* /	*Torilis faux-cherfeuil*
Hedgehog broom	Erinacea anthyllis	*Erinacea anthyllis*
Hedgehog holly	Ilex aquifolium 'Ferox'	*Houx des hérissons*
Hedgehog rose	Rosa rugosa	*Rosier rugueux*
Hedge woundwort	Stachys sylvatica	*Épiaire des bois*
Heliotrope arborescens	Heliotrope arborescens	*Fleur des dames* /
	Héliotrope de Pérou	/ *Herbe de Saint-Fiacre*
Helmet flower	Aconitum napellus	*Aconit napel*
Hemlock	Conium maculatum	*Grande ciguë*
Hemp agrimony	Eupatorium cannabinum	*Eupatoire à feuilles de chanvre*
Hen-and-chicken fern	Asplenium bulbiferum	*Asplenium bulbiferum*
Henbane	Hyoscyamus niger	*Jusquiame noire*
Henbit	Lamium amplexicaule	*Lamier amplexicaule*
Hepatica	Hepatica nobilis	*Anémone hépatique*
Herald's trumpet	Beaumontia grandiflora	*Beaumontia grandiflora*
Herb Bennet	Geum urbanum	*Benoîte commune*
Herb of grace	Ruta graveolens	*Herbe de grace* / *Rue fétide*
Herb Paris	Paris quadrifolia	*Parisette à quatre feuilles*
Herb Robert	Geranium robertianum	*Herbe à Robert*
Heropito	Pseudowintera axillaris	*Pseudowintera axillaris*
Herringbone plant	Maranta leuconeura "Erythroneura"	
	Maranta leuconeura "Erythroneura"	
Her's maple	Acer grosseri var. hersii	*Acer grosseri var. hersii*
Hiba	Thujopsis dolabrata	*Tujopsis dolabrata*
Hickory	Carya	*Hickory* / *Noyer d'Amérique*
Higan cherry	Prunus subhirtella	*Cerisier à fleurs japonais*
Highbush blueberry	Vaccinium corymbosum	*Airelle à corymbes*
Highland cudweed	Gnaphalium norvegicum	*Gnaphale de Norvège*
Highland fleabane	Erigeron borealis	*Vergerette dea Alpes*
Highland saxifrage	Saxifraga rivularis	*Saxifrage des ruisseaux*
Hill cherry	Prunus serrulata var. spontanea	*Prunus serrula*
Himalayan Balsam	Impatiens glandulifera	*Balsamind de l'Himalaya*
Himalayan birch	Betula utilis	*Betula utilis*
Himalayan box	Buxus wallichiana	*Buxus wallichiana*
Himalayan holly	Ilex dipyrena	*Houx dipyrena*
Himalayan honeysuckle	Leycesteria formosa	*Leycesteria formosa*
Himalayan hounds tongue	Cynoglossum nervosum	*Cynoglosse nervosum*
Himalayan lilac	Syringa emodi	*Lilas de l'Himalaya*
Himalayan May apple	Podophyllum emodi	*Podophylle indien*
Himalayan pine	Pinus walliciana	*Pin pleureur de l'Himalaya*
Himalayan weeping juniper	Juniperus recurva	*Juniperus recurva*

Hinoki cypress	Chamaecyparis obtusa	*Hinoki*
Hippeastrum vittatum	Hippeastrum vittatum	*Amaryllis de Rouen*
Hoarhound	Marrubum	*Marrube*
Hoary alison	Berteroa incana	*Alysson blanchatre*
Hoary cinquefoil	Potentilla argentea	*Potentille argentée*
Hoary mullein	Verbascum pulverolentum	*Molène pulvérulente*
Hoary mustard	Hirschfeldia incana	*Herschfeldie grisâtre*
Hoary plantain	Plantago media	*Plantain moyen*
Hoary ragwort	Senecio erucifolius	*Séneçon à feuilles de roquette*
Hoary rock-rose	Helianthemum canum	*Hélianthème blanchâtre*
Hoary willow	Salix elaeagnos	*Salix elaeagnos*
Hoary willow-herb	Epilobium parviflorum	*Épilobe à peties fleurs*
Hog's fennel	Peucedanum officinale	*Peucédan officinal / Queue-de-porc*
Hogweed	Heracleum sphondylium	*Berce commune / Patte d'ours*
Holford's pine	Pinus x holfordiana	*Pin x holfordiana*
Holly	Ilex aquifolium	*Houx*
Holly fern	Cyrtomium falcatum	*Cyrtomium falcatum*
Holly fern	Polystichum lonchitis	*Polystic lonchitis*
Holly flame pea	Chorizema illicifolium	*Chorizema illicifolium*
Hollyhock	Alcea	*Passe-rose / Rose trémière / Rose à bâton*
Holm oak	Quercus ilex	*Chêne vert / Yeuse*
Holy flax	Santolina rosmarinifolia	*Santolina rosmarinifolia*
Honewort	Trinia glauca	*Trinia glauque*
Honesty	Lunaria annua	*Herbe aux écus / Monnai du Pape / Monnayère*
Honey locust	Gleditsia triacanthas	*Févier d'Amérique*
Honeybush	Melianthus major	*Mélianthe*
Honeysuckle	Lonicera periclymenum	*Chèvrefeuille des bois*
Hoop pettcoat daffodil	Narcissus bulbocodium	*Narcissus bulbocodium*
Hop	Humulus lupulus	*Houblon*
Hop hornbeam	Ostrya carpinifolia	*Charme houblon*
Hop tree	Ptelea trifoliata	*Orme de Samarie / Ptélée*
Hop trefoil	Trifolium campestre	*Trèfle jaune*
Hornbeam	Carpinus	*Charme*
Hornbeam maple	Acer carpinifolium	*Érable à feuilles de charme*
Horned holly	Ilex cornuta	*Houx cornu*
Horned pondweed	Zannichellia palustris	*Zanichellie des marais*
Horned poppy	Glaucium flavum	*Glaucière jaune*
Horned tulip	Tulipa acuminata	*Tulipe cornue / Tulipe turque*
Horned violet	Viola cornuta	*Viola cornuta*
Hornwort	Ceratophyllum demersum	*Cornifle emergé*

Horse chestnut	**Aesculus hippocastanum**	*Marronnier / Pavier*
Horse radish	**Armoracia rusticana**	*Raifort*
Horseshoe vetch	**Hippocrepis comosa**	*Fer-à-cheval /*
		Hippocrépis à toupet
Hottentot fig	**Carpobrotus edulis**	*Figue des Hottentots*
Hot-water plant	**Achimenes**	*Achimenes*
Hound's tongue	**Cynoglossum officinale**	*Cynoglosse officinale /*
		Langue-de-chien
Houseleek	**Sempervivum**	*Joubarbe*
Huckleberry	**Gaylussacia**	*Gaylussacie*
Humble plant	**Mimosa pudica**	*Sensitive*
Hunangemoho grass	**Chinochloa conspicua**	*Chinochloa conspicua*
Hungarian oak	**Quercus frainetto**	*Chêne de Hongrie*
Huntingdon elm	**Ulmus 'Vegeta'**	*Ulmus 'Vegeta'*
Huntsman's cap	**Sarracenia purpurea**	*Sarracène pourpre*
Hupeh crab	**Malus hupehensis**	*Malus hupehensis*
Hupeh rowan	**Sorbus hupehensis**	*Sorbus hupehensis*
Hutchinsia	**Hornungia peteraea**	*Hutchinsie des pierres*
Hyacinth	**Hyacinthus**	*Jacinthe*
Hyacinth bean	**Lablab purpureus**	*Dolique d'Égypte*
Hydrangea	**Hydrangea**	*Hortensia*
Hyssop	**Hyssopus officinalis**	*Hysope officinale*
Hyssop-leaved loosesrife	**Lythrum hyssopifolia**	*Salicaire a feuilles d'hysoppe*

I

Iceland poppy	**Papaver nudicaule**	*Pavot d'Islande*
Iceland purslane	**Koenigia islandica**	*Koenigia d'Islande*
Ice plant	**Dorotheanthus bellidiformis**	*Dorotheanthus bellidiformis*
Ice plant	**Mesembryanthemum crystallinum**	*Ficoïdee glaciale*
Ice plant	**Sedum spectabile**	*Sedum spectabile*
Illawarra flame tree	**Brachychiton acerifolius**	*Brachychiton acerifolius*
Illawarra palm	**Archontophoenix cunninghamiana**	
		Archontophoenix cunninghamsiana
Immortelle	**Xeranthemum annuum**	*Immortelle annuelle / Xamthème*
Incense cedar	**Calocedrus decurrens**	*Libocedrus decurrens*
Incense plant	**Humea elegans**	*Humea elegans*
Incense rose	**Rosa primula**	*Rose primula*
India rubber tree	**Ficus elastica**	*Caoutchouc*
Indian almond	**Terminalia catappa**	*Terminalia catappa*
Indian bean tree	**Catalpa bignonioides**	*Catalpa commun*
Indian corn	**Zea mays**	*Blé de Turquie / Maïs*

48

Indian currant	**Symphoricarpos orbiculata**	*Symphorine orbiculata*
Indian fig	**Opuntia ficus-indica**	*Figuier de Barbarie*
Indian ginger	**Alpinia calcarata**	*Alpinia calcarata*
Indian hawthorn	**Rhaphiolepis indica**	*Rhaphioloepis indica*
Indian horse chestnut	**Aesculus indica**	*Marronnier d'Inde*
Indian laburnum	**Cassia fistula**	*Averse dorée*
Indian pink	**Dianthus chinensis**	*Œillet de Chine*
Indian plum	**Oemleria cerasiformis**	*Oemleria cerasiformis*
Indigo	**Indigofera**	*Indigotier*
Inkberry	**Ilex glabra**	*Houx glabra*
Interrupted fern	**Osmunda claytoniana**	*Osmunda claytoniana*
Ipomoea	**Ipomoea**	*Ipomée*
Iris	**Iris**	*Iris*
Irish bladderwort	**Utricularia intermedia**	*Utricularia intermedia*
Irish fleabane	**Inula salicina**	*Inule à feuilles de saule*
Irish ivy	**Hedera helix var.hibernica**	*Lierre d'Irlande*
Irish marsh orchid	**Dactylorhiza majalis**	*Orchis à feuilles larges*
Irish yew	**Taxus baccata fastigiata**	*If d'Irlande*
Iron cross begonia	**Begonia masoniana**	*Begonia masoniana*
Ironwood	**Ostrya virginiana**	*Ostryer*
Italian alder	**Alnus cordata**	*Aulne à feuilles en cœur*
Italian buckthorn	**Rhamnus alaternus**	*Neprun alaterne*
Italian cypress	**Cupressus sempervirens**	*Cyprès de Provence*
Italian maple	**Acer opalus**	*Érable d'Italie*
Italian millet	**Setaria italica**	*Sétaire d'Italie*
Ivy	**Hedera**	*Lierre*
Ivy duckweed	**Lemna trisulca**	*Lentille d'eau trilobée*
Ivy of Uraguay	**Cissus striata**	*Cissus striata*
Ivy peperomia	**Peperomia griseoargenta**	*Peperomia griseoargenta*
Ivy-leafed bellfower	**Wahlenbergia hederacea**	*Wahlenbergie à feuilles de lierre*
Ivy-leafed toadflax	**Cymbalaria muralis**	*Linaire cymbalaire / Ruine-de-Rome*
Ivy-leafed violet	**Viola hederacea**	*Viola hederacea*
Ivy speedwell	**Veronica hederifolia**	*Véronique à feuilles de lierre*

J

Jack pine	**Pinus banksiana**	*Pin de Banks*
Jack-in-the-pulpit	**Arisaema triphyllum**	*Arisaema triphyllum*
Jack-go-to-bed-at-noon	**Tragopogon pratensis**	*Salsifis des prés*
Jacobean lily	**Sprekelia formosissima**	*Amaryllis Croix Saint-Jacques*

Jacob's coat	Acalypha wilkesiana	*Ricnelle*
Jacob's ladder	Polemonium caeruleum	*Polémoine blue*
Jacob's ladder	Polemonium caeruleum	*Valériane Grecque*
Jade tree	Crassula ovata	*Crassula ovata*
Jade vine	Strongylodon macrobotrys	*Strongylodon macrobotrys*
Japan pepper	Zanthoxylum piperitum	*Clavalier / Poivrier du Japon*
Japanese anemone	Anemone x hybrida	*Anémone du Japon*
Japanese angelica tree	Aralia elata	*Angélique de Chine*
Japanese apricot	Prunus mume	*Abricot japonais / Abricotier du Japon*
Japanese aralia	Fatsia japonica	*Fatsia japonica*
Japanese arrowhead	Sagittaria sagittifolia "Flore pleno"	*Sagittaria sagittifolia "Flore pleno"*
Japanese banana	Musa basjoo	*Bananier basjoo*
Japanese big leaf magnolia	Magnolia hypoleuca	*Magnolia hypoleuca*
Japanese bitter orange	Poncirus trifoliatta	*Poncirus trifoliatta*
Japanese black pine	Pinus thunbergii	*Pin noir du Japon*
Japanese camellia	Camellia japonica	*Camellia du Japon*
Japanese cedar	Cryptomeria japonica	*Cryptomeria japonica / Sugi*
Japanese climbing fern	Lygodium japonicum	*Lygodium japonicum*
Japanese flag	Iris ensata	*Iris ensata*
Japanese hemlock	Tsuga diversifolia	*Tsuga de Japon*
Japanese hemlock	Tsuga sieboldii	*Tsuga de Japon*
Japanese holly	Ilex crenata	*Houx crenata*
Japanese honeysuckle	Lonicera japonica	*Chèvrefeuille du Japon*
Japanese horse chestnut	Aesculus turbinata	*Marronnier à fruit turbiné*
Japanese hyacinth	Ophiopogon japonicus	*Herbe aux turquoises*
Japanese hydrangea vine	Schizophragma hydrangeoides	*Schizophragma hydrangeoides*
Japanese ivy	Hedera rhombea	*Lierre de Japon*
Japanese ivy	Parthenocissus tricuspidata	*Lierre de Japon / Vigne vierge japonaise*
Japanese larch	Larix kaempferi	*Mélèze du Japon*
Japanese locust	Gleditsia japonica	*Févier du Japon*
Japanese maple	Acer japonicum / Acer palmatum	*Érable du Japon*
Japanese pittosporum	Pittosporum tobira	*Pittosporum tobira*
Japanese privet	Ligustrum japonicum	*Troène du Japon*
Japanese quince	Chaenomeles japonica	*Cognassier du Japon*
Japanese red pine	Pinus densiflora	*Pin rouge du Japon*
Japanese roof iris	Iris tectorum	*Iris evansia*
Japanese rose	Rosa multiflora	*Rosier multiflore*
Japanese sago palm	Cycas revoluta	*Cycas revoluta*

Japanese shield fern	**Dryopteris erythrosora**	*Fougère erythrosora*
Japanese snowball tree	**Viburnum plicatum**	*Boule-de-neige*
Japanese spindle	**Euonymus japonicus**	*Fusain du Japon*
Japanese umbrella pine	**Sciadopitys verticulata**	*Sciadopitys verticulata*
Japanese walnut	**Juglans ailantifolia**	*Juglans ailantifolia*
Japanese white pine	**Pinus parviflora**	*Pin parviflora*
Japanese wisteria	**Wisteria floribunda**	*Glycine du Japon*
Japanese witch hazel	**Hamamelis japonicus**	*Hamamélide du Japon*
Japanese yew	**Taxus cuspidata**	*If du Japon*
Japonica	**Chaenomeles**	*Cognassier du Japon*
Jasmine	**Jasminium**	*Jasmin*
Jeffrey pine	**Pinus jeffreyi**	*Pin de Jeffrey*
Jelly palm	**Butia capitata**	*Butia capitata*
Jersey cudweed	**Gnaphalium luteoalbum**	*Gnaphale blanc-jaunâtre*
Jersey elm	**Ulmus "Sarniensis"**	*Orme de Jersey*
Jersey forget-me-not	**Myosotis sicula**	*Myosotis de Sicile*
Jersy orchid	**Orchis laxiflora**	*Orchid des pentecôtes*
Jersey toadflax	**Linaria pelisseriana**	*Linaire de Pellisier*
Jerusalem artichoke	**Helianthus tuberosus**	*Artichchaut h'hiver /*
		Topinambour
Jerusalem cherry	**Solanum pseudocapsicum**	*Cerisier d'amour /*

Cerisier de Jérusalem / Orangier de savetier / Pommier d'amour

Jerusalem cross	**Lychnis chalcedonica**	*Croix de Malte*
Jerusalem sage	**Phlomis fruticosa**	*Sauge de Jérusalem*
Jerusalem thorn	**Paliurus spina-christi** *Argalou / Épine du Christ*	
Jerusalem thorn	**Parkinsonia aculeata**	*Parkinsonia aculeata*
Jessamine	**Jasminium officinale**	*Jasmin commun*
Jesuit's nut	**Trapa natans**	*Châtaigne d'eau / Macre*
Job's tears	**Coix lachryma-jobi**	*Larmes de Job*
Joe Pye weed	**Eupatorium purpureum**	*Eupatorium purpureum*
Jonquil	**Narcissus jonquilla**	*Petite jonquille*
Joseph & Mary	**Pulmonaria longifolia**	
		Pulmonaire à feuilles longues
Josephine's lily	**Brunsvigia josephenae**	*Amaryllis de Joséphine*
Judas tree	**Cercis siliquastrrum**	*Arbre de Judée*
Juneberry	**Amelanchier**	*Amélanchier*
Juniper	**Juniperus**	*Genévrier*

K

Kadzu vine	Pueraria lobata	*Pueraria lobata*
Kaffir fig	Carpobrotus edulis	*Figue des Hottentots*
Kaffir Lily	Schizostylis	*Schizostylis*
Kaki	Diospyros kaki	*Kaki / Plaqueminier kaki*
Kangaroo paw	Anigozanthus	*Anigozanthus*
Kangaroo vine	Cissus antarctica	*Cissus Antarctica*
Kansas gay feather	Liatris pycnostachya	*Liatris pycnostachya*
Kapok	Ceiba pentandra	*Kapokier*
Karo	Pittosporum crassifolium	*Pittosporum crassifolium*
Kashmir cypress	Cupressus cashmeriana	*Cyprès de Kashmir*
Katsura	Cercidiphyllum japonicum	*Cercidiphyllacé du Japon*
Keeled garlic	Allium carinatum	*Ail caréné*
Kenilworth ivy	Cymbalaria muralis	*Linaire cymbalaire / Ruine-de-Rome*
Kentucky coffee tree	Gymnocladus dioica	*Chicot du Canada*
Kermes oak	Quercus coccifera	*Chêne kermès*
Kerria japonica	Kerria japonica	*Corète du Japon*
Kerry lily	Simethis planifolia	*Simathis à feuilles plates*
Khasia berry	Cotoneaster simonsii	*Cotoneaster de l'Himalaya*
Kidney saxifrage	Saxifraga hirsuta	*Saxifrage herissée*
Kidney vetch	Anthyllis vulneraria	*Anthyllide vulnéraire*
Kilmarnock willow	Salix caprea	*Marsault*
King of the bromeliads	Vriesea hieroglyphica	*Vriesea hieroglyphica*
King palm	Archontophoenix alexandrae	*Archontophoenix*
King protea	Protea cynaroides	*Protea cynaroides*
King William pine	Arthrotaxis selaginoides	*Arthrotaxis selaginoides*
Kingcup	Caltha palustris	*Populage des marais*
Kingfisher daisy	Felicia bergeriana	*Felicia bergeriana*
King's crown	Justicia carnea	*Carmantine carnea*
King's spear	Eremurus	*Eremurus*
Kiwi fruit	Actinidia chinensis	*Kiwi / Souris végétale*
Knapweeed	Centaurea	*Centaurée*
Knapweed broomrape	Orobanche elatior	*Orobanche élevée*
Knautia macedonica	Knautia macedonica	*Scabieuse rumelica*
Knawel	Scleranthus annuus	*Gnavelle annuelle*
Knife-leaf wattle	Acacia cultriformis	*Mimosa couteau*
Knotgrass	Polygonum aviculare	*Renouée des oiseaux*
Knotted bur parsley	Torilis nodosa	*Torilis à feuilles glomérulées*
Knotted cranesbill	Geranium nodosum	*Géranium noueux*
Knotted pearlwort	Sagina nodosa	*Sagine noueuse*

Knotweed	**Polygonum**	*Renouée*
Korean fir	**Abies koreana**	*Sapin de Corée*
Korean mountain ash	**Sorbus alnifolia**	*Sorbier à feuilles d'aune*
Korean thuja	**Thuja koraiensis**	*Thuya de Corée*
Kowhai	**Sophora tetrapetera**	*Sophora*
Kurrajong	**Brachychiton populneus**	*Brachychiton populneus*
Kusamaki	**Podocarpus macrophyllus**	*Podocarpus macrophyllus*

L

Lablab	**Lablab purpureus**	*Dolique*
Labrador tea	**Ledum groenlandicus**	*Thé du Labrador*
Labrador tea	**Ledum palustre**	*Thé du Labrador*
Lace aloe	**Aloe aristata**	*Aloès aristata*
Lace cactus	**Mammillaria elongata**	*Mammillaria elongata*
Lace flower	**Episcia dianthiflora**	*Episcia dianthiflora*
Lace-bark	**Hoheria populnea**	*Hoheria populnea*
Laquered wine cup	**Aechmea "Foster's favourite"**	
		Aechmea "Foster's favourite"
Ladder fern	**Nephrolepis cordifolia**	*Néphrolépis cordifolia*
Lad's love	**Artemisia abrotanum**	*Aurone / Citronelle*
Lady fern	**Athyrium filix-femina**	*Fougère femelle*
Lady orchid	**Orchis purpurea**	*Orchis pourpre*
Lady tulip	**Tulipa clusiana**	*Tulipe de l'Écluse /*
		Tulipe radis
Lady of the night	**Brassavola nodosa**	*Brassavola nodosa*
Lady's bedstraw	**Galium verum**	*Gaillet jaune*
Lady's eardrops	**Fuchsia magellanica**	*Fuchsia magellanica*
Lady's mantle	**Alchemilla vulgaris**	*Alchémille commune*
Lady's slipper orchid	**Cypripedium calceolus**	*Sabot de Vénus*
Lady's smock	**Cardamine pratensis**	*Cardamine des prés*
Lamb's tongue	**Stachys byzantina**	*Oreille de chat*
Lamb's tail cactus	**Echinocereus schmollii**	*Echinocereus schmollii*
Lampshade poppy	**Meconopsis integrifolia**	*Pavot jaune*
Lancewood	**Pseudopanax crassifolius**	*Pseudopanax crassifolius*
Lantern tree	**Crinodendron hookeriana**	*Arbre aux lanternes*
Large bittercres	**Cardamine amara**	*Cardamine amère*
Large cuckoo pint	**Arum italicum**	*Arum d'Italie*
Large evening primrose	**Oenothera lamarkiana**	*Onagre de Lamarck*
Large flowered mullein	**Verbascum virgatum**	*Molène fausse-blattaire*
Large hemp-nettle	**Galeopsis speciosa**	*Galópsis orné*
Large self heal	**Prunella grandiflora**	*Brunelle grandiflora*

Large yellow restharrow	Ononis natrix	Bugrane gluante
Large yellow stonecrop	Sedum reflexum	Orpin réfléchi
Large leafed lime	Tilia platyphylos	Tilleul à grandes feuilles / Tilleul de Hollande
Larkspur	Consolida	Pied d'alouette annuel
Late Dutch honeysuckle	Lonicera periclymenum 'Serotina'	
	Lonicera periclymenum "Serotina"	
Late spider orchid	Ophrys fuciflora	Ophrys bourdon
Laurel	Laurus	Laurier
Laurel	Prunus laurocerasus	Laurier-cerise
Laurustinus	Viburnum tinus	Laurier-tin
Lavatera olbia	Lavatera olbia	Lavatère d'Hyères
Lavatera trimestris	Lavatera trimestris	Lavatère à grandes fleurs
Lavender	Lavandula	Lavande
Lavender cotton	Santolina	Santoline
Lawson Cypress	Chamaecyparis lawsoniana	Cyprès de Lawson / Faux-cyprès de Lawson
Lax sea-lavender	Limonium humile	Statice nain
Lead plants	Amorpha canescens	Amorpha canescens
Least bur-reed	Sparganium minimum	Rubanier nain
Least cinquefoil	Sibbaldia procumbens	Sibbaldie couchée
Least duckweed	Wolffia arrhiza	Wolfie sans racine
Least lettuce	Lactuca saligna	Laitue à feuilles de saulle
Least snowbell	Soldanella minima	Soldanella minima
Least willow	Salix herbacea	Salix herbacea
Leatherleaf	Chamaedaphne calyculata	Chamédaphné
Leatherleaf sedge	Carex buchananii	Laîche buchananii
Leatherwood	Cyrilla racemiflora	Bois-cuir
Lemon verbena	Aloysia triphylla	Citronella verveine
Lemon vine	Pereskia aculeata	Groseillier des Barbades
Lent Lily	Narcissus pseudonarcissus	Jonquille / Narcisse jaune
Leopard Lily	Dieffenbachia	Dieffenbachia
Leopard Lily	Lilium pardalinum	Lis pardalinum
Leopard's bane	Doronicum pardalianches	Doronic tue-pantheres
Lesser bulrush	Typha angustifolia	Massette à feuilles étroites
Lesser butterfly orchid	Platanthera bifolia	Orchis à deux feuilles
Lesser celandine	Ranunculus ficaria	Ficaire
Lesser chickweed	Stellaria pallida	Stellaire pâle
Lesser evening primrose	Oenothera biennis	Onagre bisannuelle
Lesser meadow rue	Thalictrum minus	Petit pigamon
Lesser periwinkle	Vinca minor	Petite pervenche

Lesser pondweed	**Potamogeton pusillus**	*Potamot fluet*
Lesser skullcap	**Scutellaria minor**	*Toque mineur*
Lesser snapdragon	**Misopates orontium**	*Muflier des champs*
Lesser spearwort	**Ranunculus flammula**	*Petite douve /*
		Renoncule flamette
Lesser stitchwort	**Stellaria graminea**	*Stellaire graminé*
Lesser twayblades	**Listera cordata**	*Listère à feuilles*
		cordées
Lesser water plantain	**Baldellia ranunculoides**	*Fluteau fausse-renoncule*
Leyland cypress	**Cupressocarpus leylandii**	*Cyprès de Leyland*
Lijiang spruce	**Picea likeangensis**	*Picea likeangensis*
Lilac	**Syringa**	*Lilas*
Lily	**Lilium**	*lis*
Lilt leek	**Allium moly**	*Ail doré*
Lily tree	**Magnolia denudata**	*Magnolia denudata*
Lilyturf	**Liriope**	*Liriope*
Lily of the valley	**Convallaria majalis**	*Muguet*
Lily of the valley tree	**Clethra arborea**	*Clethra arborea*
Lilyturf	**Liriope**	*Liriope*
Lime	**Tilia**	*Tilleul*
Limestone bugle	**Ajuga pyramidalis**	*Bugle pyramidale*
Limestone woundwort	**Stachys alpina**	*Épiaire des Alpes*
Linden	**Tilia**	*Tilleul*
Ling	**Calluna vulgaris** *Brande /*	*Callune fausse-bruyère*
Lion's ear	**Leonotis leonorus**	*Queue de lion*
Lipstick plant	**Aeschyanthus pulcher**	*Aeschyanthus pulcher*
Liquorice	**Glycyrrhiza glabra**	*Réglisse*
Liquorice fern	**Polypodium glycyrrhiza**	*Polypodium glycyrrhiza*
Lithospermum	**Lithodora**	*Grémil*
Little mouse-ear	**Cerastium semicandrum**	*Céraiste à 5 étamines*
Little robin	**Geranium purpureum**	*Géranium pourpré*
Little walnut	**Juglans microcarpa**	*Juglans microcarpa*
Live oak	**Quercus virginiana**	*Chêne de Caroline*
Living rock	**Ariocarpus**	*Ariocarpus*
Living rock	**Pleiospilos bolusii**	*Pleiospilos bolusii*
Living stones	**Lithops** *Pierre vivante /*	*Plante-caillou*
Livingstone daisy	**Dorotheanthus belliformis**	*Ficoïde*
Lizard orchid	**Himantoglossum hircinum**	*Orchis bouc*
Lizard's tail	**Saururus cernuus**	*Queue de lézard*
Lobel's maple	**Acer lobelii**	*Érable de Lobel*
Loblolly bay	**Gordonia lasianthus** *Gordonia à feuilles glabrées*
Lobster cactus	**Schlumbergera truncata**	*Cactus crabe*

Lobster claws	Heliconia	*Heliconia*
Locust	Robinia pseudoacacia	*Robinia faux-acacia*
Loddon pondweed	Potamogeton nodosus	*Potamot noueux*
Loddon lily	Leucojum aestivum	*Nivéole d'été*
Lodgepole pine	Pinus contorta latifolia	*Pin contorta latifolia*
Lollipop plant	Pachysatchys lutea	*Pachysatchys lutea*
Lombardy poplar	Populus nigra 'Italica'	*Peuplier d'Italie*
London plane	Platanus acerifolia	*Platane de Londres*
London pride	Saxifraga urbium	*Saxifraga urbium*
Long-headed poppy	Papaver dubium	*Pavot douteux*
Longleaf	Falcaria vulgaris	*Falcaria commun*
Long-leaved sundew	Drosera intermedia	*Rossolis intermédiaire*
Long stalked cranesbill	Geranium columbinum	*Géranium des colombes / Pied-de-pigeon*
Long stalked pondweed	Potamogeton praelongus	*Potamot allongé*
Loose-flowered orchid	Orchis laxiflora	*Orchis à fleurs laches*
Loquat	Eriobotrya japonica	*Bibacier / Loquat / Néflier du Japon*
Lord Anson's blue pea	Lathyrus nervosus	*Lathyrus nervosus*
Lords and Ladies	Arum maculatum	*Gouet maculé*
Lorraine begonia	Begonia x cheimantha "Gloire de Lorraine"	*Begonia x cheimantha "Gloire de Lorraine"*
Lotus	Nelumbo	*Lotus / Nélumbium*
Lousewort	Pedicularis sylvatica	*Pédiculaire des bois*
Lovage	Ligusticum scoticum	*Livèche d'Écosse*
Love-in-a-mist	Nigella damascena	*Cheveux de Vénus / Nigelle de Damas*
Love-lies-bleeding	Amaranthus caudatus	*Queue de renard*
Low bush blueberry	Vaccinium angustifolium laevigatum	*Brimbelle*
Lucombe oak	Quercus hispanica 'Lucombeana'	*Chêne hispanica 'Lucombeana'*
Lucerne	Medicago sativa	*Luzerne cultivée*
Lungwort	Pulmonaria officinalis	*Pulmonaire officinale*
Lupin	Lupinus	*Lupin*
Lychnis coronaria	Lychnis coronaria	*Coquelourde des jardins*
Lyme grass	Leymus arenarius	*Élyme des sable s*

M

Macadamia nut	Macadamia integrifolia	*Noyer du Queensland*
Mace sedge	Carex grayi	*Laîche grayi*
Macedonian pine	Pinus peuce	*Pin de Macédoine*
Mackay's heath	Erica mackaiana	*Bruyère de Mackay*

Madagascar dragon tree	Dracaena marginata	Dragonnier de Madagascar
Madagascar jasmine	Stephanotis floribunda	Stephanotis floribunda
Madagascar periwinkle	Vinca rosea	Pervenche de Madagascar
Madeira vine	Andredra	Andredra
Madonna lily	Lilium candidum	Lis blanc /
	Lis de la Madone / Lis de la Saint-Jean	
Madroña	Arbutus menziesii	Arbutus menziesii
Madwort	Asperugo procumbens	Rapette couchée
Magellan ragwort	Senecio smithii	Séneçon smithii
Magnolia tripetala	Magnolia tripetala	Magnolia parasol
Mahoe	Melicytus ramiflorus	Melicytus ramiflorus
Mahoe	Thespesua populnea	Thespesua populnea
Maiden pink	Dianthus deltoides	Œillet couché
Maidenhair fern	Adiantum capillus veneris	Capillaire de Montpellier /
		Cheveux de Vénus
Maidenhair spleenwort	Asplenium trichomanes	Fausse capillaire
Maidenhair tree	Ginkgo biloba	Arbe aux 40 écus
Maiten	Maytenus boaria	Maytenus boaria
Maize	Zea mays	Maïs
Majorcan poppy	Paeonia cambessedesii	Pivoine de Majorca
Malay ginger	Costus speciosus	Costus speciosus
Male fern	Dryopteris filix-mas	Fougère mâle
Mallow	Malva	Mauve
Maltese cross	Lychnis chalcedonica	Croix de Malte
Mamaku	Cythea medulalaris	Cythea medulalaris
Man orchid	Aceras anthropophorum	Orchis homme-pendu
Mandarin's hat plant	Holmskioldia sanguinea	Holmsikoldia sanguinea
Mandrake	Mandragora	Mandragore
Manipur lily	Lilium mackliniae	Lis mackliniae
Manna ash	Fraxinus ornus	Frêne à fleurs
Manna gum	Eucalyptus viminalis	Eucalyptus viminalis
Manuka	Leptospermum scoparium	Leptospermum scoparium
Many-seed goosefoot	Chenopodium polyspermum	
	Chénopode a graines nombreuses	
Manzanita	Arctostaphylos manzanita	Busserole
Maple	Acer campestre	Érable champêtre
Maple leaf begonia	Begonia dregei	Begonia dregei
Maple leaf begonia	Begonia weltoniensis	Begonia weltoniensis
Marestail	Hippuris vulgaris	Pesse d'eau
Marguerite	Chrysanthemum frutescens	Anthémis
Marigold	Calendula	Souci
Mariposa tulip	Calochortus	Tulipe de Mormons

Maritime Pine	**Pinus pinaster**	*Pin des landes / Pin maritime*
Marjoram	**Origanum vulgare**	*Marjolaine /*
		Marjolaine bâtarde / Marjolaine origan / Origan commun
Marmalade bush	**Streptosolen jamesonii**	*Streptosolen jamesonii*
Marsh arrow-grass	**Triglochin palustris**	*Troscart des marais*
Marsh bedstraw	**Galium palustre**	*Gaillet des marais*
Marsh buckler fern	**Thelypteris palustirs**	*Thelypteris palustirs*
Marsh cinquefoil	**Potentilla palustris**	*Comaret*
Marsh dock	**Rumex palustris**	*Patience des marais*
Marsh gentian	**Gentiana pneumonanthe**	*Gentiane pneumonanthe*
Marsh hawksbeard	**Crepis paludosa**	*Crépide des marais*
Marsh helleborine	**Epipactis palustris**	*Épipactis des marais*
Marsh-mallow	**Althaea officinalis**	*Guimauve officinale*
Marsh marigold	**Caltha palustris**	*Populage des marais*
Marsh pea	**Lathyrus palustris**	*Gesse des marais*
Marsh pennywort	**Hydrocotyle vulgaris**	*Écuelle d'eau*
Marsh ragwort	**Senecio aquaticus**	*Séneçon aquatique*
Marsh St. John's wort	**Hypericum elodes**	*Élodés des marais*
Marsh sow-thistle	**Sonchus palustris**	*Laiteron des marais*
Marsh speedwell	**Veronica scutellata**	*Véronique à Écusson*
Marsh stitchwort	**Stellaria palustris**	*Stellaire des marais*
Marsh thistle	**Cirsium palustre**	*Cirse des marais*
Marsh valerian	**Valeriana dioica**	*Valériane dioïque*
Marsh willow-herb	**Epilobium palustra**	*Épilobe des marais*
Marshwort	**Apium inundatum**	*Ache aquatique*
Marsh woundwort	**Stachys palustris**	*Épiaire des marais*
Marsh violet	**Viola palustris**	*Violette des marais*
Marsh yellow cress	**Rorippa islandica**	*Rorippa d'Islande*
Martagon lily	**Lilium martagon**	*Lis martagon*
Marvel of Peru	**Mirabilis**	*Belle-du-nuit*
Mask flower	**Alonsoa warscewiczii**	*Alonsoa warscewiczii*
Masterwort	**Peucedanum ostruthium**	*Peucédan impératoire*
Mastic tree	**Pistacia lentiscus**	*Arbre au mastic /*
		Lentisque
Matted sea-lavender	**Limonium bellidifolium**	*Statice à feuilles de paquerette*
May	**Crataegus laevigata**	*Aubépine / Épine blanche*
May apple	**Podophyllum peltatum**	*Podophyllum peltatum*
May lily	**Maianthemum bifolium**	*Fleur de mai /*
		Maianthème à deux feuilles/ Petit muguet
Mayflower	**Epigaea repens**	*Epigaea repens*
Meadow buttercup	**Ranunculus acris**	*Bouton d'or*
Meadow cranesbill	**Geranium pratense**	*Géranium des prés*

Meadow foam	**Limnanthes douglasii**	*Limnanthe douglasii*
Meadow lily	**Lilium canadense**	*Lis du Canada*
Meadow pea	**Lathyrus pratensis**	*Gesse des prés*
Meadow rue	**Thalictrum flavum**	*Pigamon jaune*
Meadow saffron	**Bulbocodium**	*Bulbocode*
Meadow sage	**Salvia pratensis**	*Sauge des prés*
Meadow saxifrage	**Saxifraga granulata**	*Saxifrage granulée*
Meadowsweet	**Filipendula ulmaria**	*Reine des prés / Spirée ulmaire*
Meadow thistle	**Cirsium dissectum**	*Cirse des prairies*
Meconopsis betonicifolia	**Meconopsis betonicifolia**	
		Pavot bleu de l'Himalaya
Mediterranean cypress	**Cupressus sempervirens**	*Cyprès de Provence*
Medlar	**Mespilus germanica**	*Néflier*
Melon cactus	**Melocactus communis**	*Cactus melon*
Menziesia	**Phyllodoce caerulea**	*Phyllodoce bleuatre*
Merry-bells	**Uvularia grandiflora**	*Uvularia grandiflora*
Mescal button	**Lophophora williamsii**	*Peyote /*
		Plante qui fait les yeux émerveillés
Metake	**Pseudosasa japonica**	*Pseudosasa japonica*
Metal leaf begonia	**Begonia metallica**	*Begonia metallica*
Mexican blood flower	**Distictis buccinatoria**	*Distictis buccinatoria*
Mexican bush sage	**Salvia leucantha**	*Salvia leucantha*
Mexican cypress	**Cupressus lusitanica**	*Cyprès de Busaco /*
		Cyprès de Goa / Cyprès pleureur
Mexican firecracker	**Echeveria setosa**	*Echeveria setosa*
Mexican flame vine	**Senecio confusus**	*Senecio confusus*
Mexican foxglove	**Tetranema roseum**	*Tetranema roseum*
Mexican giant hyssop	**Agastache**	*Agastache*
Mexican hat plant	**Kalanchoe diagremontiana**	
		Kalanchoe diagremontiana
Mexican orange blossom	**Choisya ternata**	*Orangier du Mexique*
Mexican palo verde	**Parkinsonia aculeata**	*Parkinsonia aculeata*
Mexican stone pine	**Pinus cembroides**	*Pin cembroides*
Mexican sunflower	**Tithonia rotundiflora**	*Soleil de Californie*
Mexican tulip poppy	**Hunnemannia fumariifolia**	
		Hunnemannia fumariifolia
Mexican violet	**Tetranema roseum**	*Tetranema roseum*
Mezereon	**Daphne mezereum**	*Bois-gentil / Bois joli / Graou*
Michaelmas daisy	**Aster**	*Aster du Jardin*
Mickey mouse plant	**Ochna serrulata**	*Ochna serrulata*

Mignonette	Reseda	*Mignonette*
Mignonette vine	Andredera	*Andredera*
Mile a minute plant	Polygonum aubertii	*Renouée aubertii*
Mile a minute plant	Polygonum baldschuanicum	*Renouée*
Milk parsley	Peucedanum palustre	*Peucédan des marais*
Milk thistle	Silybum marianum	*Chardon marie*
Milkweed	Euphorbia	*Euphorbe*
Mimicry plant	Pleiospilos bolusii	*Pleomele bolusii*
Mimosa	Acacia	*Mimosa*
Mind your own business	Soleirolia	*Soleirolia*
Miniature date palm	Phoenix roebelenii	*Datier roebelenii*
Miniature grape ivy	Cissus striata	*Cissus striata*
Mint	Mentha	*Menthe*
Mint bush	Escholtzia stauntonii	*Escholtzia stauntonii*
Mint bush	Prostanthera	*Prostanthera*
Mirbeck's oak	Quercus canariensis	*Chêne zeen*
Missouri flag	Iris missouriensis	*Iris missouriensis*
Mist flower	Eupatorium rugosum	*Eupatoire rugeux*
Mistletoe	Viscum album	*Gui*
Mistletoe cactus	Rhipsalis	*Rhipsalis*
Mistletoe fig	Ficus deltoides	*Ficus deltoides*
Moccasin flower	Cypripedium acaule	*Cypripedium acaule*
Mock orange	Philadelphus coronarius	*Seringat*
Mock orange	Pittosperum tobira	*Pittosperum tobira*
Monarch birch	Betula maximowicziana	*Betula maximowicziana*
Monarch of the East	Sauromatum venosum	*Sauromatum venosum*
Money tree	Crassula ovata	*Crassula ovata*
Moneywort	Lysimachia nummularia aurea	*Herbe aux écus*
Mongolian Lime	Tilia mongolica	*Tilleul à feuille de vigne / Tilleul de Mongolie*
Mongolian oak	Quercus mongolica	*Chêne de Mongolie*
Monkshood	Nalellus	*Napel*
Monk's pepper	Vitex agnus castus	*Agneau chaste / Arbre au poivre / Gattillier commun*
Monkey flower	Mimulus guttatus	*Mimule tacheté*
Monkey musk	Mimulus	*Mimulus*
Monkey orchid	Orchis simia	*Orchis singe*
Monkey puzzle	Araucaria araucana	*Déspoir du singe*
Monk's Rhubarb	Rumex alpinus	*Patience des Alpes*
Monkshood	Aconitum anglicum	*Aconit anglicum*
Montbretia	Crocosmia x crocosmiflora	*Montbretia*
Monterey ceanothus	Ceanothus rigidus	*Céanothe de Monterey*

Monterey cypress	**Cupressus macrocarpa**	*Cyprès de Monterey /*
		Cyprès de Lambert
Monterey pine	**Pinus radiata**	*Pin de Monterey*
Montezuma pine	**Pinus montzumae**	*Pin de Montezuma*
Montpelier maple	**Acer monspessulanum**	*Érable de Montpellier*
Moon carrot	**Seseli libanotis**	*Persil de montagne /*
		Séséli libanotis
Moon flower	**Ipomoea alba**	*Ipomoea alba*
Moon trefoil	**Medicago arborea**	*Luzerne arborescente*
Moonlight holly	**Ilex aquiflium flavescens**	*Houx aquiflium flavescens*
Moonseed	**Menispermum**	*Ménisperme*
Moonstones	**Pachyphytum oviferum**	*Pachyphytum oviferum*
Moreton Bay chestnut	**Castanospermum australe**	*Castanospermum*
Moreton Bay fig	**Ficus macrophylla**	*Ficus macrophylla*
Morinda spruce	**Picea smithiana**	*Picea smithiana*
Morning glory	**Ipomoea hederacea**	*Belle-du-jour*
Morning glory	**Convolvulus tricolor**	*Belle-du-jour*
Moroccan broom	**Cytisus battandieri**	*Cytisus battandieri*
Moschatel	**Adoxa moschatellina**	*Moschatelline*
Moses-in-the-cradle	**Tradescantia spathacea**	*Tradescantia spathacea*
Mosquito grass	**Bouteloua gracilis**	*Bouteloua gracilis*
Moss campion	**Silene acaulis**	*Silène acaule*
Mossy pearlwort	**Sagina procumbens**	*Sagine couchée*
Mossy saxifrage	**Saxifraga hypnoides**	*Saxifrage faux hypne*
Mossy stonecrop	**Crassula tillaea**	*Tillée mousse*
Moth mullein	**Verbascum blattaria**	*Herbe aux mites /*
		Molène blattaire
Mother of thousands	**Saxifraga stolonifera**	*Saxifraga stolonifera*
Mother of thousands	**Soleirolia**	*Soleirolia*
Mother spleenwort	**Asplenium bulbiferum**	*Asplenium bulbiferum*
Mother-in-law's seat	**Echinocactus grusonii**	*Echinocactus grusonii*
Mother-in-law's-tongue	**Sansiviera trifasciata**	*Sansiviera trifasciata*
Mother of pearl plant	**Graptopetalum paraguayense**	
		Graptopetalum paraguayense
Motherwort	**Leonurus cardiaca**	*Agripaume cardiaque*
Mount Etna broom	**Genista aetnensis**	*Genêt del'Etna*
Mountain ash	**Sorbus aucuparia**	*Sobier des oiseleurs*
Mountain avens	**Dryas octopetala**	*Dryade à huit pétales*
Mountain buckler fern	**Thelypteris oreopteris**	*Thelypteris oreopteris*
Mountain currant	**Ribes rubrum**	*Groseillier des Alpes*
Mountain dogwood	**Cornus nuttallii**	*Cornus nuttallii*
Mountain everlasting	**Antennaria dioica**	*Pied-de-chat dioïque*

Mountain fern	**Thelypteris oreopteris**	*Thelypteris oreopteris*
Mountain fetterbush	**Pieris floribunda**	*Pieris floribunda*
Mountain flax	**Phormium cookianum**	*Phormium cookianum*
Mountain gum	**Eucalyptus dalrympleana**	*Eucalyptus dalrympleana*
Mountain hemlock	**Tsuga mertensiana**	*Tsuga mertensiana*
Mountain pansy	**Viola lutea**	*Pensée des vosgess*
Mountain pepper	**Drimys lanceolata**	*Drimys lanceolata*
Mountain pine	**Pinus mugo**	*Pin de montagne*
Mountain pride	**Penstemon newberryi**	*Penstemon newberryi*
Mountain sorrel	**Oxyria digyna**	*Oxyria a deux styles*
Mountain sow thistle	**Cicerbita alpina**	*Cicerbita des Alpes*
Mountain spruce	**Picea englemannii**	*Épicéa d'Engelmann*
Mountain tassel	**Soldanella montana**	*Soldanelle des montagnes*
Mountain willow	**Salix arbuscula**	*Salix arbuscula*
Mountain wood fern	**Thelypteris oreopteris**	*Thelypteris oreopteris*
Mourning widow	**Iris susiana**	*Iris de Suse*
Mouse plant	**Arisarum proboscideum**	*Arisarum proboscideum*
Mousetail	**Myosurus minimus**	*Queue de souris*
Moutan	**Paeonia suffruticosa**	*Pivoine en arbre*
Mugwort	**Artemisia vulgaris**	*Armoise commune*
Mulberry	**Morus**	*Mûrier*
Mullein	**Verbascum**	*Molène*
Muriel bamboo	**Thamnocalamus spathaceus**	*Thamnocalamus spathaceus*
Murray red gum	**Eucalyptus camaldulensis**	*Eucalyptus camaldulensis*
Mushroom	**Fungus**	*Champignon*
Musk	**Mimulus moschatus**	*Mimulus musqué*
Musk mallow	**Malva moschata**	*Mauve musquée*
Musk orchid	**Herminium monarchis**	*Herminium à un bulbe*
Musk storksbill	**Erodium moschatum**	*Bec musqué*
Musk thistle	**Carduus nutans**	*Chardon penché*
Musk willow	**Salix aegyptiaca**	*Salix aegyptiaca*
Myrobalan	**Prunus cerasifera**	*Prunier myrobolan*
Myrtle	**Myrtus**	*Myrte*
Myrtle flag	**Acorus calamus variegatus**	*Acore*

N

Naked coral tree	Erythrina coralloides	*Érythrine coralloides*
Nankeen lily	Lilium x testaceum	*Lis couleur Isabelle*
Narihira bamboo	Semiarundinaria fastuosa	*Semiarundinaria fastuosa*
Narrow buckler fern	Dryopteris carthusiana	*Dryoptéris carthusiana*
Narrow cudweed	Filago gallica	*Cotonnière de France*
Narrow helleborine	Cephalanthera longifolia	
		Céphalanthéra à feuilles étroites
Narrow leafed ash	Fraxinus angustifolia	*Frêne oxyphylle*
Narrow-leaved eel-grass	Zostera angustifolia	*Zostère à feuilles étroites*
Narrow leafed pepperwort	Lepidium ruderale	*Passerage des décombres*
Narrow leaved bittercress	Cardamine impatiens	*Cardamine impatiente*
Narrow-lipped helleborine	Epipactis leptochila	*Épipactis à labelle étroite*
Narrow water plantain	Alisma lanceolatum	*Plantain d'eau lancéolé*
Narrow water starwort	Callitriche hermaphroditica	
		Callitriche hermaphrodite
Nasturtium	Tropaeolum	*Capucine*
Natal grass	Rhynchelytrum repens	*Rhynchelytrum repens*
Natal ivy	Senecio macroglossus	*Senecio macroglossus*
Natal plum	Carissa grandiflora	*Carissa grandiflora*
Native Australian frangipani	Hymenosporum flavum	*Hymenosporum flavum*
Navelwort	Cotyledon umbilicus	*Ombilic*
Necklace poplar	Populus deltoides	*Peuplier noir d'Amérique*
Needle spike rush	Eleocharis acicularis	*Scirpe épingle*
Nemesia	Nemesia	*Némésie*
Nepalese ivy	Hedera nepalensis	*Hedera nepalensis*
Nettle leaved bellflower	Campanula trachelium	*Gantelée*
Nettle leaved goosefoot	Chenopodium murale	*Chénopode des murs*
Nettle tree	Celtis australis	*Micocoulier de Provence*
Net veined willow	Salix reticulata	*Saule reticulé*
New Zealand bluebell	Wahlenbergia albomarginata	
		Wahlenbergia albomarginata
New Zealand Christmas tree	Metrosideros excelsa	*Arbre de rata*
New Zealand edelweiss	Leucogenes	*Edelweiss de Nouvelle-Zélande*
New Zealand flax	Phormium tenax	*Lin de Nouvelle-Zélande*
New Zealand honeysuckle	Knightia excelsa	*Knightia excelsa*
New Zealand palm lily	Cordyline australis	*Cordyline australis*
New Zealand satin flower	Libertia grandiflora	*Libertia grandiflora*
New Zealand tea tree	Leptospermum scoparium	*Leptospermum scoparium*
New Zealand willow-herb	Epilobium brunnescens	
		Épilobe de Nouvelle Zélande
Nicotiana alata	Nicotiana alata	*Tabac blanc odorant*

63

Night-scented catchfly	Silene noctiflora	Silène du nuit
Nikko fir	Abies homolepis	Sapin homolepis
Nikko malpe	Acer nikoense	Acer nikoense
Ninebark	Physocarpus opulifolius	Physocarpe opulifolius
Nipplewort	Lapsana communis	Graceline / Lapsane commune
Nirre	Nothofagus antarctica	Nothofagus antarctica
Noble fir	Abies procera	Sapin noble
Nodding bur-marigold	Bidens cernua	Bident penché
Nodding catchfly	Silene pendula	Silène de Crète
Nodding star of Bethlehem	Ornithogalum nutans	Étoile de Bethléhem
Nootka cypress	Chamaecyparis nootkatensis	Cyprès de Nootka
Norfolk Island hibiscus	Lagunaria patersonii	Lagunaria patersonii
Norfolk Island pine	Araucaria heterophylla	Araucarie elevée
North Island edelweiss	Leucogenes leontopodium	
		Edelweiss de Nouvelle-Zélande
Northern bedstraw	Galium boreale	Gaillet du nord
Northern bilberry	Vaccinium uliginosum	Airelle des marais
Northern bungalow palm	Archontophoenix cunnnghamia	
		Archontophoenix cunnnghamia
Northern hawksbeard	Crepis mollis	Crépide tendre
Northern Japanese hemlock	Tsuga diversifolia	Tsuga diversifolia
Northern maidenhair fern	Adiantum pedantum	Capillaire pedantum
Northern marsh orchid	Dactylorhiza purpurella	Orchis d'Ecosse
Northern pitch pine	Pinus rigida	Pin rigida
Norway maple	Acer plantanoides	Érable plane
Norway spruce	Picea abies	Épicéa commun
Norway spruce	Picea abies	Sapin de Norvège
Norway spruce	Picea abies	Sapin rouge
Nottingham catchfly	Silene nutans	Silène penché

O

Oak	Quercus	Chêne
Oak leafed hydrangea	Hydrangea quercifolia	Hortensia à feuilles de chêne
Oak-leaved goosefoot	Chenopodium glaucum	Chénopode glauque
Obedient plant	Physostegia	Physostegia
Oconee bells	Shortia galacifolia	Shortia galacifolia
Ohio buckeye	Aesculus glabra	Marronnier glabra
Old man	Artemisia abrotanum	Aurone / Citronnelle
Old man of the Andes	Borzicactus celsianus	Borzicactus celsianus
Old man of the Andes	Borzicactus trolii	Borzicactus trolii
Old man's beard	Clematis vitalba	Clémtite des haies
Old lady cactus	Mammillaria hahniana	Mammillaria hahniana

Old man cactus	**Cephalocereus senilis**	*Cierge barba de vieillard*
Old witch grass	**Panicum capillare**	*Herbe de Guinée*
Old woman cactus	**Mammillaria hahniana**	*Mammillaria hahniana*
Oleander	**Nerium oleander**	*Laurier rose*
Oleaster	**Elaeagnus angustifolia**	*Olivier de Bohême*
Olive	**Olea europaea**	*Olivier*
Onion	**Allium**	*Oignon*
Ontario poplar	**Populus candicans**	*Peuplier d'Ontario*
Opium poppy	**Papiver somniferum**	*Pavot somnifère*
Opposite pondweed	**Groenlandia densa**	*Potamot dense*
Opuntia	**Opuntia**	*Nopal /Raquette*
Orange birdsfoot	**Ornithopus pinnatus**	*Ornithope penné*
Orange jasmine	**Murraya paniculata**	*Murraya paniculata*
Orange lily	**Lilium bulbiferum**	*Lis bulbiferum*
Orange mullein	**Verbascum phlomoides**	*Molène faux-phlomide*
Orchard grass	**Dactylis glomerata**	*Dactyle aggloméré / Dactyle pelotonné*
Orchid cactus	**Epiphyllum**	*Cactus-orchidée*
Orchid tree	**Bauhinia purpurea**	*Bauhinia purpurea*
Orchid tree	**Bauhinia variegata**	*Bauhinia variegata*
Oregon grape	**Mahonia aquifolium**	*Mahonia à feuilles de houx*
Oregon maple	**Acer macrophyllum**	*Érable macrophyllum*
Oregon oak	**Quercus garryana**	*Chêne garryana*
Organ pipe cactus	**Lemaireocereus marginatus**	*Lemaireocereus marginatus*
Oriental beech	**Fagus orientalis**	*Hêtre d'Orient*
Oriental bittersweet	**Celastrus orbiculatus**	*Célastre orbiculatus*
Oriental plane	**Platanus orientalis**	*Platane d'Orient*
Oriental poppy	**Papaver orientale**	*Pavot d'Orient / Pavot de Tournefort*
Oriental sweet gum	**Liquidambar orientalis**	*Liquidambar orientalis*
Oriental white oak	**Quercus aliena**	*Chêne aliena*
Ornamental cabbage	**Brassica oleracea**	*Chou d'ornement*
Ornamental maize	**Zea mays**	*Maïs*
Ornamental pepper	**Capsicum annuum**	*Piment commun*
Ornamental yam	**Dioscorea discolor**	*Igname*
Orpine	**Sedum telephium**	*Orpin reprise*
Osage orange	**Maclura pomifera**	*Bois d'arc / Orangier des osages*
Oso berry	**Oemleria cerasiformis**	*Oemleria cerasiformis*
Ostrich fern	**Matteuccia struthiopteris**	*Matteuccia struthiopteris*
Ostrich feather fern	**Matteuccia struthiopteris**	*Matteuccia struthiopteris*
Ovens wattle	**Acacia pravissima**	*Acacia pravissima*
Owl eyes	**Huernia zebrina**	*Huernia zebrina*
Ox-eye-daisy	**Chrysanthemum leucanthemum**	*Grande marguerite*
Oxford ragwort	**Senecio squalidus**	*Séneçon négligé*
Oxlip	**Primula elatior**	*Primevère élevée*

P

Pacific dogwood	**Cornus nuttallii**	*Cornouiller nuttallii*
Pacifc fir	**Abies amabilis**	*Sapin amabilis*
Paddy's pride	**Hedera colchica 'Sulphur Heart'**	
		Hedera colchica 'Sulphur Heart'
Pagoda tree	**Sophora japonica**	*Arbre des pagodes /*
		Sophora du Japon
Paintbrush	**Haemanthus albiflos**	*Haemanthus albiflos*
Painted fern	**Athyrium nipponicum**	*Fougère femelle*
Painted net leaf	**Fittonia verschaffeltii**	*Fittonia verschaffeltii*
Painted wood lily	**Trillium undulatum**	*Trillie undulatum*
Painted trillium	**Trillium undulatum**	*Trillie undulatum*
Pale butterwort	**Pinguicula lusitanica**	*Grassette du Portugal*
Pale flax	**Linum bienne**	*Lin à feuilles étroites*
Pale heath violet	**Viola lactea**	*Violette lactée*
Pale poppy	**Papaver argemone**	*Pavot argémone*
Pale St. John's wort	**Hypericum montanum**	*Millepertuis de montagne*
Pale toadflax	**Linaria repens**	*Linaire rampante*
Pale willow-herb	**Epilobium roseum**	*Épilobe rosé*
Pampass grass	**Cortaderia selloana**	*Herbe de pampas*
Panda plant	**Kalanchoe tomentosa**	*Plante panda*
Pansy	**Viola wittrockliana**	*Pensée*
Pansy orchid	**Miltonia**	*Miltonia*
Panther lily	**Lilium pardalinum**	*Lis pardalinum*
Paper bark maple	**Acer griseum**	*Érable gris*
Paper bark tree	**Melaleuca quinquenervia**	*Melaleuca quinquenervia*
Paper birch	**Betula papyrifera**	*Bouleau à papier*
Paper mulberry	**Broussonetia papyrifera**	*Mûrier à papier*
Papyrus	**Cyperus papyrus**	*Souchet â papier*
Para para	**Pisonia umbellifera**	*Pisonia umbellifera*
Parachute plant	**Ceropegia sandersonii**	*Ceropegia sandersonii*
Paradise palm	**Howea forsteriana**	*Howea forsteriana*
Parlour palm	**Chamaedorea elegans**	*Chamaedorea elegans*
Parrot leaf	**Alternanthera ficoidea**	*Alternanthera ficoidea*
Parrot's bill	**Clianthus puniceus**	*Clianthus puniceus*
Parrot's feather	**Myriophyllum aquaticum**	*Myriophylle aquaticum*
Parrot's flower	**Heliconia psittacorum**	*Heliconia psittacorum*
Parsley	**Petroselinum crispum**	*Persil*
Parsley fern	**Cryptogramma crispa**	*Cryptogramma crispa*
Parsley piert	**Aphanes arvensis**	*Alchémille des champs*
Parsley water dropwort	**Oenanthe lachenalii**	*Œnanthe de lachenal*

Partridge berry	Mitchella repens	*Mitchella repens*
Partridge breasted aloe	Aloe variegata	*Aloès variegata*
Pasque flower	Pulsatilla vulgaris	*Anémone pulsatille / Coquelourde*
Passion flower	Passiflora	*Fleur de passion / Passiflore*
Patagonian cypress	Fitzroya cupressoides	*Alerge*
Patience dock	Rumex patientia	*Epinard-oseille*
Pawpaw	Asimina triloba / Carica papaya	*Asimina triloba*
Peace lily	Spathiphyllum wallisii	*Spathiphyllum wallisii*
Peach	Prunus persica	*Pêcher*
Peacock flower	Tigridia pavonia	*Œil de paon*
Peacock plant	Calathea makoyana	*Calathea makoyana*
Peanut cactus	Chamaecereus silvestri	*Chamaecereus silvestri*
Pear	Pyrus	*Poirier*
Pearl berry	Margyricarpus pinnatus	*Margyricarpus pinnatus*
Pearl everlasting	Annaphalis margaritacea	*Immortelle blanche / Immortelle de Virginie*
Pearlwort	Sagina	*Sagine*
Pedunculate oak	Quercus robur	*Chêne pédonculé*
Peepul	Ficus religiosa	*Ficus religiosa*
Pelican flower	Aristolochia grandiflora	*Aristoloche*
Pencil cedar	Juniperus virginiana	*Genévrier de Virginie*
Pencilled cranesbill	Geranium versicolor	*Géranium changeant*
Pendent silver lime	Tilia petiolaris	*Tilleul petiolaris*
Pendulous sedge	Carex pendula	*Laîche pendante*
Pennyroyal	Mentha pulegium	*Menthe pouliot*
Peony	Paeonia	*Pivoine*
Peppermint	Mentha x piperita	*Menthe poivrée*
Peppermint geranium	Pelargonium tomentosum	*Pelargonium tomentosum*
Peppermint tree	Agonis flexuosa	*Agonis flexuosa*
Pepper saxifrage	Silaum silaus	*Fenouil des chevaux*
Pepper tree	Pseudowintera axillaris	*Pseudowintera axillaris*
Père David's maple	Acer davidii	*Acer davidii*
Perennial centaury	Centaurium scilloides	*Petite centaurée fauss-scille*
Perennial flax	Linum perenne	*Lin vivace*
Perennial knawel	Scleranthus perennis	*Gnavelle vivace*
Perennial pea	Lathyrus latifolius	*Pois vivace*
Perfoliate honeysuckle	Lonicera caprifolium	*Chèvrefeuille des jardins*
Perfiolate pondweed	Potamogeton perfiolatus	*Potamot perfolié*
Periwinkle	Vinca	*Pervenche*
Persian buttercup	Ranunculus asiaticus	*Renoncule des fleuristes / Renoncule des jardins*
Persian everlasting pea	Lathyrus rotundifolia	*Lathyrus rotundifolia*

Persian ironwood	Parrotia persica	*Parrotia persica*
Persian ivy	Hedera colchica	*Lierre de Perse*
Persian lilac	Melia azedarach	*Margousierr azedarach*
Persian lilac	Syringa persica	*Lilas de Perse*
Persian stone cress	Aethionema grandiflorum	*Aethionema grandiflorum*
Persian violet	Exacum affine	*Exacum affine*
Persimmon	Diospyros kaki	*Kaki / Plaqueminier kaki*
Peruvian scilla	Scilla peruviana	*Scilla du Pérou*
Peruvian daffodil	Hymenocallis narcissiflora	*Hymenocallis narcissiflora*
Peruvian mastic tree	Schinus molle	*Faux poivrier*
Peruvian old man cactus	Expostoa lanata	*Expostoa lanata*
Peruvian pepper tree	Schinus molle	*Faux poivrier*
Pestle parsnip	Lomatium nudicaule	*Lomatium nudicaule*
Petty whin	Genista anglica	*Genêt d'Angleterre*
Petunia	Petunia	*Pétunia*
Pheasant grass	Stipa arundinacea	*Stipa arundinacea*
Pheasant's eye	Narcissus poeticus recurva	*Narcisse des poètes*
Pheasant's eye	Adonis annua	*Adonis d'automne*
Philippine violet	Barleria cristata	*Barleria cristata*
Piccabean palm	Archontophoenix cunninghamiana	
		Archontophoenix cunninghamiana
Pick-a-back plant	Tolmiea menziesii	*Tolmiea menziesii*
Pickerel weed	Pontederis cordata	*Pontédérie à feuilles en cœur*
Pigeon berry	Duranta repens	*Duranta repens*
Pignut	Conopodium majus	*Châtaigne de terre /*
		Conopode dénudé
Pignut	Carya glabra	*Noyer à balais /*
		Noyer des pourceaux
Pignut hickory	Carya glabra	*Noyer à balais / Noyer des pourceaux*
Pigweed	Amaranthus retroflexus	*Amarante réfléchie*
Pin cherry	Prunus pennsylvanica	*Prunier de Pennsylvanie*
Pin oak	Quercus palustris	*Chêne des marais*
Pincushion cactus	Mammillaria	*Mammillaria*
Pink stonecrop	Sedum villosum	*Orpin velu*
Pine	Pinus	*Pin*
Pineapple broom	Cytisus battandieri	*Cytisus battandieri*
Pineapple flower	Eucomis	*Eucomis*
Pineapple guava	Feijoa sellowiana	*Feijoa sellowiana*
Pine-mat manzanita	Arcotstaphylos nevadensis	
		Arcotstaphylos nevadensis
Pink	Dianthus	*Œillet mignardise*
Pink broom	Notospartium carmichaeliae	*Notospartium carmichaeliae*

Pink dandelion	**Crepis incana**	*Crepide incana*
Pink masterwort	**Astrantia major**	*Grande astrance / Radiare*
Pink purslane	**Claytonia sibirica**	*Montie de Sibérie*
Pink snowball	**Dombeya x cayeuxii**	*Dombeya x cayeuxii*
Pink trumpet	**Tabebuia rosea**	*Tabebuia rosea*
Pink water speedwell	**Veronica catenata**	*Véronique aquatique*
Pinwheel	**Aeonium haworthii**	*Aeonium haworthii*
Pinyon	**Pinus cembroides**	*Arolle / Pin cembro*
Pipewort	**Eriocaulon aquaticum**	*Joncinelle*
Pitch apple	**Clusea rosea**	*Clusea rosea*
Pitcher plant	**Nepenthes**	*Nepenthes*
Pitcher plant	**Sarracenia purpurea**	*Sarracène pourpre*
Plane	**Platanus**	*Platane*
Plantain-leaved pondweed	**Potamogeton coloratus**	*Potamot coloratus*
Plantain lily	**Hosta**	*Funkie*
Ploughman's spikenard	**Inula conyza**	*Herbe aux mouches / Inule squarreuse*
Plovers' eggs	**Adromischus festivus**	*Adromischus festivus*
Plum yew	**Cephalotaxus harringtonia**	*Cephalotaxus harringtonia*
Plum yew	**Podocarpus andinus**	*Podocarpus andinus*
Plush plant	**Echevaria pulvinata**	*Echevaria pulvinata*
Poached egg plant	**Limnanthes douglasii**	*Limnanthes douglasii*
Pocket handkerchief tree	**Davidia involucrata**	*Arbe aux mouchoirs / Arbe aux pochettes*
Poet's daffodil / Narcissus	**Narcissus poeticus**	*Jeannette / Narcisse des poètes / Porillon*
Pohutukawa	**Metrosiderus excelsa**	*Metrosiderus excelsa*
Poinsettia	**Euphorbia pulcherrima**	*Poinsettia*
Polka-dot plant	**Hypoestes phyllostachya**	*Hypoestes phyllostachya*
Polyanthus	**Primula polyanthus**	*Primevère polyanthe*
Polygala chamaebuxus	**Polygala chamaebuxus**	*Polygale faux-buis*
Polypody	**Polypodium vulgare**	*Polypode commun*
Pomegranite	**Punica granatum**	*Grenadier*
Pontine oak	**Quercus pontica**	*Chêne d'Arménie /Chêne pontin*
Pony tail	**Beaucarnea recurvata**	*Beaucarnea recurvata*
Poor man's orchid	**Schizanthus**	*Schizanthus*
Poplar	**Populus**	*Peuplier*
Poppy	**Papaver**	*Pavot*
Port Jackson fig	**Ficus rubiginosa**	*Ficus rubiginosa*
Portia oil nut	**Thespesia populnea**	*Thespesia populnea*
Portugal laurel	**Prunus lusitanica**	*Laurier du Portugal*
Portuguese heath	**Erica lusitanica**	*Bruyère du Portugal*

Pot marigold	**Calendula officinalis**	*Souci des jardins*
Potato	**Solanum tuberosum**	*Pomme de terre*
Potato creeper	**Solanum seaforthianum**	*Solanum seaforthianum*
Potato vine	**Solanum jasminoides**	*Solanum jasminoides*
Powder-puff cactus	**Mammillaria boscasana**	*Mammillaria boscasana*
Prayer plant	**Maranta leuconeura**	*Maranta leuconeura*
Prickly comfrey	**Symphytum asperum**	*Consoude hérissée*
Prickly lettuce	**Lactuca serriola**	*Laitue scariole*
Prickly Moses	**Acacia verticillata**	*Acacia verticillata*
Prickly pear	**Opuntia**	*Nopal / Raquette*
Prickly poppy	**Argemone mexicana**	*Argémone mexicana*
Prickly shield fern	**Polystichium aculeatum**	*Polystic aculeatum*
Prickly sow-thistle	**Sonchus asper**	*Laiteron rude*
Pride of Bolivia	**Tipuana tipu**	*Tipuana tipu*
Pride of India	**Koelreuteria paniculata**	*Savonnier*
Pride of India	**Lagerstroemia speciosa**	*Lilas des indes*
Primrose	**Primula vulgaris**	*Primevère acaule*
Primrose jasmine	**Jasminium mesneyi**	*Jasminium mesneyi*
Prince Albert's yew	**Saxegothaea conspicua**	*Saxegothaea conspicua*
Prince's feather	**Amaranthus hybridus erythrostachys**	
		Amarante hybride
Princess tree	**Paulownia tomentosa**	*Paulownia impérial*
Privet	**Ligustrum vulgare**	*Troène*
Prophet flower	**Arnebia pulchra**	*Arnebia pulchra*
Prostrate coleus	**Plectranthus oertendahlii**	
		Plectranthus oertendahlii
Prostrate speedwell	**Veronica prostrata**	*Véronique couchée*
Prostrate toadflax	**Linaria supina**	*Linaire couchée*
Prunus malaheb	**Prunus malaheb**	*Cerisier de Sainte-Lucie*
Pudding pipe-tree	**Cassia fistula**	*Averse dorée*
Puka	**Meryta sinclairii**	*Meryta sinclairii*
Pukapuka	**Brachyglottis repanda**	*Brachyglottis repanda*
Purple anise	**Illicium floridanum**	*Illicium floridanum*
Purple beech	**Fagus sylvatica purpurea**	*Hêtre pourpré*
Purple broom	**Cytisus purpureus**	*Genêt pourpré*
Purple coltsfoot	**Homogyne alpina**	*Homogyne des Alpes*
Purple crab	**Malus x purpurea**	*Malus x purpurea*
Purple gromwell	**Lithospermum purpuro-caerulea**	
		Grémil pourpre-violet
Purple hawkweed	**Saussurea alpina**	*Saussurée des Alpes*
Purple loosestrife	**Lythrum salicaria**	*Lysimaque rouge / Salicaire commune*
Purple milk-vetch	**Astragalus danicus**	*Astragale du Danemark*

Purple mountain milk-vetch	**Oxytropis halleri**	*Oxytropis de Haller*
Purple osier	**Salix purpurea**	*Osier rouge*
Purple rock brake	**Pellaea atropurpurea**	*Pellaea atropurpurea*
Purple saxifrage	**Saxifraga oppositifolia**	
		Saxifrage à feuilles opposées
Purple toadflax	**Linaria purpurea**	*Linaire pourprée*
Purple stemmed cliff brake	**Pellaea atropurpurea**	*Pellaea atropurpurea*
Purple viper's bugloss	**Echium plantagineum**	*Vipérine pourpre*
Purple water flag	**Iris versicolor**	*Iris versicolore*
Pussy ears	**Cyanotis somaliensis**	*Cyanotis somaliensis*
Pussy ears	**Kalanchoe tomentosa**	*Plante panda*
Pussy willow	**Salix caprea**	*Marsault*
Pygmy date palm	**Phoenix roebelenii**	*Phoenix roebelenii*
Pyramidial bugle	**Ajuga pyramidalis**	*Bugle pyramidalis*
Pyramidial orchid	**Anacamptis pyramidalis**	*Orchis pyramidial*
Pyrenean cranesbill	**Geranium pyrenaicum**	*Géranium des Pyrénées*
Pyrenean lily	**Lilium pyrenaicum**	*Lis des Pyrénées*
Pyrenean saxifrage	**Saxifraga umbrosa**	*Saxifrage des Pyrénées*
Pyrethrum	**Tanacetum coccineum**	*Pyrèrthre*
Weeping willow pear	**Pyrus salicifolia pendula**	
		Poirier pleureur à feuilles de saule

Q

Quaking aspen	**Populus tremuloides**	*Faux-tremble*
Quaking grass	**Briza**	*Brize / Tremblotte*
Quamash	**Camassia**	*Quamash*
Quater	**Vinca major**	*Grande pervenche*
Queen Anne's double daffodil	**Narcissus eystenensis**	*Narcissus eystenensis*
Queen Anne's jonquil	**Narcissus jonquilla florepleno**	
		Narcissus jonquilla florepleno
Queen palm	**Arecastrum**	*Cocos*
Queencup	**Clintonia uniflora**	*Clintonia uniflora*
Queen-of-the-night	**Hylocereus undatus**	*Hylocereus undatus*
Queen-of-the-night	**Selenicereus grandiflorus**	*Cierge à grandes fleurs*
Queen's crape myrtle	**Lagerstroemia speciosa**	*Lagerstoemia speciosa*
Queen's tears	**Billbergia nutans**	*Billbergia nutans*
Queensland nut	**Macadamia integrifolia**	*Macadamia integrifolia*
Queensland pyramidial tree	**Lagunaria patersonii**	*Lagunaria patersonii*
Queensland umbrella tree	**Schefflera actinophylla**	*Arbre ombrelle*
Quince	**Cydonia oblonga**	*Cognassier commun*

71

R

Rabbit tracks	**Maranta leuconeura kerchoviana**	
		Maranta leuconeura kerchoviana
Radish	**Raphanus sativus**	*Radis cultivé*
Ragged Robin	**Lychnis flos-cuculi**	*Fleur de coucou /*
		Fleur de Jupiter
Ragweed	**Ambrosa**	*Ambroisie*
Rain daisy	**Dimorphotheca pluvialis**	*Souci pluvial*
Rain lily	**Zephyranthes**	*Zephyranthes*
Rainbow star	**Cryptanthus bromelioides**	
		Cryptanthus bromelioides
Rampion bellfower	**Campanula rapunculus**	*Campanule raiponce*
Ramsons	**Allium ursinum**	*Ail des ours*
Rangiora	**Brachyglottis repanda**	*Brachyglottis repanda*
Rangoon creeper	**Quisqualis indica**	*Quisqualis indica*
Rannoch rush	**Scheuchzeria palustris**	*Scheuchzérie des marais*
Raoulia australis	**Raoulia australis**	*Carpette argentée*
Raspberry	**Rubus idaeus**	*Framboisir*
Rata	**Metrosideros robusta**	*Arbre de Rata*
Rat's tail cactus	**Aporocactus flagelliformis**	
		Aporocactus flagelliformis
Rat's tail plantain	**Plantago major**	*Grand plantain /*
		Plantain majeur
Rauli	**Nothofagus procera**	*Nothofagus procera*
Red ash	**Fraxinus pennsylvanica**	*Frêne rouge*
Red baneberry	**Actaea rubra**	*Actée rouge*
Red-barked dogwood	**Cornus alba**	*Cornouiller blanc*
Red bartsia	**Odontites verna**	*Euphraise rouge*
Red-berried elder	**Sambucus racemosa**	*Sureau à grappes /*
		Sureau rouge
Redbird flower	**Pedilanthus tithymaloides**	*Pedilanthus tithymaloides*
Red buckeye	**Aesculus pavia**	*Pavier rouge*
Redbud	**Cercis**	*Gainier*
Red catchfly	**Lychnis viscaria**	*Viscaire*
Red chokeberry	**Aronia arbutifolia**	*Aronia arbutifolia*
Red clover	**Trifolium pratense**	*Trèfle des prés*
Red currant	**Ribes rubrum**	*Groseillier rouge*
Red dead-nettle	**Lamium purpureum**	*Lamier pourpre / Ortie rouge*
Red goosefoot	**Chenopodium rubrum**	*Chénopode rouge*
Red and green kangaroo paw	**Anigozanthus manglesii**	*Anigozanthus manglesii*
Red helleborine	**Cephalanthera rubra**	*Céphalanthéra rose*

Red hemp-nettle	Galeopsis angustifolia	Galópsis à feuilles étroites
Red-hot cat's tail	Acalypha hispida	Acalypha hispida
Red-hot poker	Kniphofia	Kniphofia / Tritome
Red horsechestnut	Aesculus x carnea	Marronnier à fleurs rouges
Red-ink plant	Phytolacca americana	Phytolacca americana
Red maple	Acer rubrum	Érable rouge / Plaine rouge
Red morning glory	Ipomoea coccinea	Ipomoea coccinea
Red mountain spinach	Atriplex hortensis rubra	Belle-Dame rouge
Red oak	Quercus rubra	Chêne rouge
Red orach	Atriplex hortensis rubra	Belle-Dame rouge
Red orchid cactus	Nopalxochia ackermannii	Nopalxochia ackermannii
Red passion flower	Passiflora coccinea	Passiflore coccinea
Red pineapple	Ananas bracteatus	Ananas bracteatus
Red rattle	Pedicularis palustris	Pédiculaire des marais
Red sandwort	Minuartia rubella	Minuartia rougeâtre
Red spider lily	Lycoris radiata	Lycoris radiata
Red spike	Cephalophyllum alstonii	Cephalophyllum alstonii
Red valerian	Centranthus ruber	Valériane rouge
Reddish pondweed	Potamogeton alpinus	Potamot alpin
Redwood	Sequoia sempervirens	Sequoia sempervirens
Reflexed stonecrop	Sedum reflexum	Orpin réfléchi
Regal lily	Lilium regale	Lis royal
Rest-harrow	Ononis repens	Arrête-bœuf / Bugrane rampante
Resurrection plant	Selaganella lepidophylla	Selaginella lepidophylla
Rewarewa	Knightia excelsa	Knightia excelsa
Rex begonia vine	Cissus discolor	Cissus discolor
Rhubarb	Rheum	Rhubarbe
Ribbon gum	Eucalyptus viminalis	Eucalyptus à feuilles d'osier
Ribbon-leaved water plantain	Alisma gramineum	Flûteau à feuilles de graminée
Ribbon plant	Dracaena sanderiana	Dragonnier de Sander
Ribbon wood	Hoheria sexstylosa	Hoheria sexstylosa
Ribwort plantain	Plantago lanceolata	Plantain lancéolé
Rice-paper plant	Tetrapanax papyriferus	Tetrapanax papyriferus
Rienga lily	Arthropodium cirrhatum	Arthropodium cirrhatum
River red gum	Eucalyptus camaldulensis	Eucalyptus camaldulensis
Roast-beef plant	Iris foetidissima	Iris fétide
Roble	Nothofagus obliqua	Nothofagus obliqua
Rock lily	Arthropodium cirrhatum	Arthropodium cirrhatum
Rock rose	Cistus	Ciste
Rock rose	Helianthemum	Hélianthème

Rock samphire	**Crithmum maritimum**	*Criste marine / Perce-pierre*
Rock sea-lavender	**Limonium binervosum**	*Statice à deux nervures*
Rock speedwell	**Veronica fruticans**	*Véronique des rochers*
Rock stonecrop	**Sedum forsteranum**	*Orpin de Forster*
Rocky mountain juniper	**Juniperus scopulorum**	*Juniperus scopulorum*
Roman wormwood	**Artemisia pontica**	*Armoise pontica*
Roof houseleek	**Sempervivum tectorum**	*Joubarbe des toits*
Rosa mundi	**Rosa gallica versicolor**	*Rosa gallica versicolor*
Rosary vine	**Ceropegia woodii**	*Ceropegia woodii*
Rose	**Rosa**	*Rose*
Rose acacia	**Robinia hispida**	*Acacia rose*
Rose cactus	**Pereskia grandiflora**	*Pereskia grandiflora*
Rose of Jericho	**Selaginella lepidophylla**	*Selaginella lepidophylla*
Rose of Sharon	**Hypericum calycinum**	*Millepertuis a grandes fleurs*
Rose periwinkle	**Catharanthus roseus**	*Catharanthus roseus*
Rose pincushion	**Mammillaria zeilmanniana**	
		Mammillaria zeilmanniana
Rose-bay willow-herb	**Chamaenerion angustifolium**	*Épilobe en épi / Laurier St. Antoine*
Rose-root	**Sedum rosea**	*Orpin rose*
Rosebud cherry	**Prunus subhirtella**	*Prunus subhirtella*
Rosemary	**Rosmarinus officinalis**	*Romarin*
Roseroot	**Sedum rosea**	*Orpin rose / Rhodiole rose*
Rosy garlic	**Allium roseum**	*Ail rose*
Rouen lilac	**Syringa x chinensis**	*Lilas Varin*
Rough-barked Mexican pine	**Pinus montezumae**	*Pin de Montezuma*
Rough chervil	**Chaerophyllum temulentum**	*Cerfeuil penché*
Rough hawksbeard	**Crepis biennis**	*Crépide bisannuelle*
Rough mallow	**Althaea hirsuta**	*Guimauve hérisée*
Rough star thistle	**Centaurea aspera**	*Centaurée rude*
Round headed club-root	**Scirpus holoschoenus**	*Scirpe à tête ronde*
Round headed leek	**Allium sphaerocephalon**	*Ail a tête ronde*
Round-headed rampion	**Phyteuma orbiculare**	*Raiponce orbiculaire*
Round-leaved cranesbill	**Geranium rotundifolium**	*Géranium à feuilles rondes*
Round-leaved fluellen	**Kickxia spuria**	*Linaire bâtarde velvote*
Round-leaved mint-bush	**Prostanthera rotundifolia**	*Prostanthera rotundifolia*
Round-leaved wintergreen	**Pyrola rotundifolia**	*Pyrole rotundifolia*
Rowan	**Sorbus aucuparia**	*Sorbier des oiseleurs*
Royal agave	**Agave victoriae-reginae**	*Agave victoriae-reginae*
Royal fern	**Osmunda regalis**	*Fougère royale / Osmonde royale*
Royal jasmine	**Jasminium grandiflorum**	*Jasmin d'Espagne*
Royal paintbrush	**Scadoxus puniceus**	*Scadoxus puniceus*

Royal palm	**Roystonea**	*Roi des palmiers*
Royal red bugler	**Aeschynanthus pulcher**	*Aeschynanthus pulcher*
Rubber plant	**Ficus elastica**	*Caoutchouc*
Rubber vine	**Cryptostegia grandiflora**	*Cryptostegia grandiflora*
Ruby grass	**Rhynchelytrum repens**	*Rhynchelytrum repens*
Rue	**Ruta**	*Rue*
Rupture-wort	**Herniaria ciliata**	*Herniaire ciliée*
Russian comfrey	**Symphytum x uplandicum**	*Consoude de Russia*
Russian vine	**Polygonum aubertii**	*Polygonum aubertii*
Russian vine	**Polygonum baldschuanicum**	
		Polygonum baldschuanicum
Rusty woodsia	**Woodsia ilvensis**	*Woodsia ilvensis*
Rusty-back fern	**Ceterach officinarum**	*Ceterach officinarum*
Rusty-leaved fig	**Ficus rubiginosa**	*Ficus rubiginosa*

S

Sacred bamboo	**Nandina domestica**	*Nandine fruitière*
Sacred fig tree	**Ficus religiosa**	*Figuier des pagodes*
Sacred lotus	**Nelumbo nucifera**	*Lotus des Indes*
Saffron crocus	**Crocus sativus**	*Safran d'automne*
Sage	**Salvia**	*Sauge / Toute bonne*
Saguaro	**Carnegiea gigantea**	*Carnegiea gigantea*
St. Augustine's grass	**Stenotaphrium secundatum**	
		Stenotaphrium secundatum
St. Barnaby's thistle	**Centaurea solstitalis**	*Centaurée du solstice*
St. Bernard's lily	**Anthericum liliago**	*Phalangère à fleur de lis*
St. Bruno's lily	**Paradisea liliastrum**	*Lis de Saint-Bruno*
St. Catherine's lace	**Eriogonum giganteum**	*Eriogonum giganteum*
St. Dabeoc's heath	**Daboecia cantabrica**	*Bruyère de Saint-Dabeoc*
St. John's wort	**Hypericum**	*Millepertuis*
St. Olaf's candlestick	**Moneses uniflora**	*Pyrole uniflore*
St. Patrick's cabbage	**Saxifraga spathularis**	*Saxifrage spathulée*
Salsify	**Tragopogon porrifolius**	*Salsifis cultivé*
Saltwort	**Salsola kali**	*Soude salsovie*
Salvia argentea	**Salvia argentea**	*Sauge argentée*
Sand catchfly	**Silene conica**	*Silène conique*
Sand crocus	**Romulea columnae**	*Romulée à petites fleurs*
Sand leek	**Allium scorodoprasum**	*Ail rocambole*
Sand phlox	**Phlox bifida**	*Phlox bifida*
Sand spurrey	**Spergularia rubra**	*Spergulaire rouge*
Sandwort	**Arenaria**	*Arénaire / Sabline*

Sanfoin	Onobrychis viciifolia	*Esparcette / Sainfoin*
Sanicle	Sanicula europaea	*Sanicle d'Europe*
Sapphira berry	Symplocos paniculata	*Symplocos paniculata*
Saracen's woundwort	Senecio fluviatilis	*Seneçon des rivières*
Sargent cherry	Prunus sargentii	*Prunus sargentii*
Sargent's rowan	Sorbus sargentiana	*Sorbus sargentiana*
Satin poppy	Meconopsis napaulensis	*Meconopsis napaulensis*
Sausage tree	Kigelia pinnata	*Kigélie / Saucissonier*
Savin	Juniperus sabina	*Genévrier Sabine*
Savory	Satureja	*Sarriette*
Saw palmetto	Serenoa repens	*Serenoa repens*
Sawara cypress	Chamaecyparis pisifera	*Sawara*
Sawfly orchid	Ophrys tenthredinifera	*Ophrys tenthredinifera*
Sawtooth oak	Quercus acutissima	*Quercus acutissima*
Sawwort	Serratula tinctoria	*Sarrette /*
		Serratule des teinturiers
Saxifrage	Saxifraga	*Saxifrage*
Saxifraga x geum	Saxifraga x geum	*Saxifrage benoîte*
Scabious	Knautia arvensis	*Scabieuse*
Scabious	Scabiosa	*Scabieuse*
Scarlet ball cactus	Notocactus haselbergii	*Notocactus haselbergii*
Scarlet banana	Musa coccinea	*Bananier rouge*
Scarlet Fritillary	Fritillaria recurva	*Fritillaire recurva*
Scarlet oak	Quercus coccinea	*Chêne écarlate*
Scarlet pimpernel	Anagallis arvenis	*Mouron rouge*
Scarlet plume	Euphorbia fulgens	*Euphorbe fulgens*
Scarlet sage	Salvia splendens	*Sauge éclatante*
Scarlet trompetilla	Bouvardia ternifolia	*Bouvardia ternifolia*
Scarlet trumpet honeysuckle	Lonicera x brownii	*Lonicera x brownii*
Scarlet turk's cap lily	Lilium chalcedonicum	*Lis chalcedonicum*
Scented orchid	Gymnadenia canopsea	*Gymnadénia à long éperon*
Scented paper-bark	Melaleuca squarrosa	*Melaleuca squarrosa*
Scentless mayweed	Matricaria inodora	*Matricaire maritime*
Scotch heather	Calluna vulgaris	*Brande /*
		Callune fausse-bruyère
Scotch laburnum	Laburnum alpinum	*Cytise des Alpes*
Scotch rose	Rosa pimpinellifolia	*Rosier pimpernelle*
Scotch thistle	Onopordum acanthium	*Chardon aux ânes /*
		Onopordon faux-acanthe / Pet-d'âne
Scots pine	Pinus sylvestris	*Baquois / Vacoua*
Scots primrose	Primula scotica	*Primevère d'Ecosse*
Scottish asphodel	Tofieldia pusilla	*Tofieldie fluette*

Scottish lupin	**Lupinus nootkatensis**	*Lupin d'Écosse*
Scottish sandwort	**Arenaria norvegica**	*Sabline de Norvège*
Screw pine	**Pandanus**	*Pandanus*
Scrub palmetto	**Serenoa repens**	*Serenoa repens*
Sea arrow-grass	**Triglochin maritima**	*Troscart maritime*
Sea aster	**Aster tripolium**	*Aster maritime*
Sea beet	**Beta vulvaris**	*Bette maritime*
Sea bindweed	**Calystegia soldanella**	*Chou marin /*
		Liseron de mer
Sea buckthorn	**Hippophäe rhamnoides**	*Argousier*
Sea campion	**Silene vulgaris maritima**	*Silène maritime*
Sea clover	**Trifolium squamosum**	*Trèfle maritime*
Sea daffodil	**Pancratium maritimum**	*Lis matthiola /*
	Lis narcisse /	*Pancrais maritime*
Sea heath	**Frankenia laevis**	*Bruyère marine /*
		Frankenénie lisse
Sea holly	**Eryngium maritimum**	*Panicaut de mer*
Sea kale	**Crambe maritima**	*Chou marin*
Sea knotgrass	**Polygonum maritimum**	*Renouée maritime*
Sea lavender	**Limonium vulgare**	*Lavande de mer / Saladelle /*
		Immortelle bleue
Sea lily	**Pancratium maratimum**	*Pancrais maritime*
Sea milkwort	**Glaux maritima**	*Glauce*
Sea onion	**Urginea maritima**	*Scille maritima*
Sea pea	**Lathyrus japonicus**	*Gesse maritime*
Sea pearlwort	**Sagina maritima**	*Sagine maritime*
Sea pink	**Armeria maritima**	*Arméria maritime /*
		Œillet marin
Sea plantain	**Plantago maritima**	*Plantain maritime*
Sea purslane	**Halimione portulacoides**	*Arroche pourpière*
Sea rocket	**Cakile maritima**	*Coquillier maritime*
Sea sandwort	**Honkenya peploides**	*Pourpier de mer /*
		Roquette de mer
Seaside centaury	**Centaurium littorale**	*Petite centaurée du littoral*
Seaside thistle	**Carduus tenuilorus**	*Chardon à capitues grêles*
Sea spurrey	**Spergularia marina**	*Spergulaire marine*
Sea squill	**Urginea maritima**	*Urginea maritima*
Sea stock	**Matthiola incana**	*Quarantaine*
Sea storksbill	**Erodium maritimum**	*Bec-de-grue maritime*
Sea urchin	**Astrophytum asterias**	*Astrophytum asterias*
Sea wormwood	**Artemisia maritima**	*Armoise maritime*
Selaginella kraussiana	**Selaginella kraussiana**	*Lycopode du jardinier*

Self heal	**Prunella vulgaris**	*Brunelle commune*
Sensitive fern	**Onoclea sensibilis**	*Onocléa délicat*
Sensitive plant	**Mimosa pudica**	*Sensitive pudique*
Sentry palm	**Howea forsteriana**	*Howée*
Serbian spruce	**Picea omorica**	*Épicéa de Serbie*
Service tree	**Sorbus domestica**	*Cormier / Sorbier domestique*
Service tree of Fontainebleau	**Sorbus latifolia**	*Alisier de Fontainebleau*
Serviceberry	**Amelanchier**	*Amélanchier*
Sessile oak	**Quercus petraea**	*Chêne rouvre / Chêne sessile*
Shadbush	**Amelanchier canadensis**	*Amelanchier du Canada*
Shag-bark hickory	**Carya ovata**	*Noyer blanc d'Amérique*
Shallon	**Gaultheria shallon**	*Gaultheria shallon*
Shamrock pea	**Parochetus communis**	*Fleur des dieux*
Sharp-leaved fluellen	**Kickxia elatine**	*Linaire élatine*
Sharp-leafed pondweed	**Potamogeton acutifolius**	*Potamot à feuilles aiguës*
Shasta daisy	**Chrysanthemum x superbum**	*Chrysanthemum x superbum*
Sheep laurel	**Kalmia angustifolia**	*Laurier des moutons*
Sheepberry	**Viburnum lentago**	*Viorne lentago*
Sheep's bit	**Jasione montana**	*Jasione des montagnes*
Sheep's sorrel	**Rumex acetosella**	*Petite oseille*
Shell flower	**Alpinia zerumbet**	*Alpinia zerumbet*
Shell flower	**Moluccella laevis**	*Clochette d'Irlande*
Shell ginger	**Moluccella laevis**	*Clochette d'Irlande*
Shepherd's cress	**Teesdalia nudicaulis**	*Teesdalie à tige nue*
Shepherd's needle	**Scandix pecten-veneris**	*Scandix peigne-de-Vénus*
Shepherd's purse	**Capsella bursa-pastoris**	*Bourse à pasteur*
Shepherd's rod	**Dipsacus pilosus**	*Cardère poilue*
Shield ivy	**Hedera helix deltoides**	*Hedera helix deltoides*
Shingle oak	**Quercus imbricaria**	*Chêne à lattes*
Shingle plant	**Monstera acuminata**	*Monstera acuminata*
Shining cranesbill	**Geranium lucidum**	*Géranium luisant / Rouget*
Shining pondweed	**Potamogeton lucens**	*Potamot luisant*
Shoofly	**Nicandra physalodes**	*Nicandra physalodes*
Shooting stars	**Dodecatheon**	*Gyroselle*
Shore dock	**Rumex rupestris**	*Patience des rochers*
Shore juniper	**Juniperus conferta**	*Genévrier des rivages*
Shore pine	**Pinus contorta**	*Pin vrillé*
Shore-weed	**Littorella uniflora**	*Littorelle uniflore*
Short-fruited willow-herb	**Epilobium obscurum**	*Épilobe foncé*
Showy lady's slipper orchid	**Cypripedium reginae**	*Cypripedium reginae*

Shrimp plant	**Justicia brandegeana**	*Carmantine brandegeana*
Shrubby cinquefoil	**Potentilla fruticosa**	*Potentille ligneuse*
Shrubby germander	**Teucrium fruticans**	*Germandrée fruticans*
Shrubby hare's ear	**Bupleurum fruticosum**	*Oreille-de-lièvre*
Shrubby restharrow	**Ononis fruticosa**	*Bugrane fruticosa*
Siberian bugloss	**Brunnera macrophylla**	*Brunnera macrophylla*
Siberian crab	**Malus baccata**	*Pommier à baies*
Siberian elm	**Ulmus pumila**	*Orme de Sibérie*
Siberian flag	**Iris sibirica**	*Iris de Sibérie*
Siberian melic	**Melica altissima**	*Mélique*
Siberian squill	**Scilla sibirica**	*Scille de Sibérie*
Siberian wallflower	**Erysimum hieraciifolium**	*Vélar*
Sickle Hare's-ear	**Bupleurum falcatum**	*Buplèvre des haies*
Silene coeli-rosa	**Silene coeli-rosa**	*Coquelourde rose de ciel*
Silk cotton tree	**Ceiba pentandra**	*Arbre à kapok*
Silk tree	**Albizia julibrissin**	*Arbre de soie*
Silk vine	**Periploca graeca**	*Périploque*
Silk weed	**Asclepias**	*Asclépiade*
Silk-tassel bush	**Garrya elliptica**	*Garrya elliptica*
Silky oak	**Grevillea robusta**	*Grevillea robusta*
Silky wisteria	**Wisteria venusta**	*Wisteria venusta*
Silver ball cactus	**Notocactus scopa**	*Notocactus scopa*
Silver beech	**Nothofagus menziesii**	*Nothofagus menziesii*
Silver bell	**Halesia carolina**	*Arbre aux cloches*
Silver cassia	**Cassia artemisioides**	*Casse argentée*
Silver chain	**Dendrochilum glumaceum**	*Dendrochilum glumaceum*
Silver dollar cactus	**Astrophytum asterias**	*Astrophytum asterias*
Silver fir	**Abies alba**	*Sapin argenté / Sapin commun / Sapin des Vosges*
Silver heart	**Peperomia marmorata**	*Peperomia marmorat*
Silver hedgehog holly	**Ilex aquifolium 'Ferox Argentea'**	*Houx aquifolium ferox argentea*
Silver inch plant	**Tradescantia zebrina**	*Misère*
Silver jade plant	**Crassula arborescens**	*Crassula arborescens*
Silver lime	**Tilia tomentosa**	*Tilleul argenté*
Silver maple	**Acer saccherinum**	*Érable argenté / Plaine blanche*
Silver morning glory	**Argyreia splendens**	*Volubilis argenté*
Silver net-leaf	**Fittonia verschaffeltii**	*Fittonia verschaffeltii*
Silver torch	**Cleistocactus strausii**	*Cleistocactus strausii*
Silver tree	**Leucadendron argenteum**	*Arbre d'argent*

Silver vase plant	Aechmea fasciata	Bilbergia rhodocyanea

Silver vine	Actinidia polygama	Actinidie polygame
Silver vine	Epipremnum pictum	Epipremnum pictum
Silver wattle	Acacia dealbata	Mimosa
Silver willow Salix alba	Saule argenté / Saule blanc / Saule vivier	
Silver-leaf peperomia	Peperomia griseo'Argentea Marginata'	
	Houx commun 'Argentea Marginata'	
Silverweed	Potentilla anserina	Ansérine
Sitka spruce	Picea sitchensis	Épicéa de Sitka
Skullcap	Scutellaria	Scutellaire /Toque
Skunk cabbage	Symplocarpus	Symplocarpe
Sky plant	Fittonia verschaffeltii	Tillandsia ionantha
Skyflower	Duranta repens	Durante
Sleeping beauty	Oxalis corniculata	Oxalis corniculé
Sleepy mallow	Malvaviscus arboreus	Malvaviscus arboreus
Slender centaury	Centaurea nemoralis	Petite centaurée délicat
Slender cicendia	Cicendia filiformis	Cicendies filiforme
Slender hare's ear	Bupleurum tenuissimum	Buplèvre grêle
Slender lady palm	Rhapis excelsa	Rhapis excelsa
Slender leafed pondweed	Potamogeton filiformis	Potamot filiforme
Slender naid	Najas flexilis	Naiade flexible
Slender wart cress	Coronopus didymus	Sénebière didyme
Slender pondweed	Potamogeton berchtoldii	Potamot de Berchtold
Slipper orchid	Cypripedium calceolus	Sabot deVénus
Sloe	Prunus spinosa	Épine noire / Prunellier
Small alison	Alyssum alyssoides	Alysson à calice persistant
Small balsam	Impatiens parviflora	Balsamine à petites fleurs
Small goosegrass	Galium tricornutum	Gaillet à trois cornes
Small bladderwort	Utricularia minor	Utriculaire fluette
Small cow-wheat	Melampyrum sylvaticum	Mélampyre des bois
Small cudweed	Filago minima	Cotonnière naine
Small fleabane	Pulcaria vulgaris	Pulicaire commune
Small flowered buttercup	Ranunculus parviflorus	Renoncule a peites fleurs
Small flowered cranesbill	Geranium pusillum	Géranium fluet
Small-flowered melilot	Melilotus indica	Mélilot des Indes
Small leaved box	Buxus microphylla	Buis à petites feuilles
Small leaved lime	Tilia cordata	Tilleul à petites feuilles
Small nettle	Urtica urens	Ortie brûlante
Small rest-harrow	Ononis reclinata	Bugrane renversée
Small scabious	Scabiosa columbaria	Scabieuse colombaire
Small toadflax	Chaenorhinum minus	Petite linaire

Small toadflax	Chaenorhinum minus	*Petite linaire*
Smoke tree	Cotinus coggygria	*Arbre à perruques / Sumac fustet*
Smooth catsear	Hypochoeris glabra	*Porcelle glabre*
Smooth cypress	Cupressus glabra	*Cupressus glabra*
Smooth rupture-wort	Herniaria glabra	*Herniare glabre*
Smooth sow-thistle	Sonchus oleraceus	*Laiteron potager*
Smooth sumach	Rhus glabra	*Sumac à bois glabre / Vinaigrier*
Smooth tare	Vicia tetrasperma	*Vesce à quatre graines*
Smooth winterberry	Ilex laevigata	*Houx laevigata*
Smooth-leaved elm	Ulmus carpinifolia	*Orme à feuilles de charme*
Snail flower	Vigna caracalla	*Vigna caracalla*
Snake bush	Justicia adhatoda	*Carmantine en arbre*
Snake gourd	Trichosanthes anguina	*Patole / Serpent végétal*
Snake-bark maple	Acer capillipes	*Érable capillipes*
Snake-bark maple	Acer davidii	*Érable davidii*
Snake-bark maple	Acer pennsylvanicum	*Érable jaspé*
Snake-bark maple	Acer rufinerve	*Érable rufinerve*
Snake's head fritillery	Fritillaria meleagris	*Méléagre / Œuf e pintade / Œuf de vanneau*
Snapdragon	Antirrhinum	*Guele-de-loup / Muflier*
Sneezeweed	Helenium	*Hélénie*
Sneezewort	Achillea ptarmica	*Achillée sternutatoire / Bouton d'argent*
Snow brake	Pteris ensiformis	*Pteris ensiformis*
Snow bush	Breynia disticha	*Breynia disticha*
Snow creeper	Porana paniculata	*Porana paniculata*
Snow gum	Eucalyptus niphophila	*Eucalyptus niphophila*
Snow poppy	Eomecon chionantha	*Eomecon chionantha*
Snow trillium	Trillium nivale	*Trillie nivale*
Snowball pincushion	Mammillaria candida	*Mammillaria candida*
Snowbell	Soldanella	*Soldanelle*
Snowberry	Symphoricarpus albus	*Symphorine*
Snowbush tree	Rosa 'Dupontii'	*Rosier Dupontii*
Snowdon lily	Lloydia serotina	*Lloydie tardive*
Snowdrop	Galanthus nivalis	*Clochette d'hiver / Galantine / Nivéol Perce-neige / Violette de la Chandeleur*
Snowdrop plicatus byzantinus	Galanthus plicatus byzantinus	*Byzantine*
Snowdrop tree	Halesia	*Arbre aux cloches d'argent*
Snowdrop windflower	Anemone sylvestris	*Anémone sylvestre*

81

Snowflake	Leucojum	*Nivéole du printemps*
Snow-in-summer	Cerastium tomentosum	*Céraiste tomentosum*
Snow-in-summer	Euphorbia marginata	*Euphorbe panaché*
Snow-on-the-mountain	Euphorbia marginata	*Euphorbe panaché*
Snowy woodrush	Luzula nivea	*Luzule nivea*
Soapwort	Saponaria officinalis	*Saponaire officinale / Savonnière*
Soft clover	Trifolium striatum	*Trèfle strié*
Soft shield fern	Polystichum setiferum	*Polystic setiferum*
Soft comfrey	Symphytum orientale	*Consoude d'Orient*
Soldier orchid	Orchis militaris	*Orchis militaire*
Solomon's seal	Polygonatum	*Sceau-de-Salomon*
Sorrel tree	Oxydendron arboreum	*Oxydendron en arbre*
South American air plant	Kalanchoe fedtschenko	*Kalanchoe fedtschenkoi*
South sea arrowroot	Tacca leontopetaloides	*Tacca leontopetaloides*
Southern hawksbeard	Crepis foetida	*Crépide fétide*
Southern Japanese hemlock	Tsuga sieboldii	*Tsuga sieboldii*
Southern marsh orchid	Dactylorhiza praetermissa	*Orchis négligé*
Southernwood	Artemisia abrotanum	*Aurone / Citronelle*
Sowbane	Chenopodium hybridum	*Chénopode hybride*
Sowbread	Cyclamen hederifolium	*Cyclamen de Naples*
Sow thistle	Sonchus	*Laiteron*
Spade leaf	Philodendron domesticum	*Philodendron domesticum*
Spanish bayonet	Yucca aloifolia	*Yucca aloifolia*
Spanish bluebell	Hyacinthoides hispanica	*Jacinthe d'Espagne*
Spanish bluebell	Brimeura amethystina	*Jacinthe d'Espagne / Jacinthe des pyrénées*
Spanish broom	Spartium junceum	*Genêt d'Espagne*
Spanish chestnut	Castanea sativa	*Châtaignier*
Spanish dagger	Yucca gloriosa	*Yucca gloriosa*
Spanish gorse	Genista hispanica	*Genêt d'Espagne*
Spanish heath	Erica australis	*Bruyère d'Espagne*
Spanish jasmine	Jasminium grandiflorum	*Jasmin d'Espagne*
Spanish moss	Tillandsia usneoides	*Barbe de vieillard / Fille de l'air / Mousse espagnole*
Spanish tree heath	Erica australis	*Bruyère d'Espagne*
Spear-leaved willow-herb	Epilobium lanceolatum	*Épilobe à feuilles lancéolées*
Spear-mint	Mentha spicata	*Menthe en épi*
Spear thistle	Cirsium vulgare	*Cirse à feuilles lancéolées*
Speedwell	Veronica	*Véronique*
Spiceberry	Lindera benzoin	*Laurier benzoin*

Spider fern	Pteris multifida	Pteris multifida
Spider flower	Cleome	Cléome
Spider orchid	Ophrys sphegodes	Ophrys araignée
Spider plant	Anthericum	Anthericum
Spider plant	Chlorophytum comosum	Chlorophytum comosum
Spider web houseleek	Sempervivum arachnoideum	
		Joubarbe à toile d' araignée
Spiderwort	Tradescantia	Tradescantia
Spignel-meu	Meum athamanticum	Fenouil des Alpes
Spike heath	Bruckenthalia spiculifolia	Bruckenthalia spiculifolia
Spiked water-milfoil	Myriophyllum spicatum	Myriophylle à épis
Spiked rampion	Phyteuma spicatum	Raiponce en épi
Spiked speedwell	Veronica spicata	Véronique en épi
Spiked star of Bethlehem	Ornithogalum pyrenaicum	Aspergette
Spindle tree	Euonymus europaeus	Bonnet-de-prêtre /
		Fusain d'Europe
Spinning gum	Eucalyptus perriniana	Eucalyptus perriniana
Spiny cocklebur	Xanthium spinosum	Lampourde épineuse
Spiny rest-harrow	Ononis spinosa	Bugrane épineuse
Spotted catsear	Hypochoeris maculata	Porcelle maculée
Spotted dead-nettle	Lamium maculatum	Lamier maculé
Spotted medick	Medicago arabica	Luzerne d'Arabie
Spreading bellflower	Campanula patula	Campanule Étalée
Spreading bur parsley	Torilis arvensis	Torilis des champs
Spring adonis	Adonis vernalis	Adonide printanière
Spring beauty	Claytonia virginica / perfiolata	Montie perfolée
Spring bell	Sisyrinchium douglasii	Sisyrinchium douglasii
Spring crocus	Crocus vernus	Crocus printanier
Spring gentian	Gentiana verna	Gntiane printanière
Spring sandwort	Minuartia verna	Minuartia du printemps
Spring snowflake	Leucojum vernum	Nivéole perce-neige
Spring speedwell	Veronica verna	Véronique printanière
Spring squill	Scilla verna	Scille printanière
Spring vetch	Vicia lathyroides	Vesce printanière
Spruce	Picea	Épicéa
Spurge	Euphorbia	Euphorbe
Spurge laurel	Daphne laureola	Daphné lauréole /
		Lauréole des bois
Square St. John's wort	Hypericum tetrapterum	Millepertuis a quatre
		ailes
Squawroot	Trillium erectum	Trillie erectum
Squinancywort	Asperula cynanchia	Aspérule des sables /
		Herbe à l'esquinancie

Squirrel's foot fern	**Davallia maresii**	*Davallia maresii*
Squirrel tail grass	**Hordeum jubatum**	*Orge barbue*
Staff tree	**Celastrus scandens**	*Bourreau des arbres / Célastre grimpant*
Staff vine	**Celastrus orbiculatus**	*Célastre orbicule*
Stag's horn fern	**Platycerium**	*Platycérium*
Stag's horn sumach	**Rhus typhina**	*Sumac amarante / Sumac de Virginie*
Stanford manzanita	**Arctostaphylos stanfordiana**	*Arctostaphylos stanfordiana*
Star daisy	**Lindheimera texana**	*Lindheimera texana*
Star flower	**Stapelia variegata**	*Stapelia variegata*
Star-fruit	**Damasonium alisima**	*Damasonium étoilé*
Star ipomoea	**Ipomoea coccinea**	*Ipomoea coccinea*
Star jasmine	**Trachelospermum jasminoides**	*Jasmin étoilé*
Star magnolia	**Magnolia stellata**	*Magnolia étoilé*
Star-cluster	**Pentas lanceolata**	*Pentas lanceolata*
Star-of-Bethleham	**Ornithogalum umbelletum**	*Dame d'onze heures / Étoile de Bethléem*
Star-of-Bethleham orchid	**Angraecum sesquipedale**	*Étoile de Bethléem*
Star thistle	**Centaurea calcitrapa**	*Chausse-trappe / Chardon Étoilé*
Starry saxifrage	**Saxifraga stellaris**	*Saxifrage etoile*
Starwort mouse ear	**Cerastium cerastoides**	*Céraiste faux-céraiste*
Statice	**Limonium**	*Lavande de mer / Statice*
Stemless gentian	**Gentiana acaulis**	*Gentiana acaulis*
Sticky groundsel	**Senecio viscosus**	*Séneçon visqueux*
Sticky mouse-ear	**Cerastium glomeratum**	*Céraiste à fleurs agglomérée*
Stinging nettle	**Urtica dioica**	*Grande ortie*
Stinking chamomile	**Anthemis cotula**	*Camomille puante*
Stinking goosefoot	**Chenopodium vulvaria**	*Arroche puante*
Stinking hellebore	**Helleborus foetidus**	*Ellébore fétide / Pied-de-griffon*
Stinking iris	**Iris foetidissima**	*Iris gigot*
Stink weed	**Diplotaxis muralis**	*Diplotaxis des murailles*
Stock	**Matthiola**	*Giroflée quarantaine*
Stone bramble	**Rubus saxatilis**	*Ronce des rochers*
Stonecrop	**Sedum**	*Orpin*
Stone parsley	**Sison amomum**	*Sison amome*
Stone pine	**Pinus pinea**	*Pin parasol*
Stone plant	**Lithops**	*Plante-caillou / Pierre vivante*

84

Strap cactus	Epiphyllum	*Cactus orchidée*
Strapwort	**Corrigiola littoralis**	*Corrigiola dsa grèves*
Strawberry cactus	**Mammillaria prolifera**	*Mammillaria prolifera*
Strawberry clover	**Trifolium fraggiferum**	*Trèfle fraisier*
\Strawberry geranium	**Saxifraga stolonifera 'Tricolor'**	
		Saxifraga stolonifera 'Tricolor'
Strawberry tomato	**Physalis peruviana**	*Alkékenge de Pérouc /*
		Coqueret de Pérou / Lanterne japonaise
Strawberry tree	**Arbutus unedo**	*Arbousier / Arbre aux fraises*
Strawflower	**Helichrysum bracteatum**	*Immortelle à bractés*
String-of-beads	**Senecio rowleyanus**	*Senecio rowleyanus*
String-of-hearts	**Ceropegia woodii**	*Ceropegia woodii*
Striped squill	**Puschkinia scilloides**	*Puschkinia scilloides*
Striped torch	**Guzmania monostachia**	*Guzmania monostachia*
Subalpine fir	**Abies lasiocarpa**	*Sapin lasiocarpa*
Suffocated clover	**Trifolium suffocatum**	*Trèfle étouffé*
Sugar bush	**Protea repens**	*Protea repens*
Sugar maple	**Acer saccharum**	*Érable à sucre*
Sugar-almond plum	**Pachyphytum oviferum**	*Pachyphytum oviferum*
Sulpher cinquefoil	**Potentilla recta**	*Potentille dressée*
Sulphur clover	**Trifolium ochroleucon**	*Trèfle jaunâtre*
Sumach	**Rhus**	*Sumac*
Summer cypress	**Kochia scoparia trichophylla**	*Kochie*
Summer holly	**Comarostaphylis diversifolia**	
		Comarostaphylis diversifolia
Summer hyacinth	**Galtonia candicans**	*Jacinthe du Cap*
Summer snowflake	**Leucojum aestivum**	*Niveole d'été*
Sunplant	**Portulaca grandiflora**	*Pourpier grandiflora*
Sundew	**Drosera**	*Rossolis*
Sunflower	**Helianthus**	*Soleil / Tournesol*
Sunrise horse-chestnut	**Aesculus x neglecta**	*Aesculus x neglecta*
Sutherlandia frutescens	**Sutherlandia frutescens**	*Baguenaudier d'Éthiopie*
Swamp cypress	**Taxodium distichum**	*Cyprès chauve*
Swamp lily	**Lilium superbum**	*Lis superbum*
Swamp lily	**Saururus cernuus**	*Queue de lézard*
Swamp pink	**Helonias bullata**	*Helonias bullata*
Swan flower	**Aristolocia grandiflora**	*Aristoloche grandiflora*
Swan river daisy	**Brachycome iberidifolia**	*Brachycome iberidifolia*
Swedish birch	**Betula pendula 'Dalecarlica'**	*Bouleau lacinié*
Swedish ivy	**Plectranthus australis**	*Plectranthus australis*
Swedish ivy	**Plectranthus oertendahlii**	
		Plectranthus oertendahlii

Swedish whitebeam	**Sorbus intermedia**	*Sorbus intermedia*
Sweet alyssum	**Lobularia maritima**	*Alysson maritime / Corbeille d'argent*
Sweet bay	**Laurus nobilis**	*Lauie-sauce*
Sweet bay magnolia	**Magnolia virginiana**	*Magnolia de Virginie*
Sweet box	**Sarcococca**	*Sarcococca*
Sweet briar	**Rosa eglanteria**	*Églantine / Églantier odorant*
Sweet buckeye	**Aesculus flava**	*Marronnier jaune*
Sweet chestnut	**Castanea sativa**	*Chataignier*
Sweet Cicely	**Myrrhis odorata**	*Cerfeuil musqué*
Sweet corn	**Zea mays**	*Maïs*
Sweet flag	**Acorus calamus variegatus**	*Acore vrai*
Sweet gum	**Liquidambar styraciflua**	*Copalme d'Amerique*
Sweet pea	**Lathyrus odoratus**	*Pois de senteur*
Sweet pepper-bush	**Clethra alnifolia**	*Clethra alnifolia*
Sweet rocket	**Hesperis matronalis**	*Julienne des dames / Julienne des jardins*
Sweet scabious	**Scabiosa atropurpurea**	*Scabieuse des jardins*
Sweet sop	**Annona**	*Corossolier à fruit hérissé*
Sweet sultan	**Centaurea moschata**	*Centaurée barbeau*
Sweet viburnum	**Viburnum odoratissimum**	*Viorne odorante*
Sweet violet	**Viola odorata**	*Violette odorante*
Sweet William	**Dianthus barbatus**	*Œillet de poète / Jalousie*
Sweetheart ivy	**Hedera helix 'Deltoides'**	*Hedera helix Deltoides*
Swine's succory	**Arnoseris minima**	*Chicorée de mouton*
Swiss mountain pine	**Pinus mugo**	*Pin de montagne*
Swiss cheese plant	**Monstera deliciosa**	*Monstera deliciosa*
Sword fern	**Nephrolepis exaltata**	*Nephrolépis exaltata*
Sycamore	**Acer pseudoplatanus**	*Érable sycomore*
Sydney golden wattle	**Acacia longifolia**	*Chenille*
Syrian juniper	**Juniperus drupacea**	*Genévrier de Syrie*
Szechuan birch	**Betula szechuanica**	*Bouleau szechuanica*

T

Tacamahac	**Populus balsamifera**	*Peuplier baumier*
Tail flower	**Anthurium andraeanum**	*Anthurium andraeanum*
Taiwan cherry	**Prunus campanulata**	*Prunus campanulata*
Taiwan spruce	**Picea morrisonicola**	*Picea morrisonicola*
Tall melic	**Melica altissima**	*Melica altissima*
Tamarind	**Tamarindus indica**	*Tamarin / Tamarinier*

Tamarisk	**Tamarix**	*Tamaris*
Tamarisk	**Tamarix gallica**	*Tamaris de France*
Tanbark oak	**Lithocarpus densiflorus**	*Lithocarpus densiflorus*
Tansy	**Tanacetum vulgare**	*Tanaisie commune*
Tansy-leaved thorn	**Crataegus tanacetifolia**	*Épine a feuilles de tanasie*
Tape grass	**Vallisneria spiralis**	*Vallisnérie spiralée*
Tarajo holly	**Ilex latifolia**	*Houx latifolia*
Taro	**Alocasia macrorrhiza**	*Grande tayove / Taro*
Taro	**Colocasia esculenta**	*Madère / Taro*
Tarragon	**Artemesia dracunculus**	*Dragone / Estragon*
Tasman celery pine	**Phyllocladus aspleniifolius**	
		Phyllocladus aspleniifolius
Tasmanian blue gum	**Eucalyptus globulus**	*Gommier bleu*
Tasmanian podocarp	**Podocarpus alpinus**	*Podocarpe monagnard*
Tasmanian sassafras	**Atherosperma moschatum**	*Atherosperma moschatum*
Tasmanian snow gum	**Eucalyptus coccifera**	*Eucalyptus coccifera*
Tasmanian waratah	**Telopea truncata**	*Telopea truncata*
Tassel flower	**Amaranthus caudatus**	*Queue de renard*
Tassel flower	**Emilia javanica**	*Cacalie éclarte / Émile*
Tassel grape hyacinth	**Muscari comosum**	*Muscari à toupet /*
		Poireau roux
Tassel maidenhair	**Adiantum raddianum 'Grandiceps'**	
		Capillaire raddianum 'Grandiceps'
Tassel pondweed	**Ruppia maritima**	*Ruppia maritime*
Tawny day lily	**Hemerocallis fulva**	*Ls jaune*
Teasel	**Dipsacus fullonium**	*Cardère sauvage /*
		Chardon à foulon
Teddy-bear vine	**Cyanotis kewensis**	*Cyanotis kewensis*
Teesdale sandwort	**Minuartia stricta**	*Minuartia raide*
Temple bells	**Smithiantha cinnabarina**	*Smithiantha cinnabarina*
Temple juniper	**Juniperus rigida**	*Juniperus rigida*
Tenby daffodil	**Narcissus obvallaris**	*Narcissus obvallaris*
Terebinth tree	**Pistacia terebinthus**	*Térébinthe*
Texan walnut	**Juglans microcarpa**	*Noyer des rochers*
Thale cress	**Arabidopsis thaliana**	*Arabette thaliana*
Thatch-leaf plant	**Howea forsteriana**	*Howea forsteriana*
Thick-leaved stonecrop	**Sedum dasyphyllum**	*Orpin à feuilles épaisses*
Thimbleberry	**Rubus odoratus**	*Ronce odorante*
Thistle	**Cirsium**	*Cirse / Chardon*
Thorn	**Crataegus**	*Aubépine / Épine / Mai*
Thorn-apple	**Datura stramonium**	*Herbe a la taupe /*
		Pomme épineause / Stramoine

Thornless rose	Rosa 'Zéphirine Drouhin'	
		Rosier 'Zéphirine Drouhin'
Thorow-wax	Bupleurum rotundifolium	Buplèvre à feuilles rondes
Thread agave	Agave filifera	Agave filifera
Thread palm	Washingtonia robusta	Washingtonia robusta
Three-cornered leek	Allium triquetrum	Ail triquêtre
Three-veined sandwort	Moehringia triniveria	Moehringie à troisnervures
Thrift	Armeria maritima	Arméria maritime / Œillet marin
Throatwort	Trachelium caeruleum	Trachélie
Thyme	Thymus	Thym
Thyme broomrape	Orobanche alba	Orobanche blanche / Orobanche du thym
Thyme-leaved sandwort	Arenaria serpyllifolia	Sabline à feuilles de serpolet
Ti tree	Cordyline fruticosa	Cordyline fruticosa
Tickseed	Coreopsis	Coreopsis
Tidy tips	Layia platyglossa	Layie platyglossa
Tiger flower	Tigridia pavonia	Œil de paon / Tigridie
Tiger lily	Lilium lancifolium	Lis tigré
Tiger-jaws	Faucaria tigrina	Guele de tigre
Timber bamboo	Phyllostachys bambusoides	Bambou bambusoides
Tigiringi gum	Eucalyptus glaucescens	Eucalyptus glaucescens
Tipa tree	Tipuana tipu	Tipuana tipu
Toad lily	Tricyrtis	Tricyrtis
Toadflax	Linaria	Linaire
Toadshade	Trillium sessile	Trillie sessile
Toothwort	Lathraea clandestina	Dentaire
Torch cactus	Trichocereus spachianus	Trichocereus spachianus
Torch lily	Kniphofia	Kniphofia
Torch plant	Aloe aristata	Aloès aristata
Tormentil	Potentilla erecta	Potentille dressée
Touch -me-not	Impatiens noli-tangere	Impatiente / Ne-me-touchez-pas
Toyon	Heteromeles arbutifolia	Heteromeles arbutifolia
Trailing arbutus	Epigaea repens	Epigée
Trailing azalea	Loiseleuria procumbens	Loiseleuria procumbens
Trailing St. John's wort	Hypericum humifusum	Millepertuis couché
Traveller's joy	Clematis vitalba	Clématite des haies
Traveller's tree	Ravenala madegascariensis	
		Ravenala madegascariensis
Treacle mustard	Erysimum cheiranthoides	Vélar fause-giroflée
Tree cotoneaster	Cotoneaster frigidus	Cotoneaster frigidus

Tree fuchsia	Fuchsia arborescens	*Fuchsia arborescent*
Tree germander	Teucrium fruticans	*Germandrée fruticans*
Tree heath	Erica arborea	*Bruyère en arbre*
Tree ivy	Fatshedera lizei	*Fatshedera lizei*
Tree lupin	Lupinus arboreus	*Lupin arborescent*
Tree mallow	Lavatera arborea	*Lavatère arborescente /*
		Mauve du jardin
Tree medick	Medicago arborea	*Luzerne arborescente*
Tree of heaven	Ailanthus altissima	*Ailante / Faux-Vernis du Japon*
Tree purslane	Atriplex halimus	*Arroche halime /*
		Pourpier de mer
Tree tomato	Cyphomandra betacea	*Tomate en arbre /*
		Tomate de La Paz
Trident maple	Acer buergerianum	*Acer buergerianum*
Trifid bur-marigold	Bidens tripartita	*Bident trifoliolé*
Trigger plant	Stylidium graminifolium	*Stylidium graminifolium*
Trinity flower	Trillium	*Trillie*
Tropical almond	Terminalia catappa	*Badamier*
Trumpet creeper	Campsis radicans	*Jasmin trompette /*
		Jasmin de Virginie
Trumpet flower	Bignonia capreolata	*Bignonia capreolata*
Trumpet gentian	Gentiana clusii	*Gentiane clusii*
Trumpet honeysuckle	Lonicera sempervirenss	*Chèvrefeuille toujours vert*
Trumpet vine	Campsis radicans	*Jasmin trompette /*
		Jasmin de Virginie
Trumpets	Sarracenia flava	*Sarracène à fleurs jaunes*
Tuberose	Polianthes tuberosa	*Tubéreuse*
Tuberous comfrey	Symphytum tuberosum	*Consoude à tubercules*
Tuberous thistle	Cirsium tuberosum	*Cirse tubéreux*
Tubular water dropwort	Oenanthe fistulosa	*Œnanthe fistuleuse*
Tufted hair grass	Deschampsia caespitosa	*Canche cespiteuse*
Tufted loosestrife	Lysimachia thyrsiflora	*Corneille en bouquets*
		/ Lysimaque à grappes
Tufted saxifrage	Saxifraga caespitosa	*Saxifrage gazonnante*
Tufted sedge	Carex elata	*Laîche en gazon*
Tufted vetch	Vicia cracca	*Vesce cracca*
Tulip	Tulipa	*Tulipe*
Tulip tree	Liriodendron tulipifera	*Tulipier*
Tumbing Ted	Saponaria ocymoides	*Saponaire ocymoides*
Tumbling mustard	Sisymbrium altissimum	*Sisymbre fausse-moutarde*
Tunic flower	Petrorhagia saxifraga	*Toupélo*
Tupelo	Nyssa	*Tupelo*

Turkey oak	Quercus cerris	Chêne de Bourgogne / Chêne chevelu
Turkish hazel	Corylus colurna	Coudrier de Byzance / Coudrier do Levant / Noisetier de Constantinople
Turk's cap	Melocactus	Cactus malon
Turkscap lily	Lilium martagon	Lis martagon
Turtle-head	Chelone	Galane
Tutsan	Hypericum androsaemum	Androsème officinal / Toute-bonnne
Tway blades	Listera	Listère
Twin flower	Linnaea borealis	Linée boréale
Twin flowered violet	Viola biflora	Violette à deux fleurs
Twisted whitlow-grass	Draba incana	Drave grisâtre

U

Ulmo	Eucryphia cordifolia	Eucryphia cordifolia
Umbrella leaf	Diphylleia cymosa	Diphyllée
Umbrella pine	Pinus pinea	Pin parasol
Umbrella pine	Sciadopitys verticillata	Pin parasol du Japon
Umbrella plant	Peltiphyllum peltatum	Peltiphyllum peltatum
Unicorn plant	Martynia annua	Martynia annua
Um plant	Aechmea fasciata	Aechmea fasciata
Upland enchanter's nightshade	Circaea intermedia	Circée intermédiare
Upright goosefoot	Chenopodium urbicum	Chénopode des villages
Upright vetch	Vicia orobus	Vesce orobe

V

Valerian	Valeriana	Valériane
Valonia oak	Quercus macrolepis	Chêne Vélani
Van Volxem's maple	Acer velutinum vanvolxemii	Érable velutinum vanvolxemii
Variegated apple mint	Mentha suavolens variegata	Mentha suavolens variegata
Variegated Bishop's weed	Aegopodium podagraria 'Variegatum'	Égopode panaché / Herbe aux goutteux panaché
Variegated creeping soft grass	Holcus mollis 'Variegatus'	Holcus mollis 'Variegatus'
Variegated croton	Codiaeum variegatum	Croton panaché

Variegated gout weed	Aegopodium podagraria 'Variegatum'	
	Harbe aux goutteux à feuilles panachées	
Variegated ground ivy	Glechoma hederacea variegata	
	Lierre terrestre panachée	
Variegated iris	Iris variegata	Iris variegata
Variegated purple moor grass	Molinia caerulea 'Variegata'	
	Molinia caerulea 'Variegata'	
Various-leaved pondweed	Potamogeton gramineus	
	Potamot à feuilles de graminée	
Varnish tree	Rhus verniciflua	Sumac verniciflua
Veitch fir	Abies veitchii	Sapin de Veitch
Veitch's screw pine	Pandanus veitchii	Pandanus veitchii
Velvet plant	Gynura aurantiaca	Gynure
Venetian sumach	Cotinus coggygria	Arbre à perruques
Venetian sumach	Cotinus coggygria	Sumac fustet
Venus flytrap	Dionáea muscipula	Dionée attrape mouches /
		Dionée gobe-mouches
Venus's looking -glass	Legousia hybrida	Miroir de Vénus
Venus's navelwort	Omphalodes linifolia	Gazon blanc /
		Nombril-de-Venus
Verbena rigida	Verbena rigida	Verveine veineuse /
		Verveine ruguese
Vervain	Verbena officinalis	Verveine
Vetch	Vica	Vesce
Viburnum acerifolium	Viburnum acerifolium	Viorne à feuilles
		d'érable
Victorian box	Pittosporum undulatum	Pittosporum undulatum
Vine	Vitis	Vigne
Vine lilac	Hardenbergia violacea	Hardenbergia violacea
Vine maple	Acer circinatum	Érable à feuilles rondes
Violet	Viola	Violette
Violet cress	Ionopsidium acaule	Ionopsidium acaule
Violet helleborine	Epipactis purpurata	Épipactis pourprée
Violet willow	Salix daphnoides	Saule daphné / Saule noir
Viper's bugloss	Echium vulgare	Vipérine commune
Viper's grass	Scorzonera humilis	Scorzonère basse
Virginia creeper	Parthenocissus quinquefolia	Vigne vierge vrai
Virginia pine	Pinus virginiana	Pin de Jersey /Pin de Virginie
Virginia bird cherry	Prunus virginiana	Prunus virginiana
Virginia chain fern	Woodwardia virginica	Woodwardia virginica
Virginia pokeweed	Phytolacca americana	Phytolacca americana

Virginia stock	Malcolmia maritima	*Giroflée de Mahon / Julienne de Mahon / Mahonille*
Virginia witch hazel	**Hamamelis virginiana**	*Hamamelis virginiana*
Virgin's palm	**Dioon edule**	*Dioon edule*
Voodoo lily	**Sauromatum venosum**	*Sauromatum venosum*
Voss's laburnum	**Laburnum x warterei 'Vossii'**	*Laburnum x warterei 'Vossii'*

W

Wake-robin	**Trillium grandiflorum**	*Trillie*
Walking fern	**Camptosorus rhizophyllus**	*Camptosore rhizophyllus*
Wallflower	**Cheiranthus cheiri**	*Giroflée / Giroflée jaune / Rameau / Helleborine d'or / Violier*
Wall germander	**Teucrium chamaedrys**	*Germandrée petit-chêne*
Wall lettuce	**Mycelis muralis**	*Laitue des murs*
Wall pennywort	**Umbilicus rupestris**	*Ombilic*
Wall-pepper	**Sedum acre**	*Poivre de muraille*
Wall rocket	**Diplotaxis muralis**	*Diplotaxis des murailles*
Wall speedwell	**Veronica arvensis**	*Véronique des champs*
Wall-spray	**Cotoneaster horizontalis**	*Cotoneaster horizontalis*
Walnut	**Juglans**	*Noyer*
Wandering Jew	**Tradescantia fluminensis**	*Tradescantia fluminensis*
Wandflower	**Dierama**	*Diérame*
Waratah	**Telopea speciosissima**	*Telopea speciosissima*
Warminster broom	**Cytisus x praecox**	*Genêt*
Warty cabbage	**Bunias orientalis**	*Bunias d'orient*
Washington grass	**Cabomba caroliniana**	*Cabomba caroliniana*
Washington thorn	**Crataegus phaenopyrum**	*Aubépine phaenopyrum*
Water avens	**Geum rivale**	*Benoîte de rivage*
Water Chestnut	**Trapa natans**	*Châtaignier d'eau / Macre*
Water chickweed	**Myosoton aquaticum**	*Stellaire aquatique*
Water-cress	**Rorippa nasturtium-aquaticum**	*Cresson de fontaine*
Water dragon	**Saururus cernuus**	*Queue de lézard*
Water fern	**Azolla caroliniana**	*Azolla caroliniana*
Water figwort	**Scrophularia auriculata**	*Scrofulaire aquatique*
Water forget-me-not	**Myosotis scorpioides**	*Myosotis des marais*
Water fringe	**Nymphoides peltata**	*Nymphoides peltata*
Water germander	**Teucrium scordium**	*Germandrée scordium*
Water hawthorn	**Aponogeton distachyos**	*Aponogeton distachyos*
Water hyacinth	**Eichornia crassipes**	*Jacinthe d'eau*
Water lettuce	**Pistia stratiotes**	*Laitue d'eau*

		Nymphéa
Water lily tulip	**Tulipa kaufmaniana**	*Tulipa kaufmaniana*
Water lobelia	**Lobelia dortmanna**	*Lobélie de Dortmann*
Water mint	**Mentha aquatica**	*Menthe aquatique*
Water moss	**Fontinalis antipyretica**	*Fontinale*
Water oak	**Quercus nigra**	*Chêne noir*
Water plantain	**Alisma plantago-aquatica**	*Flûteau*
Water poppy	**Hydrocleys nymphoides**	*Hydrocléis*
Water soldier	**Stratiotes aloides**	*Stratiote faux-aloès*
Water speedwell	**Veronica anagallis-aquatica**	*Mouron aquatique*
Water violet	**Hottonia palustris**	*Hottonie des marais*
Waterer's gold holly	**Ilex aquifolium 'Watereriana'**	
		Houx aquifolium 'Watereriana'
Watermelon begonia	**Pellionia daveauana**	*Pellionia daveauana*
Watermelon plant	**Peperomia argyreia**	*Peperomia argyreia*
Waterwort	**Elatine hexandra**	*Elatine à six étamines*
Watling street thistle	**Eryngium campestre**	*Panicaut champêtre*
Watling street thistle	**Eryngium campestre**	*Chardon-Roland*
Wax flower	**Stephanotis floribunda**	*Stephanotis floribunda*
Wax plant	**Hoya carnosa**	*Hoya carnosa*
Wax privet	**Peperomia glabella**	*Peperomia glabella*
Wax tree	**Rhus succedanea**	*Sumac faux-vernis*
Wax vine	**Senecio macroglossus**	*Senecio macroglossus*
Wayfaring tree	**Viburnum lantana**	*Viorne cotoneuse /*
		Viorne manciennne
Wedding-cake tree	**Cornus controversa 'Variegata'**	
		Cornouiller controversa 'Variegata'
Weeping ash	**Fraxinus excelsior 'Pendula'**	*Frêne pleureur*
Weeping aspen	**Populus tremula 'Pendula'**	*Tremble pleureur*
Weeping beech	**Fagus sylvatica pendula**	*Hêtre pleureur*
Weeping birch	**Betula pendula**	*Bouleau pleureur*
Weeping fig	**Ficus benjamina**	*Ficus benjamina*
Weepng willow	**Salix babylonica**	*Saule pleureur*
Weeping willow pear	**Pyrus salicifolia pendula**	
		Poirier pleureur à feuilles de saule
Weld	**Reseda luteola**	*Gaude / Réséda dea teinturiers*
Wellingtonia	**Sequoiadendron giganteum**	
		Sequoiadendron giganteum
Welsh gentian	**Gentiana uliginosa**	*Gentiane des marais*
Welsh poppy	**Meconopsis cambrica**	
		Méconopsis du pays de Galles

Welted thistle	**Carduus crispus**	*Chardon faux-acanthe*
West Himalayan birch	**Betula utilis var. jacquemontii**	
		Betula utilis jacquemontii
West Himalayan spruce	**Picea smithiana**	*Picea smithiana*
West Indian jasmine	**Plumeria alba**	*Plumeria alba*
West Indian tree fern	**Cyathea arborea**	*Cyathea arborea*
Western balsam poplar	**Populus trichocarpa**	*Baumier de l'Ouest*
Western hemlock	**Tsuga heterophylla**	*Tsuga de Californie*
Western prickly Moses	**Acacia pulchella**	*Acacia pulchella*
Western red cedar	**Thuja plicata**	*Thuja plicata*
Western tea-myrtle	**Melaleuca nesophylla**	*Melaleuca nesophylla*
Western yellow pine	**Pinus ponderosa**	*Pin jaune*
Weymouth pine	**Pinus strobus**	*Pin Weymouth*
Wheatley elm	**Ulmus 'Sarniensis'**	*Orme de Jersey*
White ash	**Fraxinus americana**	*Frêne blanc*
White asphodel	**Asphodelus albus**	*Asphodèle albus*
White baneberry	**Actaea pachypoda**	*Actée pachypoda*
White beam	**Sorbus aria**	*Alisier / Alisier blanc /*
		Allouchier
White broom	**Cytisus albus**	*Genêt blanc*
White bryony	**Bryonia cretica**	*Bryone dioîque*
White butterbur	**Petasites albus**	*Pétasite blanc*
White Chinese birch	**Betula albo-sinensis**	*Betula albo-sinensis*
White cinquefoil	**Potentilla rupestris**	*Potentille des rochers*
White clover	**Trifolium repens**	*Trèfle blanc /*
		Trèfle rampante
White cypress	**Chamaecyparis thyoides**	*Chamaecyparis thyoides*
White dead-nettle	**Lamium album**	*Lamier blanc / Ortie blanche*
White elm	**Ulmus americana**	*Orme d'Amérique /*
		Orme à larges feuilles
White false hellebore	**Veratrum album**	*Vératre blanc*
White fir	**Abies concolor**	*Sapin concolor*
White ginger lily	**Hedychium coronarium**	*Hedychium coronarium*
White horehound	**Marrubium vulgare**	*Marrube commun*
White melilot	**Melilotus alba**	*Mélilot blanc*
White mignonette	**Reseda alba**	*Réséda blanc*
White mugwort	**Artemisia lactiflora**	*Armoise lactiflora*
White mulberry	**Morus alba**	*Mûrier blanc*
White mullein	**Verbascum lychnitis**	*Molène lychnide*
White mustard	**Sinapis alba**	*Moutarde blanche*
White oak	**Qyercus alba**	*Chêne blanc*
White pigweed	**Amaranthus albus**	*Amarante blanche*

White poplar	Populus alba	Peuplier blanc
White rock-rose	Helianthemum apenninum	
		Hélianthème des Appennines
White rosebay	Epilobium angustifolium album	
		Laurier de Saint-Antoine album
White sails	Spathiphyllum wallisii	Spathiphyllum wallisii
White Sally	Eucalyptus pauciflora	Eucalyptus pauciflora
White snakeroot	Eupatorium rugosum	Eupatoire rugeux
White spruce	Picea glauca	Épinette blanche /
		Sapinette blanche
White stonecrop	Sedum album	Orpin blanc
White trumpet lily	Lilium longiflorum	Lilium longiflorum
White water lily	Nymphaea alba	Nénuphar blanc
White willow	Salix alba	Saule blanc
White-backed hosta	Hosta hypoleuca	Hosta hypoleuca
Whitebeam	Sorbus aria	Alisier blanc
Whiteywood	Melicytus ramiflorus	Melicytus ramiflorus
Whorl flower	Morina	Morina
Whorled caraway	Carum verticillatum	Carum verticillé
Whorled Solomon's seal	Polygonatum verticillatum	
		Sceau de Salomon verticillé
Whorled water-milfoil	Myriophyllum verticillatum	Myriophylle verticille
Whortleberry	Vaccinium myrtillus	Myrtillier commun
Widow iris	Hermodactylus tuberosus	Hermodactylus tuberosus
Wild angelica	Angelica sylvestris	Angélique des bois
Wild azalea	Loiseleuria procumbens	Azalée des Alpes /
		Azalée couchée
Wild basil	Clinopodium vulgare	Sarriette commune
Wild buckwheat	Eriogonum	Eriogonum
Wild candytuft	Iberis amara	Iberis amer
Wild carrot	Daucus carota	Carotte commune
Wild catmint	Nepeta cataria	Herbe aux chats /
		Nepeta des chats
Wild celery	Apium graveolens	Céleri
Wild cherry	Prunus avium	Merisier des oiseaux
Wild coffee	Polyscias guilfoylei	Polyscias guilfoylei
Wild daffodil	Narcissus pseudonarcissus	Aiault / Faux narcisse
Wild ginger	Asarum europaeum	Asaret
Wild iris	Iris versicolor	Iris versicolore
Wild Irishman	Discaria toumatou	Discaria toumatou
Wild leek	Allium ampeloprasum	Gros ail

Wild lily of the valley	Pyrola rotundifolia	*Prolle à feuilles rondes*
Wild liquorice	Astragalus glycyphyllos	
	Astragale a feuilles de réglisse / *Réglisse bâtarde*	
Wild madder	Rubia peregrina	*Garance voyageuse*
Wild marjoram	Origanum vulgare	*Origan commun*
Wild mignonette	Reseda lutea	*Réséda jaune*
Wild pansy	Viola tricolor	*Pensée sauvage*
Wild parsnip	Pastinaca sativa	*Panais cultivé*
Wild pineapple	Ananas bracteatus	*Ananas bracteatus*
Wild radish	Raphanus raphanistrum	*Ravenelle*
Wild rum cherry	Prunus serotina	*Cerisier noir*
Wild service tree	Sorbus torminalis	*Alisier torminal*
Wild service tree	Pyrus torminalis	*Alisier torminal*
Wild strawberry	Fragaria vesca	*Fraisier commun*
Wild tulip	Tulipa sylvestris	*Tulipe sauvage*
Wild yellow lily	Lilium canadense	*Lilium canadense*
Willow	Salix	*Saule*
Willow gentian	Gentiana asclepiadea	*Gentiane asclepiadea*
Willow herb	Epilobium	*Épilobe*
Willow moss	Fontinalis antipyretica	*Fontinalis antipyretica*
Willow myrtle	Agonis	*Agonis*
Willow oak	Quercus phellos	*Chêne saule*
Willow-leaved magnolia	Magnolia salicilfolia	*Magnolia salicilfolia*
Willow-leaved sunflower	Helianthus salicifolius	*Helianthus salicifolius*
Windflower	Anemone	*Anémone*
Windflower	Zephranthes	*Zephranthes*
Windmill palm	Trachycarpus fortunei	*Trachycarpus fortunei*
Winecups	Babiana rubro-cyanea	*Babiana rubro-cyanea*
Wing nut	Pterocarya	*Pterocarya*
Winged spindle	Euonymus alatus	*Fusain ailé*
Winter aconite	Eranthis hyemalis	*Ellebore d'hiver* / *Éranthe*
Winterberry	Ilex verticillata	*Houx verticillata*
Winter cherry	Cardiospermum halicacabum	*Cardiospermum halicacabum*
Winter cherry	Physalis alkekengi	*Alkékenge* / *Amour-en-cage* / *Lanterne japonais*
Winter cress	Barbarea vulgaris	*Barbarée commune*
Wintergreen	Pyrola	*Pyrole*
Winter heath	Erica carnea	*Bruyère des neiges*
Winter heliotrope	Petasites fragrans	*Héliotrope d'hiver*
Winter iris	Iris unguicularis	*Iris unguicularis*
Winter jasmine	Jasminium nudiflorum	*Jasmin d'hiver*
Winter savory	Satureja montana	*Sarriette vivace*

Winter's bark	**Drimys winteri**	*Drimys winteri*
Wintersweet	**Acokanthera oblongifolia**	*Acokanthera oblongifolia*
Wintersweet	**Chimonanthus praecox**	*Chimonanthe précoce*
Wire netting bush	**Corokia cotoneaster**	*Corokia cotoneaster*
Wish-bone flower	**Torenia fournieri**	*Torenia fournieri*
Wisteria	**Wistaria**	*Glycine*
Witch alder	**Fothergilla gardenii**	*Fothergilla gardenii*
Witch hazel	**Hamamelis**	*Noisetier de sorcière*
Woad	**Isatis tinctoria**	*Pastel des teinturiers*
Wolf's bane	**Aconitum vulparia**	*Aconit tu-loup*
Wonga-wonga vine	**Pandorea pandorana**	*Pandorea pandorana*
Wood anemone	**Anemone nemorosa**	*Anémone des bois*
Wood chickweed	**Stellaria nemorum**	*Stellaire des bois*
Wood cranesbill	**Geranium sylvaticum**	*Géranium des bois*
Wood or Red-veined dock	**Rumex sanguineus**	*Patience sanguine*
Wood dog violet	**Viola reichenbachiana**	*Violette des bois*
Wood forget-me-not	**Myosotis sylvatica**	*Myosotis dea bois*
Wood goldilocks	**Ranunculus auricomus**	*Renoncule à tête d'or*
Wood lily	**Trillium**	*Trillie*
Wood millet	**Milium effusum**	*Milium effusum*
Wood rose	**Merremia tuberosa**	*Merremia tuberosa*
Woodruff	**Galium odoratum**	*Aspérule odorante / Belle-étoile / Petit muguet*
Wood-sage	**Teucrium scorodonia**	*Germandrée / Sauge des bois*
Wood sorrel	**Oxalis acetosella**	*Pain de coucou*
Wood spurge	**Euphorbia amygdaloides**	*Euphorbe des bois*
Wood vetch	**Vicia sylvatica**	*Vesce des forêts*
Woodbine	**Lonicera periclymenum**	*Chèvrefeuille des bois*
Woodruff	**Galium odoratum**	*Gaillet / Caille-lait*
Woodrush	**Luzula**	*Luzule*
Woolly netbush	**Calothamnus villosus**	*Calothamnus villosus*
Woolly thistle	**Cirsium eriophorum**	*Cirse laineux*
Woolly willow	**Salix lanata**	*Salix lanata*
Wormwood	**Artemisia absinthium**	*Artemisia absinthium*
Wormwood cassia	**Cassia artemisioides**	*Casse argentée*
Wrack-like pondweed	**Potamogeton compressus**	*Potamot comprimé*
Wych elm	**Ulmus glabra**	*Orme blanc*

Y

Yarrow	Achillea millefolium	*Achillée millefeuille*
Yarrow broomrape	Orobanche purpurea	*Orobanche pourprée*
Yatay palm	Butia	*Butia*
Yavering bells	Orthilia secunda	*Pyrole unilatérale*
Yellow asphodel	Asphodeline lutea	*Bâton de Jacob*
Yellow autumn crocus	Colchicun luteum	*Colchique jaune*
Yellow bartsia	Parentucellia viscosa	*Bartsie visqueuse*
Yellow banksia	Rosa banksiae lutea	*Rosier jaune de Banks*
Yellow bells	Tecoma stans	*Tecoma stans*
Yellow birch	Betula alleghaniensis	*Bouleau jaune*
Yellow birdsnest	Monotropa hypopitys	*Monotrope sucepin*
Yellow buckeye	Aesculus flava	*Marronnier jaune*
Yellow chamomile	Anthemis tinctoria	*Anthémis des teinturiers*
Yellow day lily	Hemerocallis lilio-asphodelus	*Hémérocalle jaune /*
		Lis jaune
Yellow elder	Tecoma stans	*Tecoma stans*
Yellow figwort	Scrophularia vernalis	*Scrofulaire du printemps*
Yellow flag	Iris pseudacorus	*Iris faux-acore / Iris des marais*
Yellow flax	Linum flavum	*Lin jaune*
Yellow flax	Reinwardtia indica	*Reinwardtia indica*
Yellow foxglove	Digitalis grandiflora	*Digitale jaune à grandes fleurs*
Yellow fritillary	Fritillaria pudica	*Fritillaire pudica*
Yellow haw	Crataegus flava	*Épine à fruits jaunes*
Yellow horned poppy	Glaucium flavum	*Glaucière jaune / Pavot cornu*
Yellow jasmine	Jasminium humile	*Jasmin d'Italie*
Yellow kangaroo paw	Anigozanthos flavidus	*Anigozanthos flavidus*
Yellow lady's slipper orchid	Cypripedium calceolus	*Cypripedium calceolus*
Yellow loosestrife	Lysimachia vulgaris	*Lysimaque commune*
Yellow mariposa	Calochorus luteus	*Calochorus luteus*
Yellow marsh saxifrage	Saxifraga hirculus	*Saxifrage œil de bouc*
Yellow milk-vetch	Oxytropis campestris	*Oxytropis champêtre*
Yellow morning glory	Merremia tuberosa	*Merremia tuberosa*
Yellow mountain saxifrage	Saxifraga aizoides	*Saxifrage jaune des montagnes*
Yellow musk	Mimulus luteus	*Mimulus luteus*
Yellow oleander	Thevetia peruviana	*Laurier rose à fleurs jaune*
Yellow ox-eye	Buphthalmum salicifolium	*Buphthalmum salicifolium*
Yellow palm	Chrysalidocarpus lutescens	*Chrysalidocarpus lutescens*
Yellow parilla	Menispermum canadense	*Menispermum canadense*
Yellow pimpernel	Lysimachia nemorum	*Lysimaque des bois*
Yellow pitcher plant	Sarracenia flava	*Sarracène à fleurs jaunes*

Yellow pond lily	**Nuphar advena**	*Nénuphar advena*
Yellow rattle	**Rhinanthus crista-galli**	*Petit cocriste*
Yellow-root	**Xanthorhiza simplicissima**	
		Xanthorhiza simplicissima
Yellow scabious	**Cephalaria gigantea**	*Cephalaria gigantea*
Yellow skunk cabbage	**Lysichiton americanus**	*Lysichiton americanus*
Yellow star of Bethlehem	**Gagea lutea**	*Gagée jaune*
Yellow turkscap lily	**Lilium pyrenaicum**	*Lis pyrenaicum*
Yellow vetch	**Vicia lutea**	*Vesce jaune*
Yellow vetchling	**Lathyruus aphaca**	*Gesse aphylle*
Yellow water lily	**Nuphar lutea**	*Nénuphar jaune*
Yellow whitlow grass	**Draba aizoides**	*Drave faux-aizoon*
Yellow wood	**Cladrastis lutea**	*Virginier à bois jaune*
Yellow-wort	**Blackstonia perfiolata**	*Centaurée jaune /*
		Chlora perfiolé
Yesterday-today-and-tomorrow	**Brunfelsia pauciflora**	*Brunfelsia pauciflora*
Yew	**Taxus baccata**	*If*
Yoshino cherry	**Prunus x yedoensis**	*Prunus x yedoensis*
Young's weeping birch	**Betula pendula 'Youngii'**	
		Bouleau pleureur 'Youngii'
Youth and age	**Tolmiea menziesii**	*Tolmiea menziesii*
Yulan	**Magnolia denudata**	*Magnolia de Yulan*

Z

Zebra plant	**Aphelandra squarrosa**	*Aphelandra squarrosa*
Zebra plant	**Calathea zebrina**	*Calathea zebrina*
Zigzag bamboo	**Phyllostachys flexuosa**	*Bambou flexuosa*
Zigzag clover	**Trifolium medium**	*Trèfle flexueux*

Français	English	Latin
A		
Abricotier	Apricot	**Prunus armeniaca**
Abricot japonais	Japanese apricot	**Prunus mume**
Acacia baileyana.	Cootmandra wattle.	**Acacia baileyana**
Acacia blanc	False acacia / Locust	**Robinia pseudoacacia**
Acacia pravissima	Ovens wattle	**Acacia pravissima**
Acacia pulchella	Western prickly Moses	**Acacia pulchella**
Acacia rose	Rose acacia	**Robinia hispida**
Acacia verticillata	Prickly Moses	**Acacia verticillata**
Acalypha hispida	Red-hot cat's tail	**Acalypha hispida**
Acanthe à feuilles molles	Bear's breeches	**Acanthus mollis**
Ache aquatique	Marshwort	**Apium inundatum**
Ache nodiflore	Fool's watercress	**Apium nodiflorum**
Achillée	Achillea	**Achillea**
Achillée millefeuille	Yarrow	**Achillea millefolium**
Achillée sternutatoire	Sneezewort	**Achillea ptarmica**
Aciphylla aurea	Golden Spaniard	**Aciphylla aurea**
Aciphylla scott-thomsonii	Giant Spaniard	**Aciphylla scott-thomsonii**
Aciphylla Squarrosa	Bayonet plant	**Aciphylla squarrosa**
Acokanthera oblongifolia	Wintersweet	**Acokanthera oblongifolia**
Aconit anglicum	Monkshood	**Aconitum anglicum**
Aconit napel	Helmet flower	**Aconitum napellus**
Aconit tu-loup	Wolf's bane.	**Aconitum vulparia**
Acore vrai	Sweet flag / Myrtle flag	**Acorus calamus variegatus**
Actée en épi	Baneberry.	**Actaea**
Actée pachypoda	Doll's eyes / White baneberry	**Actaea pachypoda**
Actée rouge	Red baneberry	**Actaea rubra**
Actinidie	Bower vine	**Actinidia arguta**
Actinidie polygama	Silver vine	**Actinidia polygama**
Adansonia	Boabab	**Adansonia**
Adenophora	Gland bellflower	**Adenophora**
Adlumia fungosa	Alleghany vine / Climbing fumitory	**Adlumia fungosa**
Adonide d'automne	Pheasant's eye	**Adonis annua**
Adonide de printemps	Spring adonis	**Adonis vernalis**
Aechmea fasciata	Um plant / Silver vase plant	**Aechmea fasciata**
Aechmea 'Foster's favourite'	Laquered wine cup	**Aechmea 'Foster's favourite'**
Aechmea fulgens	Coral berry	**Aechmea fulgens**

Aegopode podagraire	Ground elder	**Aegopodium podagraria**
Aegopode podagraire	Bishop's weed (In Scotland)	**Aegopodium podagraria**
Aeonium haworthii	Pinwheel	**Aeonium haworthii**
Aeschynanthus pulcher	Lipstick plant / Royal red bugler	
		Aeschyanthus pulcher
Aesculus x neglecta	Sunrise horse-chestnut	**Aesculus x neglecta**
Aethionema grandiflorum	Persian stone cress	**Aethionema grandiflorum**
Agapanthe	Agapanthus	**Agapanthus**
Agapanthe	African lily	**Agapanthus africanus**
Agastache	Mexican giant hyssop	**Agastache**
Agave d'Amérique	Century plant	**Agave americana**
Agave filifera	Thread agave	**Agave filifera**
Agave victoriae-reginae	Royal agave	**Agave victoriae-reginae**
Agérate bleue	Floss flower	**Ageratum**
Agneau chaste	Chastity bush / Monk's pepper	**Vitex agnus castus**
Aglaonema	Chinese evergreen	**Aglaonema**
Agonis	Willow myrtle	**Agonis**
Agonis flexuosa	Peppermint tree	**Agonis flexuosa**
Agripaume cardiaque	Motherwort	**Lepidium campestre**
Agropyre	Couch grass	**Agropyrum**
Aichryson x domesticum varieg.	Cloud grass	
		Aichryson x domesticum varieg.
Aigremoine eupatoire	Agrimony	**Aigremoine eupatoire**
Ail blanc	Allium neapolitanum	**Allium neapolitanumi**
Ail caréné	Keeled garlic	**Allium carinatum**
Ail doré	Allium moly / Lily leek	**Allium moly**
Ail des endroits cultivés	Field garlic	**Allium oleraceum**
Ail des ours	Ramsons	**Allium ursinum**
Allium paradoxum	Few flowered leek	**Allium paradoxum**
Ail rocambole	Sand leek	**Allium scorodoprasum**
Ail rose	Rosy garlic	**Allium roseum**
Ail à tête ronde	Round headed leek	**Allium sphaerocephalon**
Ail triquêtre	Three-cornered leek	**Allium triquetrum**
Ail des vignes	Crow garlic	**Allium vineale**
Ailante	Tree of heaven	**Ailanthus altissima**
Aiault	Wild daffodil	**Narcissus pseudonarcissus**
Airelle	Bilberry	**Vaccinium myrtillus**
Airelle à corymbes	Highbush blueberry	**Vaccinium corymbosum**
Airelle des marais	Northern bilberry	**Vaccinium uliginosum**
Airelle rouge	Cowberry	**Vaccinium vitis-idaea**

Ajonc d'Europe	Gorse	**Ulex europaeus**
Akebia quinata	Chocolate vine	**Akebia quinata**
Alchémille des Alpes	Alpine lady's mantle	**Alchemilla alpina**
Alchémille commune	Common lady's mantle / Lady's mantle	
		Alchemilla vulgaris
Alchémille des champs	Parsley piert	**Aphanes arvensis**
Alerce	Patagonian cypress	**Fitzroya cupressoides**
Alisier blanc	Whitebeam	**Sorbus aria**
Alisier de Fontainebleau	French hales / Service tree of Fontainebleau	
		Sorbus latifolia
Alisier torminal	Wild service tree	**Pyrus torminalis / Sorbus torminalis**
Alkékenge	Winter cherry	**Physalis alkekengi**
Alkéenege du Pérou	Bladder cherry / Strawberry tomato	**Physalis Alkekengi**
Alkékenge de Pérou	Cape gooseberry	**Physalis peruviana**
Allamanda cathartica	Golden trumpet	**Allamanda cathartica**
Alliare officinale	Garlic mustard	**Alliaria petiolata**
Allier	Whitebeam	**Sorbus aria**
Alloplectus nummularia	Clog plant	**Alpinia zerumbet**
Allouchier	Whitebeam	**Sorbus aria**
Aloè	Aloe	**Aloe**
Aloès aristata	Lace aloe / Torch plant	**Aloe aristata**
Aloès variegata	Partridge breasted aloe	**Aloe variegata**
Alonsoa warscewiczii	Mask flower	**Alonsoa warscewiczii**
Alopecurus pratensis aureomarginata	Golden foxtail	
		Alopecurus pratensis aureomarginata
Alpinia calcarata	Indian ginger	**Alpinia calcarata**
Alpinia zerumbet	Shell flower	**Alpinia zerumbet**
Alternanthera ficoidea	Parrot leaf	**Alternanthera ficoidea**
Alysson blanchatre	Hoary alison	**Berteroa incana**
Alysson à calice persistant	Small alison	**Alyssum alyssoides**
Alysson maritime	Sweet alyssum	**Lobularia maritima**
Amandier	Almond	**Prunus dulcis**
Amarante blanche	White pigweed	**Amaranthus albus**
Amarante crête-de-coq	Fairy fountain	**Celosia cristata**
Amarante hybride	Prince's feather	**Amaranthus hybridus erythrostachys**
Amarante réfléchie	Pigweed	**Amaranthus retroflexus**
Amarantoïde	Globe amaranth	**Gomphrena globosa**
Amaryllis	Amaryllis	**Hippeastrum**
Amaryllis belladonna	Belladonna Lily	**Amaryllis belladonna**
Amaryllis croix Saint-Jacqes	Aztec lily / Jacobean lily	
		Sprekelia formosissima

Amaryllis de Guernsey	Guernsey lily	**Nerine sarniensis**
Amaryllis de Joséphine	Josephine's lily	**Brunsvigia josephenae**
Amaryllis de Rouen	Hippeastrum vittatum	**Hippeastrum vittatum**
Ambroisie	Ragweed	**Ambrosia**
Amélanchier du Canada	Juneberry / Serviceberry	/ Shadbush
		Amelanchier canadensis
Amorpha canescens	Lead plants	**Amorpha canescens**
Amour-en-cage	Winter cherry	**Physalis alkekengi**
Amourette	Greater quaking grass	**Briza maxima**
Amsonia	Blue star	**Amsonia**
Ananas bracteatus	Red pineapple / Wild pineapple	**Ananas bracteatus**
Ancolie	Aquelegia	**Aquelegia**
Ancolie	Granny's bonnets	**Aquelegia vulgaris**
Ancolie des Alpes	Alpine columbine	**Aquelegia alpina**
Ancolie du Canada	Canadian columbine	**Aquilegia canadensis**
Ancolie commune	Columbine	**Aquelegia vulgaris**
Andredera	Madiera vine / Mignonette vine	**Andredera**
Andromède a feuilles de polium	Bog rosemary	**Andromeda polifolia**
Adromischus festivus	Plovers' eggs	**Adromischus festivus**
Androsème officinal	Tutsan	**Hypericum androsaemum**
Anémone	Anemone / Windflower	**Anemone**
Anémone des Alpes	Alpine anemone	**Pulsatilla alpina**
Anémone apennina	Apennine anemone	**Anemone apennina**
Anémone des bois	Wood anemone	**Anemone nemorosa**
Anémone hépatique	Hepatica	**Hepatica nobilis**
Anémone fausse renoncule	Anemone ranunculoides	**Anemone ranunculoides**
Anémone des fleuristes	Anemone coronaria	**Anemone coronaria**
Anémone du Japon	Japanese anemone	**Anemone x hybrida**
Anémone des jardins	Anemone pavonia	**Anemone pavonia**
Anémone pulsatille	Pasque flower	**Pulsatilla vulgaris**
Anémone sylvestre	Snowdrop windflower	**Anemone sylvestris**
Anemonopsis	False anemone	**Anemonopsis**
Angélique	Angelica	**Angelica archangelica**
Angélique des bois	Wild angelica	**Angelica sylvestris**
Angélique de Chine	Japanese angelica tree	**Aralia**
Anguloa clowesii	Cradle orchid	**Anguloa clowesii**
Anhalonie	Living rock	**Ariocarpus**
Anigozanthus	Kangaroo paw	**Anigozanthus**
Anigozanthos flavidus	Yellow kangaroo paw	**Anigozanthos flavidus**
Anigozanthus manglesii	Red and green kangaroo paw	
		Anigozanthus manglesii
Anone reticulée	Bullock's heart	**Annona reticulata**

Ansérine	Silverweed	**Potentilla anserina**
Antennaria	Cat's ears	**Antennaria**
Anthémis	Marguerite	**Chrysanthemum frutescens**
Anthemis	Chamomile / Dog fennel	**Anthemis**
Anthémis d'Arabie	Cladanthus arabicus	**Cladanthus arabicus**
Anthémis des champs	Corn chamomile	**Anthemis arvensis**
Anthémis des teinturiers	Yellow chamomile	**Anthemis tinctoria**
Anthericum	Spider plant	**Anthericum**
Anthrisque commun	Bur chervil	**Anthriscus caucalis**
Anthrisque sauvage	Cow parsley	**Anthriscus sylvestris**
Anthurium andraeanum	Tail flower	**Anthurium andraeanum**
Anthurium crystallinum	Crystal anthurium	**Anthurium crystallinum**
Anthurium scherzerianum	Flaming flower	**Anthurium scherzerianum**
Anthyllide vulnéraire	Kidney vetch	**Anthyllis vulneraria**
Antigonon leptopus	Coral vine	**Antigonon leptopus**
Aphelandra squarrosa	Zebra plant	**Aphelandra squarrosa**
Aponogéton	Cape pondweed / Water hawthorn	
		Aponogeton distachyos
Aporocactus flagelliformis	Rat's tail cactus	**Aporocactus flagelliformis**
Arabette	Arabis	**Arabis caucasica**
Arabette poilu	Hairy rock-cress	**Arabis hirsuta**
Arabette thaliana	Thale cress	**Arabidopsis thaliana**
Araucarie elevée	Norfolk Island pine / Northern bungalow palm	
		Archontophoenix cunninghamia
Araujia sericofera	Cruel plant	**Araujia sericofera**
Arbousier	Strawberry tree	**Arbutus unedo**
Arbousier andrachne	Grecian strawberry tree	**Arbutus andrachne**
Arbousier nain	Arctous alpina	**Arctous alpina**
Arbre aux anémones	Carolina allspice	**Calycanthus floridus**
Arbre d'argent	Silver tree	**Leucadendron argenteum**
Arbre aux cloches	Silver bell	**Halesia carolina**
Arbre aux cloches d'argent	Snowdrop tree	**Halesia**
Arbre aux fraises	Strawberry tree	**Arbutus unedo**
Arbre à franges	Fringe tree	**Chionanthus virginicus**
Arbre à franges de Chine	Chinese fringe tree	**Chionanthus retusus**
Arbre de Judée	Judas tree	**Cercis siliquastrum**
Arbre à kapok	Kapok / Silk cotton tree	**Ceiba pentandra**
Arbre aux lanternes	Lantern tree	**Crinodendron hookeriana**
Arbre au mastic	Mastic tree	**Pistacia lentiscus**
Arbre aux mouchoirs	Dove tree / Ghost tree / Pocket handkerchief tree	
		Davidia involucrata
Arbre de neige	Fringe tree	**Chionanthus virginicus**

Arbre ombrelle	Queensland umbrella tree	**Schefflera actinophylla**
Arbre des pagodes	Pagoda tree	**Sophora japonica**
Arbre à perruques	Smoke tree / Venetian sumach	
		Cotinus coggygria
Arbre aux pochettes	Dove tree / Ghost tree / Pocket handkerchief tree	
		Davidia involucrata
Arbre au poivre	Chastity bush / Monk's pepper	**Vitex agnus castus**
Arbre Pompadour	Carolina allspice	**Calycanthus floridus**
Arbe aux 40 écus	Maidenhair tree	**Ginkgo biloba**
Arbre de rata New Zealand Christmas tree / Rata		**Metrosideros robusta**
Arbre de soie	Silk tree	**Albizia julibrissin**
Arbuste à papillons	Butterfly bush	**Buddleia davidii**
Arbutus menziesii	Madroña	**Arbutus menziesii**
Archontophoenix alexandrae	Alexandra palm / King palm	
		Archontophoenix alexandrae
Archontophoenix cunninghamsiana Illawarra palm / Piccabean palm		
		Archontophoenix cunninghamiana
Arcotstaphylos nevadensis	Pine-mat manzanita	
		Arcotstaphylos nevadensis
Arctostaphylos stanfordiana	Stanford manzanita	
		Arctostaphylos stanfordiana
Arctotheca calendula	Cape dandelion	**Arctotheca calendula**
Arctotis stoechadifolia	African daisy	**Arctotis stoechadifolia**
Arénaire	Sandwort	**Arenaria**
Argalon	Christ's thorn	**Paliurus spina-christi**
Argémone mexicana	Prickly poppy	**Argemone mexicana**
Argousier	Sea buckthorn	**Hippophäe rhamnoides**
Arisaema triphyllum	Jack-in-the-pulpit	**Arisaema triphyllum**
Arisarum proboscideum	Mouse plant	**Arisarum proboscideum**
Aristoloche	Calico flower	**Aristolochia elegans**
Aristoloche clématite	Birthwort	**Aristolochia clematitis**
Aristoloche grandiflora	Pelican flower / Swan flower	
		Aristolocia grandiflora
Artichaut commun	Globe artichoke	**Cynara scolymus**
Arméria maritime	Thrift / Sea pink	**Armeria maritima**
Armoise	Artemisia	**Artemisia**
Armoise arborescente	Artemisia arborescens	**Artemisia arborescens**
Armoise champêtre	Breckland mugwort	**Artemisia campestris**
Armoise commune	Mugwort	**Artemisia vulgaris**
Armoise lactiflora	White mugwort	**Artemisia lactiflora**
Armoise maritime	Sea wormwood	**Artemisia maritima**
Armoise pontica	Roman wormwood	**Artemisia pontica**

Arnebia pulchra	Prophet flower	**Arnebia pulchra**
Arnigo	Hairy greenweed	**Genista pilosa**
Aronia	Chokeberry	**Aronia**
Aronia arbutifolia	Red chokeberry	**Aronia arbutifolia**
Aronia melanocarpa	Black chokeberry	**Aronia melanocarpa**
Arroche puante	Stinking goosefoot	**Chenopodium vulvaria**
Arolle	Arolla pine / Pinyon	**Pinus cembroides**
Arrête-bœuf	Rest-harrow	**Ononis repens**
Arroche étalée	Common orache	**Atriplex patula**
Arroche halime	Tree purslane	**Atriplex halimus**
Arroche lacinée	Frosted orache	**Atriplex laciniata**
Arroche du littoral	Grass leaved orache	**Atriplex littoralis**
Arroche pourpière	Sea purslane	**Halimione portulacoides**
Artemisia absinthium	Absinthe / Wormwood	**Artemisia absinthium**
Arthropodium cirrhatum	Rienga lily /Rock lily	**Arthropodium cirrhatum**
Arthrotaxis selaginoides	King William pine	**Arthrotaxis selaginoides**
Artichaut commun	Globe artichoke	**Cynara scolymus**
Artichaut d'hiver	Jerusalem artichoke	**Helianthus tuberosus**
Arum de Éthiopie	Arum Lily	**Zantedeschia aeothiopica**
Arum d'Italie	Large cuckoo pint	**Arum italicum**
Arundinaria anceps	Anceps bamboo	**Arundinaria anceps**
Asaret d'Europe	Asrabacca / Wild ginger	**Asarum europaeum**
Asclépiade	Silk weed	**Asclepias**
Asclepias curassavica	Blood flower	**Asclepias curassavica**
Asclepias tuberosa	Butterfly weed	**Asclepias tuberosa**
Asiminier	Pawpaw	**Asimina triloba / Carica papaya**
Asparagus densiflorus 'Myersii'	Foxtail fern	**Asparagus densiflorus 'Myersii'**
Aspelenium bulbiferum	Hen-and-chicken fern / Mother spleenwort	**Aspelenium bulbiferum**
Aspelenium nidus	Bird's nest fern	**Aspelenium nidus**
Asperge officinale	Asparagus	**Asparagus officinalis**
Aspergette	Spiked star of Bethlehem	**Ornithogalum pyrenaicum**
Aspérule odorante	Woodruff	**Galium odoratum**
Aspérule des sables	Squinancywort	**Asperula cynanchia**
Asphodèle	Asphodel	**Asphodelus aestivus**
Asphodèle albus	White asphodel	**Asphodelus albus**
Aspidistra elatior	Cast-iron plant	**Aspidistra elatior**
Aster de Chine	China aster	**Callistephus**
Aster du Jardin	Michaelmas daisy	**Aster**
Aster maritime	Sea aster	**Aster tripolium**
Astragale des Alpes	Alpine milk-vetch	**Astragalus alpinus**

Astragale du Danemark	Purple milk-vetch	**Astragalus danicus**
Astragale à feuilles de réglisse	Wild liquorice	**Astragalus glycyphyllos**
Astrophytum asterias	Sea urchin / Silver dollar cactus	
		Astrophytum asterias
Atherosperma moschatum	Tasmanian sassafras	**Atherosperma moschatum**
Aubépine	May / Thorn	**Crataegus laevigata**
Aubépine	Glastonberry thorn / Hawthorn	
		Crataegus monogyna
Aubépine phaenopyrum	Washington thorn	**Crataegus phaenopyrum**
Aubour	Common laburnum / Golden chain	**Laburnum anagryoides**
Aubriette	Aubrietia	**Aubrietia**
Aucuba de Japon	Aucuba japonica	**Aucuba japonica**
Aulne blanc	Grey alder	**Alnus incana**
Aulne à feuilles en cœur	Italian alder	**Alnus cordata**
Aulne glutineux	Alder	**Alnus glutinosa**
Auricule	Auricula	**Primula auricula**
Aurone	Lad's love / Old man / Southernwood	**Artemisia abrotanum**
Austrocedrus chilensis	Chilean incense cedar	**Austrocedrus chilensis**
Avelinier	Filbert	**Corylus maxima**
Averse dorée	Golden shower / Indian laburnum / Pudding pipe-tree	**Cassia fistula**
Avoine élevée	False oat grass	**Arrhenatherum elatius**
Azalée	Azalea	**Rhododendron**
Azalée des Alpes	Trailing azalea / Alpine azalea	**Loiseleuria procumbens**
Azalée couchée	Trailing azalea / Wild azalea	**Loiseleuria procumbens**
Azalée naine	Trailing azalea / Alpine azalea	**Loiseleuria procumbens**
Azalée pontique	Azalea ponticum	**Rhododendron luteum**
Azolla caroliniana	Water fern	**Azolla caroliniana**

B

Babiana rubro-cyanea	Winecups	**Babiana rubro-cyanea**
Badamier	Indian almond / Tropical almond	**Terminalia catappa**
Badianier	Chinese anise	**Illicium anisatum**
Baguenaudier commun	Bladder senna	**Colutea arborescens**
Baguenaudier d'Éthiopie	Sutherlandia frutescens	**Sutherlandia frutescens**
Balisier	Canna	**Canna**
Ballote noire	Black horehound	**Ballota nigra**
Balsamine	Balsam	**Impatiens balsamina**
Balsamind de l'Himalaya	Himalayan Balsam	**Impatiens glandulifera**
Balsamine à petites fleurs	Small balsam	**Impatiens parviflora**

Bambou aureosulcata	Golden-groove bamboo	**Phyllostachys aureosulcata**
Bambou bambusoides	Timber bamboo	**Phyllostachys bambusoides**
Bambou doré	Fishpole bamboo / Golden bamboo	**Phyllostachys aurea**
Bambou flexuosa	Zigzag bamboo	**Phyllostachys flexuosa**
Bambou noir	Black bamboo	**Phyllostachys nigra**
Bananier	Banana	**Musa**
Bananier d'Abyssinie	Abyssinian banana	**Musa arnoldiana**
Bananier basjoo	Japanese banana	**Musa basjoo**
Bananier à fleurs décoratives	Flowering banana	**Musa ornata**
Bananier rouge	Scarlet banana	**Musa coccinea**
Banksia ericifolia	Heath banksia	**Banksia ericifolia**
Baquois	Screw pine	**Pandanus**
Barbadine	Giant granadilla	**Passiflora quadrangularis**
Barbarée commune	Winter cress / Common winter-cress	**Barbarea vulgaris**
Barbe bleue	Caryopteris	**Caryopteris**
Barbe-du-bouc	Goat's beard / Jack-go-to-bed-at-noon	
		Tragopogon pratensis
Barbe de-bouc	Goat's beard	**Aruncus dioicus**
Barbe de vieillard	Spanish moss	**Tillandsia usneoides**
Barbeau bleu	Bluebottle	**Centaurea cyanus**
Bardane à petites têtes	Burdock	**Arctium minus**
Barleria cristata	Philippine violet	**Barleria cristata**
Bartonia dorée	Golden bartonia	**Mentzelia lindleyi**
Bartsie des Alpes	Alpine bartsia	**Bartsia alpina**
Bartsie visqueuse	Yellow bartsia	**Parentucellia viscosa**
Bâton de Jacob	Yellow asphodel	**Asphodeline lutea**
Bauhinia purpurea	Butterfly tree / Orchid tree	**Bauhinia purpurea**
Bauhinia variegata	Orchid tree	**Bauhinia variegata**
Baumier de l'Ouest	Black cottonwood / Western balsam poplar	
		Populus trichocarpa
Beaucarnea recurvata	Elephant's foot / Pony tail	**Beaucarnea recurvata**
Beaumontia grandiflora	Herald's trumpet	**Beaumontia grandiflora**
Bec-de-grue commun	Common storksbill	**Erodium cicutarium**
Bec-de-grue maritime	Sea storksbill	**Erodium maritimum**
Bec musqué	Musk storksbill	**Erodium moschatum**
Bégonia	Begonia	**Begonia**
Begonia bowerae	Eyelash begonia	**Begonia bowerae**
Begonia x cheimantha	Christmas begonia	**Begonia x cheimantha**
Begonia x cheimant 'Gloire de Lorraine'	Lorraine begonia	
		Begonia x cheimantha 'Gloire de Lorraine'
Begonia coccinea	Angelwing begonia	**Begonia coccinea**
Begonia dregei	Maple leaf begonia	**Begonia dregei**

Begonia fuchsiodes	Fuchsia begonia	**Begonia fuchsiodes**
Begonia masoniana	Iron cross begonia	**Begonia masoniana**
Begonia metallica	Metal leaf begonia	**Begonia metallica**
Begonia weltoniensis	Maple leaf begonia	**Begonia weltoniensis**
Belladone	Deadly nightshade	**Atropa belladonna**
Belle-Dame rouge	Red mountain spinach / Red orach	
		Atriplex hortensis rubra
Belle-étoile	Woodruff	**Galium odoratum**
Belle-du-jour	Morning glory	**Convolvulus tricolor**
Belle-du-jour	Morning glory	**Ipomoea hederacea**
Belle-de-nuit	Four o'clock flower / Marvel of Peru	**Mirabilis**
Benoîte	Avens	**Geum**
Benoîte commune	Herb Bennet	**Geum urbanum**
Benoîte à fleurs jaunes	Geum "Lady Stratheden"	**Geum chiloense**
Benoîte des montagnes	Alpine avens	**Geum montanum**
Benoîte de rivage	Water avens	**Geum rivale**
Berberidopsis coralina	Coral plant	**Berberidopsis coralina**
Berce du Cauccase	Giant hogweed	**Heracleum mantegazzianum**
Berce commune	Hogweed	**Heracleum sphondylium**
Berle a larges feuilles	Greater water parsnip	**Sium latifolium**
Bermudienne	Blue-eyed grass	**Sisyrinchium bermudianum**
Bessera elegans	Coral drops	**Bessera elegans**
Bétoine	Betony	**Stachys officinalis**
Bette maritime	Sea beet	**Beta vulvaris**
Bibacier	Loquat	**Eriobotrya japonica**
Bident penché	Nodding bur-marigold	**Bidens cernua**
Bident trifoliolé	Trifid bur-marigold	**Bidens tripartita**
Bignone de Chili	Chilean glory flower / Eccremocarpus / Glory vine	
		Eccremocarpus scaber
Bignone de Chine	Bignonia / Chinese trumpet creeper	**Campsis grandiflora**
Bignonia capreolata	Cross vine / Trumpet flower	**Bignonia capreolata**
Billbergia nutans	Queen's tears	**Billbergia nutans**
Billbergia X windii	Angel's tears	**Billbergia x windii**
Bistorte	Bistort	**Polygonum bistorta / Persicaria bistorta**
Blé noir	Buckwheat	**Fagopyrum esculentum**
Blechne	Hard fern	**Blechnum spicant**
Blé de Turquie	Indian corn / Maize / Ornamental maize / Sweet corn.	**Zea mays**
Blé de vache	Field cow-wheat	**Melampyrum arvense**
Bleuet	Bluebottle	**Centaurea cyanus**
Bleuet des champs	Cornflower	**Centaurea cyanus**
Bleuet vivace	Centaurea montana	**Centaurea montana**
Bois d'arc	Osage orange	**Maclura pomifera**

Bois-cuir	Leatherwood	Cyrilla racemiflora
Bois-cuir	Leatherwood	**Cyrilla racemiflora**
Bois-gentil	Mezereon	**Daphne mezereum**
Bois joli	Mezereon	**Daphne mezereum**
Bon-Henri	Good King Henry	**Chenopodium bonus-henricus**
Bonhomme	Common mullein	**Verbascum thapsus**
Bonnet-de-prêtre	Spindle tree	**Euonymus europaeus**
Borzicactus celsianus	Old man of the Andes	**Borzicactus celsianus**
Borzicactus trolii	Old man of the Andes	**Borzicactus trolii**
Boswellie	Frankincense	**Boswellia**
Bougainvillée	Bougainvillea	**Bougainvillea**
Bouillon blanc	Common mullein	**Verbascum thapsus**
Boule-de-neige	Japanese snowball tree.	**Viburnum plicatum**
Boule d'or.	Globe flower.	**Trollius europaeus**
Bouleau	Birch	**Betula**
Bouleau albo-sinensis	White Chinese birch	**Betula albo-sinensis**
Bouleau jaune	Yellow birch	**Betula alleghaniensis**
Bouleau à canots	Canoe birch / Paper birch	**Betula papyrifera**
Bouleau lacinié	Swedish birch	**Betula pendula 'Dalecarlica'**
Bouleau maximowicziana	Monarch birch	**Betula maximowicziana**
Bouleau nain	Arctic birch / Dwarf birch	**Betula nana**
Bouleau pleureur	Weeping birch	**Betula pendula**
Bouleau pleureur 'Youngii'	Young's weeping birch	**Betula pendula 'Youngii'**
Bouleau pubescent	Downy birch	**Betula pubescens**
Bouleau szechuanica	Szechuan birch	**Betula szechuanica**
Bouleau utilis	Himalayan birch	**Betula utilis**
Bouleau utilis jacquemontii	West Himalayan birch	**Betula utilis jacquemontii**
Bourdaine	Alder buckthorn	**Frangula alnus**
Bourrache	Borage	**Borago officinalis**
Bourreau des arbres	American bittersweet	**Celastrus scandens**
Bourse à pasteur	Shepherd's purse	**Capsella bursa-pastoris**
Bouteloua gracilis	Blue grama / Mosquito grass	**Bouteloua gracilis**
Bouton d'argent.	Sneezewort.	**Achillea ptarmica**
Bouton d'or	Meadow buttercup	**Ranunculus acris**
Bouton d'or Double meadow buttercup		**Ranunculus acris flore pleno**
Bouvardia ternifolia	Scarlet trompetilla	**Bouvardia ternifolia**
Branc-ursine	Bear's breeches	**Acanthus mollis**
Brande	Besom heath	**Erica scoparia**
Brande	Ling / Scotch heather	**Calluna vulgaris**
Brachychiton acerifolius	Illawarra flame tree / Scarlet trompetilla	**Brachychiton acerifolius**

Brachychiton populneus	Kurrajong	**Brachychiton populneus**
Brachycome iberidifolia	Swan river daisy	**Brachycome iberidifolia**
Brachyglottis repanda	Pukapuka / Rangiora	**Brachyglottis repanda**
Brassavola nodosa	Lady of the night	**Brassavola nodosa**
Brésillet	Caesalpinia	**Caesalpinia**
Breynia disticha	Snow bush	**Breynia disticha**
Brimbelle	Low bush blueberry	
		Vaccinium angustifolium laevigatum
Brize	Quaking grass	**Briza**
Brize commune	Common quaking grass	**Briza media**
Bromelia balansae	Heart of flame	**Bromelia balansae**
Brome rameux	Hairy brome grass	**Bromus ramosus**
Browallia speciosa	Bush violet	**Browallia speciosa**
Bruckenthalia spiculifolia	Spike heath	**Bruckenthalia spiculifolia**
Brunelle commune	Self heal	**Prunella vulgaris**
Brunelle grandiflora	Large self heal	**Prunella grandiflora**
Brunelle laciniée	Cut-leaved self-heal	**Prunella laciniata**
Brunfelsia pauciflora	Yesterday-today-and-tomorrow	
		Brunfelsia pauciflora
Brunnera macrophylla	Siberian bugloss	**Brunnera macrophylla**
Bruyère en arbre	Tree heath	**Erica arborea**
Bruyère à balai	Besom heath	**Erica scoparia**
Bruyère canaliculata	Channelled heath	**Erica canaliculata**
Bruyère ciliée	Dorset heath	**Erica ciliaris**
Bruyère cendrée	Bell heather	**Erica cinerea**
Bruyère de Corse	Corsican heath	**Erica terminalis**
Bruyère d'Espagne	Spanish tree heath	**Erica australis**
Bruyère de Mackay	Mackay's heath	**Erica mackaiana**
Bruyère marine	Sea heath	**Frankenia laevis**
Bruyère des neiges	Alpine heath / Winter heath	**Erica carnea**
Bruyère du Portugal	Portuguese heath	**Erica lusitanica**
Bruyère de Saint-Dabeoc	St. Dabeoc's heath	**Daboecia cantabrica**
Bruyère tétragone	Cross-leaved heath	**Erica tetralix**
Bruyère vagabonde	Cornish heath	**Erica vagans**
Bryone dioîque	White bryony	**Bryonia cretica**
Buddleia	Buddleia / Butterfly bush	**Buddleia davidii**
Bunias d'orient	Warty cabbage	**Bunias orientalis**
Bugle jaune	Ground-pine	**Ajuga chamaepitys**
Bugle pyramidalis	Limestone bugle / Pyramidial bugle	
		Ajuga pyramidalis
Bugle rampante	Bugle	**Ajuga reptans**
Buglosse	Bugloss	**Anchusa**

Buglosse vivace	Green alkanet	**Pentaglottis sempervirens**
Bugrane épineuse	Spiny rest-harrow	**Ononis spinosa**
Bugrane fruticosa	Shrubby restharrow	**Ononis fruticosa**
Bugrane gluante	Large yellow restharrow	**Ononis natrix**
Bugrane rampante	Rest-harrow	**Ononis repens**
Bugrane renversée	Small rest-harrow	**Ononis reclinata**
Buis	Box	**Buxus**
Buis de Mahon	Balearic box	**Buxus balearicus**
Buis à petites feuilles	Small leaved box	**Buxus microphylla**
Buis wallichiana	Himalayan box	**Buxus wallichiana**
Buisson ardent	Firethorn	**Pyracantha coccinea**
Bulbocode	Autumn crocus / Meadow saffron	**Bulbocodium**
Buphthalmum salicifolium	Yellow ox-eye	**Buphthalmum salicifolium**
Buplèvre des haies	Sickle hare's-ear	**Bupleurum falcatum**
Buplèvre a feuilles rondes	Thorow-wax	**Bupleurum rotundifolium**
Buplèvre grêle	Slender hare's ear	**Bupleurum tenuissimum**
Busserole	Bearberry	**Arctostaphylos uva-ursi**
Busserole	Manzanita	**Arctostaphylos manzanita**
Butia	Yatay palm	**Butia**
Butia capitata	Jelly palm	**Butia capitata**
Butome	Flowering rush	**Butomus umbellatus**
Byzantine	Snowdrop plicatus byzantinus	**Galanthus plicatus byzantinus**

C

Cabombe de Caroliana	Fanwort / Fish grass / Washington grass	
		Cabomba caroliana
Cacalie éclarte	Tassel flower	**Emilia javanica**
Cactus crabe	Crab cactus / Lobster cactus	**Schlumbergera truncata**
Cactus melon	Melon cactus /Turk's cap	**Melocactus communis**
Cactus orchidée	Strap cactus / Orchid cactus	**Epiphyllum**
Cactus de Pâques	Easter cactus	**Rhipsalidopsis gaertneri**
Caille-lait	Woodruff	**Galium odoratum**
Caladium x hortulanum	Angels' wings	**Caladium x hortulanum**
Calathea makoyana	Peacock plant	**Calathea makoyana**
Calathea zebrina	Zebra plant	**Calathea zebrina**
Calcéolaire	Calceolaria	**Calceolaria**
Calla palustris	Bog arum	**Calla palustris**
Calliandra eriophylla	Fairy duster	**Calliandra eriophylla**
Callistemon	Bottlebrush	**Callistemon**
Callistemon speciosus	Albany bottlebrush	**Callistemon speciosus**
Callitriche hermaphrodite	Narrow water starwort	
		Callitriche hermaphroditica

Callitriche des marais	Common water starwort	**Callitriche palustris**
Callune fausse-bruyère	Ling / Scotch heather	**Calluna vulgaris**
Calochortus	Cat's ears / Mariposa tulip	**Calochortus**
Calochortus albus	Globe lily	**Calochortus albus**
Calochortus luteus	Yellow mariposa	**Calochortus luteus**
Calothamnus villosus	Woolly netbush	**Calothamnus villosus**
Calycanthe	Calycanthus	**Calycanthus**
Calycanthe occidentalis	California allspice	**Calycanthus occidentalis**
Camarine noire	Crowberry	**Empetrum nigrum**
Camellia du Japon	Japanese camellia	**Camellia japonica**
Caméline cultivée	Gold of pleasure	**Camelina sativa**
Caminet	Cross-leaved heath	**Erica tetralix**
Camomille puante	Stinking chamomile	**Anthemis cotula**
Campanule	Bellflower / Campanula	**Campanula**
Campanule agglomérée	Clustered bellflower	**Campanula glomerata**
Campanule barbue	Bearded bellflower	**Campanula barbata**
Campanule carillon	Canterbury bell	**Campanula medium**
Campanule étalée	Spreading bellflower	**Campanula patula**
Campanule fausse-raiponce	Creeping bellflower	
		Campanula rapunculoides
Campanule à feuilles larges	Giant bellflower	**Campanula latifolia**
Campanule à feuilles rondes	Harebell / Bluebell (In Scotland)	
		Campanula rotundifolia
Campanule à grosses fleurs	Canterbury bell	**Campanula medium**
Campanule menue	Fairy thimbles	**Campanula cochlearifolia**
Campanule pyramidale	Chimney bellflower	**Campanula pyramidalis**
Campanule raiponce	Rampion bellfower	**Campanula rapunculus**
Campanule vidalii	Campanula vidalii	**Azorina vidalii**
Camphorier	Cinnamomum camphora	**Cinnamomum camphora**
Camphora vrai	Cinnamomum camphora	**Cinnamomum camphora**
Camptosore	Walking fern	**Camptosorus rhizophyllus**
Canarina canariensis	Canary Island bellflower	**Canarina canariensis**
Canche cespiteuse	Tufted hair grass	**Deschampsia caespitosa**
Canne de Provence	Giant reed	**Arundo donax**
Canneberge.	Cranberry.	**Vaccinium oxycoccus**
Caoutchouc	Rubber plant / India rubber tree	**Ficus elastica**
Capillaire de Montpellier	Maidenhair fern	**Adiantum capillus veneris**
Capillaire pedantum	Northern maidenhair fern	**Adiantum pedantum**
Capillaire cunéforme	Delta maidenhair	**Adiantumcuneatum**
Capillaire radianum 'Grandiceps'	Tassel maidenhair	
		Adiantum raddianum 'Grandiceps'
Capucine	Nasturtium	**Tropaeolum**

Capucine des Canaris	Canary creeper	**Tropaeolum peregrinum**
Capucine élégante	Flame creeper / Flame nasturtium	**Tropaeolum speciosum**
Cardamine amère	Large bittercress	**Cardamine amara**
Cardamine impatiente	Narrow leaved bittercress	**Cardamine impatiens**
Cardamine des prés	Bitter cress / Cuckoo flower / Lady's smock	
		Cardamine pratensis
Cardère poilue	Shepherd's rod	**Dipsacus pilosus**
Cardère sauvage	Teasel	**Dipsacus fullonium**
Cardiocrinum giganteum	Giant lily	**Cardiocrinum giganteum**
Cardon	Cardoon	**Cynara cardunculus**
Carex elata aurea	Bowles's golden sedge	**Carex elata aurea**
Carex riparia	Greater pond sedge	**Carex riparia**
Carissa grandiflora	Natal plum	**Carissa grandiflora**
Carline	Thistle	**Carlina**
Carline des Alpes	Alpine thistle	**Carlina acaulis**
Carline commune	Carline thistle	**Carlina vulgaris**
Carmantine en arbre	Snake bush	**Justicia adhatoda**
Carmantine brandegeana	Shrimp plant	**Justicia brandegeana**
Carmantine carnea	King's crown	**Justicia carnea**
Carnegiea gigantea	Saguaro	**Carnegiea gigantea**
Carpette argentée	Raoulia australis	**Raoulia australis**
Carotte commune	Wild carrot	**Daucus carota**
Carum verticillé	Whorled caraway	**Carum verticillatum**
Casse argentée	Silver cassia / Wormwood cassia	**Cassia artemisioides**
Casse-lunettes	Eyebright	**Euphrasia officinalis**
Cassis	Black currant	**Ribes nigrum**
Castanospermum	Black bean tree / Moreton Bay chestnut	
		Castanospermum australe
Catalpa commun	Indian bean tree	**Catalpa bignonioides**
Catharanthus roseus	Rose periwinkle	**Catharanthus roseus**
Céanothe	Californian lilac / Ceanothus	**Ceanothus**
Céanothe de Monterey	Monterey ceanothus	**Ceanothus rigidus**
Céanothe thyrsiflorus repens	Creeping blue blossom	
		Ceanothus thyrsiflorus repens
Cèdre	Cedar	**Cedrus**
Cèdre de l'Atlas	Atlas cedar	**Cedrus atlantica**
Cèdre de l'Altas bleu	Blue Atlas cedar	**Cedrus atlantica glauca**
Cèdre de l'Himalaya	Deodar	**Cedrus deodara**
Cèdre du Liban	Cedar of Lebanon	**Cedrus libani**
Célastre orbicule	Oriental bittersweet / Staff vine	**Celastrus orbiculatus**
Célastre grimpant	American bittersweet / Staff tree	**Celastrus scandens**
Céleri	Wild celery	**Apium graveolen**

115

Célosie crête de coq "Fairy fountains"	Fairy fountain	**Celosia cristata**
Centaurée	Knapweeed	**Centaurea**
Centaurée jacée	French hardhead	**Centaurea jacea**
Centaurée jaune	Yellow-wort	**Blackstonia perfiolata**
Centaurée barbeau	Sweet sultan	**Centaurea moschata**
Centaurée noire	Hardhead	**Centaurea nigra**
Centaurée rude	Rough star thistle	**Centaurea aspera**
Centaurée scabieuse	Greater knapweed	**Centaurea scabieuse**
Centaurée du solstice	St. Barnaby's thistle	**Centaurea solstitalis**
Cephalaria gigantea	Giant scabious / Yellow scabious	**Cephalaria gigantea**
Cephalophyllum alstonii	Red spike	**Cephalophyllum alstonii**
Cephalotaxus harringtonia	Cow's tail pine / Plum yew	
		Cephalotaxus harringtonia
Céphalanthéra pale	Broad helleborine	**Cephalanthera damasonium**
Céphalanthéra a feuilles étroites	Narrow helleborine	
		Cephalanthera longifolia
Céphalanthéra rose	Red helleborine	**Cephalanthera rubra**
Céraiste des Alpea	Alpine mouse ear	**Cerastium alpinum**
Céraiste des champs	Field mouse-ear	**Cerastium arvense**
Céraiste à 5 étamines	Little mouse-ear	**Cerastium semicandrum**
Céraiste à courts pétales	Grey mouse-ear	**Cerastium brachypetalum**
Céraiste faux-céraiste	Starwort mouse ear	**Cerastium cerastoides**
Céraiste à fleurs agglomérée	Sticky mouse-ear	**Cerastium glomeratum**
Céraiste tomentosum	Snow-in-summer	**Cerastium tomentosum**
Céraiste visqueux	Curtis's mouse-ear	**Cerastium pumilum**
Cercidiphyllacé du Japon	Katsura	**Cercidiphyllum japonicum**
Ceropegia sandersonii	Fountain flower / Parachute plant	
		Ceropegia sandersonii
Ceropegia woodii	Heart vine / Rosary vine / String-of-hearts	**Ceropegia woodii**
Cerfeuil doré	Golden chervil	**Chaerophyllum aureum**
Cerfeuil musqué	Sweet Cicely	**Myrrhis odorata**
Cerfeuil penché	Rough chervil	**Chaerophyllum temulentum**
Cerisier	Cherry	**Prunus**
Cerisier d'amour	Jerusalem cherry	**Solanum pseudocapsicum**
Cerisier à fleurs japonais	Higan cherry	**Prunus subhirtella**
Cerisier à grappes	Bird cherry	**Prunus padus**
Cerisier de Jérusalem	Jerusalem cherry	**Solanum pseudocapsicum**
Cerisier noir	Black cherry / Wild rum cherry	**Prunus serotina**
Cerisier de Sainte-Lucie	Prunus malaheb	**Prunus malaheb**
Ceterach officinarum	Rusty-back fern	**Ceterach officinarum**
Chalef	Elaeagnus	**Elaeagnus**
Chamaecereus silvestri	Peanut cactus	**Chamaecereus silvestri**

Chamaecyparis thyoides	White cypress	**Chamaecyparis thyoides**
Chamédaphné calyculata	Leatherleaf	**Chamaedaphne calyculata**
Chamaedorea elegans	Dwarf mountain palm / Parlour palm	
		Chamaedorea elegans
Chamaelaucium uncinatum	Geraldton waxflower	
		Chamaelaucium uncinatum
Chamaerops humilis	Dwarf fan palm / European fan palm	
		Chamaerops humilis
Chamomille romaine	Chamomile / Common chamomile	
		Chamaemelum nobile
Chapeau-du-diable	Butterbur	**Petasites hybridus**
Champignon	Muxhroom	**Fungus**
Chardon	Thistle	**Cirsium**
Chardon aux ânes	Cotton thistle	**Onopordum acanthium**
Chardon bleu des Alpes	Eryngium alpinum	**Eryngium alpinum**
Chardon à capitues grêles	Seaside thistle	**Carduus tenuilorus**
Chardon d'Écosse	Cotton thistle	**Onopordum acanthium**
Chardon Étoilé	Star thistle	**Centaurea calcitrapa**
Chardon à foulon	Teasel	**Dipsacus fullonium**
Chardon Marie	Blessed Mary's thistle / Milk thistle	**Silybum marianum**
Chardon penché	Musk thistle	**Carduus nutans**
Chardon-Roland	Watling street thistle	**Eryngium campestre**
Charme	Hornbeam	**Carpinus**
Charme d'Amérique	American hornbeam	**Carpinus caroliniana**
Charme commun	Common hornbeam	**Carpinus betulus**
Charme houblon	Hop hornbeam	**Ostrya carpinifolia**
Châtaigne d'eau.	Jesuit's nut / Water Chestnut.	**Trapa natans**
Châtaigne de terre	Pignut	**Conopodium majus**
Châtaignier	Chestnut	**Castanea sativa**
Châtaignier	Spanish chestnut / Sweet chestnut	**Castanea sativa**
Châtaigner d'Amérique	American chestnut	**Castanea dentata**
Chausse-trappe	Star thistle	**Centaurea calcitrapa**
Chanvre d'eau	Gipsywort	**Lycopus europaeus**
Chélidoine	Celandine	**Chelidonium**
Chénopode blanc	Fat hen	**Chenopodium album**
Chénopode à feuilles de figuier	Fig leafed goosefoot	
		Chenopodium ficifolium
Chénopode glauque	Oak-leaved goosefoot	**Chenopodium glaucum**
Chénopode hybride	Sowbane	**Chenopodium hybridum**
Chénopode des murs	Nettle leaved goosefoot	**Chenopodium murale**
Chénopode a graines nombreuses	Many-seed goosefoot	
		Chenopodium polyspermum

Chénopode rouge	Red goosefoot	**Chenopodium rubrum**
Chénopode des villages	Upright goosefoot	**Chenopodium urbicum**
Chêne	Oak	**Quercus**
Chêne acutissima	Sawtooth oak	**Quercus acutissima**
Chêne agrifolia	Californian live oak	**Quercus agrifolia**
Chêne aliena	Oriental white oak	**Quercus aliena**
Chêne alnifolia	Golden oak of Cyprus	**Quercus alnifolia**
Chêne d'Arménie	Armenian oak / Pontine oak	**Quercus pontica**
Chêne blanc	Whjte oak	**Quercus alba**
Chêne blanc d'Amérique	American white oak	**Quercus alba**
Chêne de Bourgogne	Turkey oak	**Quercus cerris**
Chêne de Carolina	Live oak	**Quercus virginiana**
Chêne chevelu	Turkey oak	**Quercus cerris**
Chêne denté	Daimio oak	**Quercus dentata**
Chêne écarlate	Scarlet oak	**Quercus coccinea**
Chêne à feuilles de châtaigner	Chestnut leaved oak	**Quercus casteifolia**
Chêne garryana	Oregon oak	**Quercus garryana**
Chêne à gros fruits	Bur oak	**Quercus macrocarpa**
Chêne x heterophylla	Bartram's oak	**Quercus x heterophylla**
Chêne hispanica 'Lucombeana'	Lucombe oak	**Quercus hispanica 'Lucombeana'**
Chêne de Hongrie	Hungarian oak	**Quercus frainetto**
Chêne à lattes	Shingle oak	**Quercus imbricaria**
Chêne kermès	Kermes oak	**Quercus coccifera**
Chêne-liège	Cork oak	**Quercus suber**
Chêne macranthera	Caucasian oak	**Quercus macranthera**
Chêne des marais	Pin oak	**Quercus palustris**
Chêne de Mongolie	Mongolian oak	**Quercus mongolica**
Chêne noir	Water oak	**Quercus nigra**
Chêne noir	Black oak	**Quercus velutina**
Chêne pédonculé	Pedunculate oak	**Quercus robur**
Chêne pédonculé pyramidial	Fastigiate pedunculate oak	**Quercus robur fastigiata**
Chêne pontin	Pontine oak	**Quercus pontica**
Chêne rouge	Red oak	**Quercus rubra**
Chêne rouvre	Durmast oak / Sessile oak	**Quercus petraea**
Chêne saule	Willow oak	**Quercus phellos**
Chêne sessile	Durmast oak / Sessile oak	**Quercus petraea**
Chêne des teinturiers	Black oak	**Quercus velutina**
Chêne Vélani	Valonia oak	**Quercus macrolepis**
Chêne vert	Holm oak	**Quercus ilex**
Chêne Zeen	Algerian oak / Mirbeck's oak	**Quercus canariensi**

Chenille	Scorpion's tail / Sydney golden wattle	**Acacia longifolia**
Chèvrefeuille	Honeysuckle	**Lonicera**
Chèvrefeuille des bois	Honeysuckle / Woodbine	**Lonicera periclymenum**
Chèvrefeuille des bois	Fly honeysuckle	**Lonicera xylasteum**
Chèvrefeuille x brownii	Scarlet trumpet honeysuckle	**Lonicera x brownii**
Chèvrefeuille du Cap	Cape honeysuckle	**Tecomaria capensis**
Chèvrefeuille des jardins	Perfoliate honeysuckle	**Lonicera caprifolium**
Chèvrefeuille d'Italie	Etruscan honeysuckle	**Lonicera etrusca**
Chèvrefeuille du Japon	Japanese honeysuckle	**Lonicera japonica**
Chèvrefeuille toujours vert	Trumpet honeysuckle	**Lonicera sempervirens**
Chèvrefeuille de Virginie	Coral honeysuckle	**Lonicera sempervirens**
Cheveux de Vénus	Love-in-a-mist	**Nigella damascena**
Cheveux de Vénus	Maidenhair fern	**Adiantum capillus veneris**
Chicorée de mouton	Swine's succory	**Arnoseris minima**
Chicorée sauvage	Chicory	**Chicorium intybus**
Chicot du Canada	Kentucky coffee tree	**Gymnocladus dioica**
Chimonanthe précoce	Wintersweet	**Chimonanthus praecox**
Chinochloa conspicua	Hunangemoho grass	**Chinochloa conspicua**
Chlora perfiolé	Yellow-wort	**Blackstonia perfiolata**
Chlorophytum comosum	Spider plant	**Chlorophytum comosum**
Chorisia speciosa	Floss silk tree	**Chorisia speciosa**
Chorizema illicifolium	Holly flame pea	**Chorizema illicifolium**
Chou marin	Sea bindweed	**Calystegia soldanella**
Chou marin	Sea kale	**Crambe maritima**
Chou d'ornement	Ornamental cabbage	**Brassica oleracea**
Chrysalidocarpus lutescens	Golden-feather palm / Yellow palm	**Chrysalidocarpus lutescens**
Chrysanthème	Chrysanthemum	**Chrysanthemum**
Chrysanthème de blés	Corn marigold	**Chrysanthemum segetum**
Chrysanthemum x superbum	Shasta daisy	**Chrysanthemum x superbum**
Chusquea culeou	Chilean bamboo	**Chusquea culeou**
Ciboulette sauvage	Chives	**Allium schoenoprasum**
Cicendia fluette	Guernsey centaury	**Exaculum pusillum**
Cicendies filiforme	Slender cicendia	**Cicendia filiformis**
Cicutaire vireuse	Cowbane	**Cicuta virosa**
Cierge barba de vieillard	Old man cactus	**Cephalocereus senilis**
Cierge à grandes fleurs	Queen-of-the-night	**Selenicereus grandiflorus**
Ciguë aquatique	Cowbane	**Cicuta virosa**
Cimicifuge	Bugbane	**Cimicifuga**
Cinéraire hybrides	Cineraria	**Senecio x hybridus**
Circée des Alpes	Alpine enchanter's nightshade	**Circaea intermedia**

Circée intermédiare	Upland enchanter's nightshade	**Circaea intermedia**
Circée de Paris	Common enchanter's nightshade	**Circaea lutetiana**
Cirse	Thistle	**Cirsium**
Cirse acaule	Dwarf thistle	**Cirsium acaulon**
Cirse des champs	Creeping thistle	**Cirsium arvense**
Cirse a feuilles lancéolées	Spear thistle	**Cirsium vulgare**
Cirse laineux	Woolly thistle	**Cirsium eriophorum**
Cirse des marais	Marsh thistle	**Cirsium palustre**
Cirse des prairies	Meadow thistle	**Cirsium dissectum**
Cirse tubéreux	Tuberous thistle	**Cirsium tuberosum**
Cissus antarctica	Kangaroo vine	**Cissus antarctica**
Cissus discolor	Rex begonia vine	**Cissus discolor 1**
Cissus rhombifolia	Grape ivy	**Cissus rhombifolia**
Cissus striata	Ivy of Uraguay / Miniature grape ivy	**Cissus striata**
Ciste	Rock rose	**Cistus**
Ciste à gomme	Cistus ladanifer	**Cistus ladanifer**
Citrofortunella mitis	Calamondin	**Citrofortunella mitis**
Citronelle	Lad's love / Old man / Southernwood	**Artemisia abrotanum**
Citronella verveine	Lemon verbena	**Aloysia triphylla**
Clarin	Cross-leaved heath	**Erica tetralix**
Clavalier	Japan pepper	**Zanthoxylum piperitum**
Cleistocactus strausii	Silver torch	**Cleistocactus strausii**
Clématite	Clematis	**Clematis**
Clématite des haies	Old man's beard / Traveller's joy	**Clematis vitalba**
Cléome	Spider flower	**Cleome**
Clethra alnifolia	Sweet pepper-bush	**Clethra alnifolia**
Clethra arborea	Lily of the valley tree	**Clethra arborea**
Clianthus puniceus	Parrot's bill	**Clianthus puniceus**
Clinopode	Calamint	**Calamintha**
Clintonia uniflora	Queencup	**Clintonia uniflora**
Clochette d'hiver	Snowdrop	**Galanthus nivalis**
Clochette d'Irlande	Bells of Ireland / Shell flower / Shell ginger	
		Moleccella laevis
Clusia rosea	Autograph tree / Copey / Fat pork tree / Pitch apple	**Clusia rosea**
Cobée grimpante	Cup and saucer vine	**Cobaea scandens**
Cocos	Queen palm	**Arecastrum**
Cocotier du Chili	Chilean wine palm / Coquito	**Jubaea chilensis**
Cocriste	Greater yellow rattle	**Rhinanthus crista-galli**
Cœur de Jeannette	Dutchman's breeches	**Dicentra cucullaria**
Cœur de Marie	Bleeding heart	**Dicentra spectabilis**
Cognassier commun	Quince	**Cydonia oblonga**

Cognassier du Japon	Flowering quince / Japanese quince / Japonica	
		Chaenomeles japonica
Colchique jaune	Yellow autumn crocus	**Colchicun luteum**
Columnea gloriosa	Goldfish plant	**Columnea gloriosa**
Comaret	Marsh cinquefoil	**Potentilla palustris**
Comarostaphylis diversifolia	Summer holly	**Comarostaphylis diversifolia**
Comméline	Day flower	**Commelina coelistis**
Conopode dénudé	Pignut	**Conopodium majus**
Consoude	Comfrey	**Symphytum**
Consoude hérissée	Prickly comfrey	**Symphytum asperum**
Consoude d'Orient	Soft comfrey	**Symphytum orientale**
Consoude à tubercules	Tuberous comfrey	**Symphytum tuberosum**
Consoude de Russia	Russian comfrey	**Symphytum x uplandicum**
Cooperie	Rain lily	**Zephyranthes**
Copalme d'Amerique	Sweet gum	**Liquidambar styraciflua**
Coquelicot	Corn poppy / Field poppy	**Papaver rhoeas**
Coquelourde des jardins	Lychnis coronaria	**Lychnis coronaria**
Coquelourde rose de ciel	Silene coeli-rosa	**Silene coeli-rosa**
Coqueret	Chinese lantern	**Physalis**
Coqueret du Pérou	Bladder cherry	**Physalis alkekengi**
Coqueret du Perou	Cape gooseberry	**Physalis peruviana**
Coqueret de Pérou	Strawberry tomato	**Physalis peruviana**
Coquillier maritime	Sea rocket	**Cakile maritima**
Corbeille d'argent	Sweet alyssum	**Lobularia maritima**
Corbeille d'argent	Arabis / Garden arabis	**Arabis caucasica**
Corbeille d'argent	Candytuft	**Iberis**
Corbeille d'or	Gold dust	**Aurinia saxatilis**
Cordyline australis	New Zealand palm lily	**Cordyline australis**
Cordyline fruticosa	Good-luck plant / Ti tree	**Cordyline fruticosa**
Coreopsis	Tickseed	**Coreopsis**
Corète du Japon	Kerria japonica	**Kerria japonica**
Coriandre cultivée	Coriander	**Coriandrum sativum**
Cormier	Service tree	**Sorbus domestica**
Corne de bélier	Aloe arborescens	**Aloe arborescens**
Corne de cerf	Aloe arborescens	**Aloe arborescens**
Corneille des bouquets	Tufted loosestrife	**Lysimachia thyrsiflora**
Cornifle emergé	Hornwort	**Ceratophyllum demersum**
Cornouiller blanc	Red-barked dogwood	**Cornus alba**
Cornouiller canadensis	Creeping dogwood	**Cornus canadensis**
Cornouiller capitata	Bentham's cornel	**Cornus capitata**
Cornouiller controversa Varieg.	Wedding-cake tree	
		Cornus controversa Varieg.

121

Cornouiller à fleurs	Flowering dogwood	**Cornus florida**
Cornouiller mâle	Cornelian cherry	**Cornus mas**
Cornouiller nuttallii	Mountain dogwood / Pacific dogwood	
		Cornus nuttallii
Cornouiller de Suède	Dwarf cornel	**Cornus suecica**
Corokia cotoneaster	Wire netting bush	**Corokia cotoneaster**
Coronille	Coronilla	**Coronilla**
Corossolier à fruit hérissé	Cherimoya / Custard apple / Sweet sop	**Annona**
Corrigiola dsa grèves	Strapwort	**Corrigiola littoralis**
Cosmos atrosanguineus	Chocolate cosmos	**Cosmos atrosanguineus**
Costus speciosus	Malay ginger	**Costus speciosus**
Cotoneaster frigidus	Tree cotoneaster	**Cotoneaster frigidus**
Cotoneaster horizontalis	Wall-spray	**Cotoneaster horizontalis**
Cotoneaster de l'Himalaya	Khasia berry	**Cotoneaster simonsii**
Cotonnière d'Allemagne	Common cudweed	**Filago germanica**
Cotonnière de France	Narrow cudweed	**Filago gallica**
Cotonnière naine	Small cudweed	**Filago minima**
Cotule coronopifolia	Brass buttons	**Cotula coronopifolia**
Cotule à feuilles de senebière	Buttonweed	**Cotula coronopifolia**
Coucou	Cowslip	**Primula veris**
Coudrier	Cobnut / Hazel	**Corylus avellana**
Coudrier de Byzance	Turkish hazel	**Corylus colurna**
Coudrier do Levant	Turkish hazel	**Corylus colurna**
Couronne d'épine	Crown of thorns	**Euphorbia milii**
Couronne impériale	Crown imperial	**Fritillaria imperialis**
Crambé à feuille en cœur	Crambe cordifolia	**Crambe cordifolia**
Cranson du Danemark	Early scurvy-grass	**Cochlearia danica**
Cranson officinal	Common scurvey-grass	**Cochlearia officinalis**
Crassula arborescens	Silver jade plant	**Crassula arborescens**
Crassula falcata	Aeroplane propellor	**Crassula falcata**
Crassula ovata	Friendship tree / Jade tree / Money tree	**Crassula ovata**
Crataegomespilus dardarii	Bronvaux medlar	**+Crataegomespilus dardarii**
Crépide bisannuelle	Rough hawksbeard	**Crepis biennis**
Crépide fétide	Southern hawksbeard	**Crepis foetida**
Crepide incana	Pink dandelion	**Crepis incana**
Crépide des marais	Marsh hawksbeard	**Crepis paludosa**
Crépide tendre	Northern hawksbeard	**Crepis mollis**
Crépide à vésicules	Beaked hawksbeard	**Crepis vesicaria**
Cresson alénois	Cress	**Lapidium sativum**
Cresson de cheval.	Brooklime.	**Veronica beccabunga**
Cresson doré	Golden saxifrage	**Chrysosplenium oppositifolium**
Cresson de fontaine	Water-cress	**Rorippa nasturtium-aquaticum**

Cressonnette	Bitter cress / Cuckoo flower / Lady's smock	**Cardamine pratensis**
Criste marine	Rock samphire	**Crithmum maritimum**
Crocus angustifolius	Cloth of gold crocus	**Crocus angustifolius**
Crocus d'automne	Autumn crocus	**Crocus nudiflorus**
Crocus du Chili	Chilean blue crocus	**Tecophilaea cyanocrocus**
Crocus printanier	Spring crocus	**Crocus vernus**
Crocus rouge	Bulbocodium vernum	**Bulbocodium vernum**
Crocus vernus	Dutch crocus	**Crocus vernus**
Croix de Malte	Jerusalem cross / Maltese cross	**Lychnis chalcedonica**
Crotalaria agatiflora	Canary bird bush	**Crotalaria agatiflora**
Croton	Croton	**Codiaeum**
Croton panaché	Variegated croton	**Codiaeum variegatum**
Cryptanthus acaulis	Green earth star	**Cryptanthus acaulis**
Cryptanthus bromelioides	Rainbow star	**Cryptanthus bromelioides**
Cryptogramma crispa	Parsley fern	**Cryptogramma crispa**
Cryptomeria japonica	Japanese cedar	**Cryptomeria japonica**
Cryptostegia grandiflora	Rubber vine	**Cryptostegia grandiflora**
Cucubale	Bladder campion	**Cucubalus**
Cumin des prés	Caraway	**Carum carvi**
Cunonia du Cap	African red alder	**Cunonia capensis**
Cuphea hyssopifolia	False heather	**Cuphea hyssopifolia**
Cuphea ignea	Cigar flower	**Cuphea ignea**
Cupidone	Blue cupidone	**Catananche**
Cuscute d'Europe	Greater dodder	**Cuscuta europaea**
Cuscute du thym	Common dodder	**Cuscuta epithymum**
Cyanotis kewensis	Teddy-bear vine	**Cyanotis kewensis**
Cyanotis somaliensis	Pussy ears	**Cyanotis somaliensis**
Cyathea arborea	West Indian tree fern	**Cyathea arborea**
Cyathea australis	Australian tree fern	**Cyathea australis**
Cyathea medullaris	Black tree fern	**Cyathea medullaris**
Cycas revoluta	Japanese sago palm	**Cycas revoluta**
Cyclamen	Cyclamen	**Cyclamen**
Cyclamen de Naples	Sowbread	**Cyclamen hederifolium**
Cynoglosse d'Allemagne	Great hound's tongue	**Cynoglossum germanicum**
Cynoglosse nervosum	Himalayan hounds tongue	**Cynoglossum nervosum**
Cyprès	Cypress	**Cupressus**
Cyprès de l'Arizona	Arizona cypress / Smooth cypress	**Cupressus arizonica**
Cyprès de Busaco	Mexican cypress	**Cupressus lusitanica**
Cyprès chauve	Bald cypress / Swamp cypress	**Taxodium distichum**

Cyprès de Goa	Cedar of Goa / Mexican cypress	**Cupressus lusitanica**
Cyprès de Kashmir	Kashmir cypress	**Cupressus cashmeriana**
Cyprès de Lambert	Monterey cypress	**Cupressus macrocarpa**
Cyprès de Lawson	Lawson cypress	**Chamaecyparis lawsoniana**
Cyprès de Leyland	Leyland cypress	**Cupressocyparis leylandii**
Cyprès de Monterey	Monterey cypress	**Cupressus macrocarpa**
Cyprès de Nootka	Nootka cypress	**Chamaecyparis nootkatensis**
Cyprès pleureur	Mexican cypress	**Cupressus lusitanica**
Cyprès de Provence	Italian cypress / Mediterranean cypress	
		Cupressus sempervirens
Cypripedium acaule	Moccasin flower	**Cypripedium acaule**
Cypripedium calceolus	Yellow lady's slipper orchid	**Cypripedium calceolus**
Cypripedium reginae	Showy lady's slipper orchid	**Cypripedium reginae**
Cyrtomium falcatum	Fishtail fern / Holly fern	**Cyrtomium falcatum**
Cystopteris bulbifera	Berry bladder fern	**Cystopteris bulbifera**
Cystopteris fragile	Brittle bladder fern	**Cystopteris fragilis**
Cythea medulalaris	Mamaku	**Cythea medulalaris**
Cytise	Common laburnum	**Laburnum anagyroides**
Cytise des Alpes	Scotch laburnum	**Laburnum alpinum**
Cytisus battandieri	Moroccan broom / Pineapple broom	**Cytisus battandieri**

D

Dactyle aggloméré	Cock's foot / Orchard grass	**Dactylis glomerata**
Dactyle peltonné	Cock's foot / Orchard grass	**Dactylis glomerata**
Damasonium étoilé	Star-fruit	**Damasonium alisima**
Dame d'onze heures	Star-of-Bethleham	**Ornithogalum umbelletum**
Daphné	Daphne	**Daphne cneorum**
Daphné lauréole	Spurge laurel	**Daphne laureola**
Dasylirion	Bear grass	**Dasylirion**
Dattier	Date palm	**Phoenix dactylyfera**
Dattier des Canaries	Canary Island date palm	**Phoenix canariensis**
Dauphinelle	Delphinium	**Delphinium**
Davallia canariensis	Hare's foot fern	**Davallia canariensis**
Davallia maresii	Squirrel's foot fern	**Davallia maresii**
Dendrochilum glumaceum	Silver chain	**Dendrochilum glumaceum**
Dentelaire du Cap	Cape leadwort	**Plumbago auriculata**
Dent-de-chien	Dog's-tooth violet	**Erythronium dens-canis**
Dent-de-lion	Dandelion	**Taraxacum officinale**
Dentaire	Toothwort	**Lathraea clandestina**
Dentaire bulbifère	Coral root	**Cardamine bulbifera**

Déspoir des singes	Chile pine / Monkey puzzle	**Araucaria araucana**
Dianella	Flax lily	**Dianella**
Diapensie	Diapensia	**Diapensia lapponica**
Dicksonia antarctica	Australian tree fern	**Dicksonia antarctica**
Dictame	Dittany	**Dctamnus**
Dieffenbachia	Dumb cane / Leopard Lily	**Dieffenbachia**
Diéramr	Angel's fishing rod / Wandflower	**Dierama**
Digitale	Foxglove	**Digitalis purpurea**
Digitale jaune à grandes fleurs	Yellow foxglove	**Digitalis grandiflora**
Digitale pourpre	Foxglove	**Digitalis purpurea**
Dillénie	Elephant apple	**Dillenia indica**
Dimophotèque	African daisy / Cape marigold	**Dimorphotheca**
Dionée attrape mouches	Venus flytrap	**Dionaea muscipula**
Dionée gobe-mouches	Venus flytrap	**Dionaea muscipula**
Dioon edule	Virgin's palm	**Dioon edule**
Diosma ericoides	Breath of heaven	**Diosma ericoides**
Diphyllée	Umbrella leaf	**Diphylleia cymosa**
Diplotaxis des murailles	Stink weed / Wall rocket	**Diplotaxis muralis**
Discaria toumatou	Wild Irishman	**Discaria toumatou**
Disporum	Fairy bells	**Disporum**
Distictis buccinatoria	Mexican blood flower	**Distictis buccinatoria**
Dizygotheca elegantissima	False aralia	**Dizygotheca elegantissima**
Dolique d'Égypte	Australian pea / Hyacinth bean / Lablab	
		Lablab purpureus
Dombeya x cayeuxii	Pink snowball	**Dombeya x cayeuxii**
Dorine à feuilles alternes	Alternate golden saxifrage	
		Chrysosplenium alternifolium
Dorine à feuilles opposées	Golden saxifrage	
		Chrysosplenium oppositifolium
Doronic tue-pantheres	Leopard's bane	**Doronicum pardalianches**
Dorotheanthus bellidiformis	Ice plant / Livingstone daisy	
		Dorotheanthus bellidiformis
Douce-amère	Bittersweet	**Solanum dulcamara**
Douglas bleu	Blue Douglas fir	**Pseudotsuga menzieii glauca**
Douglas vert	Douglas fir	**Pseudotsuga menziesii**
Dracoléphale	Dragon's head	**Dracocephalum**
Dragone	Tarragon	**Artemisia dracunculus**
Dragonnier odorant	Corn plant	**Dracaena fragrans**
Dragonnier de Madagascar	Madagascar dragon tree	**Dracaena marginata**
Dragonnier de Sander	Ribbon plant	**Dracaena sanderiana**
Drave faux-aizoon	Yellow whitlow grass	**Draba aizoides**
Drave grisâtre	Twisted whitlow-grass	**Draba incana**

Drave des murs	Common whitlow-grass	**Draba muralis**
Drimys lanceolata	Mountain pepper	**Drimys lanceolata**
Drimys winteri	Winter's bark	**Drimys winteri**
Dryade à huit pétales	Mountain avens	**Dryas octopetala**
Durante	Pigeon berry / Skyflower	**Duranta repens**

E

Echevaria pulvinata	Plush plant	**Echevaria pulvinata**
Echinacea	Coneflower	**Echinacea**
Echinocactus grusonii	Golden barrel cactus / Mother-in-law's-seat **Echinocactus grusonii**	
Echinocereus schmollii	Lamb's tail cactus	**Echinocereus schmollii**
Échinopanax	Devil's club	**Oplopanax horridus**
Échinope à tête ronde	Globe thistle	**Echinops spaerocepha**
Éclaire	Greater celandine	**Chelidonium majus**
Écuelle d'eau	Marsh pennywort	**Hydrocotyle vulgaris**
Edelweiss	Edelweiss	**Leontopodium**
Edelweiss de Nouvelle-Zélande	North Island edelweiss **Leucogenes leontopodium**	
Églantine	Eglantine / Sweet briar	**Rosa eglanteria**
Églantier odorant	Eglantine / Sweet briar	**Rosa eglanteria**
Égopode panaché	Variegated Bishop's weed **Aegopodium podagraria 'Variegatum'**	
Elaeocarpus reticulatus	Blueberry ash	**Elaeocarpus reticulatus**
Elatine poivre d'eau	Eight stamened waterwort	**Elatine hydropiper**
Elatine à six étamines	Waterwort	**Elatine hexandra**
Ellébore fétide	Stinking hellebore	**Helleborus foetidus**
Ellebore d'hiver	Winter aconite	**Eranthis hyemalis**
Ellébore vert	Green hellebore	**Helleborus viridis**
Élodée	Elodea	**Elodea**
Élodée du Canada	Canadian waterweed	**Elodea canadensis**
Élodée de Nuttall	Esthwaite waterweed	**Elodea nuttallii**
Élodés des marais	Marsh St. John's wort	**Hypericum elodes**
Élyme des sables	Lyme grass	**Leymus arenarius**
Embothrium coccineum	Chilean firebush	**Embothrium coccineum**
Émile	Tassel flower	**Emilia javanica**
Eomecon chionantha	Snow poppy	**Eomecon chionantha**
Épervière	Hawkweed	**Hieracium**
Épiaire d'Allemagne	Downy woundwort	**Stachys germanica**
Épiaire des Alpes	Limestone woundwort	**Stachys alpina**

Épiaire des bois	Hedge woundwort	**Stachys sylvatica**
Épiaire byzantina	Bunnies' ears	**Stachys byzantina**
Épiaire des champs	Field woundwort	**Stachys arvensis**
Épiaire des marais	Marsh woundwort	**Stachys palustris**
Epicaris impressa	Australian heath	**Epicaris impress**
Épicéa	Spruce	**Picea**
Épicéa de Brewer	Brewer's spruce	**Picea breweriana**
Épicéa du Colorado	Colorado spruce	**Picea pungens**
Épicéa commun	Norway spruce	**Picea abies**
Épicéa d'Englemann	Englemann spruce / Mountain spruce	
		Picea englemannii
Épicéa likeangensis	Lijiang spruce	**Picea likeangensis**
Épicéa morrisonicola	Taiwan spruce	**Picea morrisonicola**
Épicéa de Serbie	Serbian spruce	**Picea omorica**
Épicéa de Sitka	Sitka spruce	**Picea sitchensis**
Épicéa smithiana	Morinda spruce / West Himalayan spruce	
		Picea smithiana
Epigaé	Mayflower / Trailing arbutus	**Epigaea repens**
Épilobe	Willow herb	**Epilobium**
Épilobe des Alpes	Alpine willow-herb	**Epilobium anagallidifolium**
Épilobe en épi	Rose-bay willow-herb	**Chamaenerion angustifolium**
Épilobe à feuilles d'alsine	Chickweed willow-herb	
		Epilobium alsinifolium
Épilobe à feuilles lancéolées	Spear-leaved willow-herb	
		Epilobium lanceolatum
Épilobe foncé	Short-fruited willow-herb	**Epilobium obscurum**
Épilobe hirsute	Great willow-herb	**Epilobium hirsutum**
Épilobe des marais	Marsh willow-herb	**Epilobium palustra**
Épilobe de montagne	Broad-leaved willow-herb	**Epilobium montanum**
Épilobe de Nouvelle Zélande	New Zealand willow-herb	
		Epilobium brunnescens
Épilobe à peties fleurs	Hoary willow-herb	**Epilobium parviflorum**
Épilobe rosé	Pale willow-herb	**Epilobium roseum**
Epimedium alpinum	Barrenwort	**Epimedium alpinum**
Epinard-oseille	Patience dock	**Rumex patientia**
Épinard sauvage	Good King Henry	**Chenopodium bonus-henricus**
Épine	Thorn	**Crataegus**
Épine blanche	May / Thorn	**Crataegus laevigata**
Épine du Christ	Christ's thorn /Jerusalem thorn	**Paliurus spina-christi**
Épine ergot de coq	Cockspur thorn	**Crataegus crus-galli**
Épine à fruits jaunes	Yellow haw	**Crataegus flava**
Épine à feuilles de tanasie	Tansy-leaved thorn	**Crataegus tanacetifolia**

Épine noire	Blackthorn / Sloe	**Prunus spinosa**
Épine-vinette	Barberry	**Berberis**
Epipactis a feuilles larges	Common helleborine	**Epipactis helleborine**
Épipactis a fleurs vertes	Green-flowered helleborine	**Epipactis phyllanthes**
Épipactis à labelle étroite	Narrow-lipped helleborine	**Epipactis leptochila**
Épipactis des marais	Marsh helleborine	**Epipactis palustris**
Épipactis pourprée	Violet helleborine	**Epipactis purpurata**
Épipactis sanguine	Dark red helleborine	**Epipactis atrorubens**
Epiphyllum anguliger	Fishbone cactus	**Epiphyllum anguliger**
Épipognon sans feuilles	Ghost orchid	**Epipogium aphyllum**
Epipremnum pictum	Silver vine	**Epipremnum pictum**
Episcia cupreata	Flame violet	**Episcia cupreata**
Episcia dianthiflora	Lace flower	**Episcia dianthifolia**
Érable argenté	Silver maple	**Acer saccherinum**
Érable buergerianum	Trident maple	**Acer buergerianum**
Érable champêtre	Maple	**Acer campestre**
Érable capillipes	Snake-bark maple	**Acer capillipes**
Érable de Cappadocie	Cappadocian maple	**Acer cappadocium**
Érable à feiulles d'aubepine	Hawthorn maple	**Acer crataegifolium**
Érable à feiulles rondes	Vine maple	**Acer circinatum**
Érable davidii	Père David's maple /Snake-bark maple	**Acer davidii**
Érable à feuilles de charme	Hornbeam maple	**Acer carpinifolium**
Érable du fleuve Amour	Amur maple	**Acer ginnala**
Érable de gris	Paper bark maple	**Acer griseum**
Érable grosseri var. hersii	Her's maple	**Acer grosseri var. hersii**
Érable d'Italie	Italian maple	**Acer opalus**
Érable du Japon Full moon maple		**Acer japonicum / Acer palmatum**
Érable du Japon Japanese maple		**Acer japonicum / Acer palmatum**
Érable jaspé	Snake-bark maple	**Acer pensylvanicum**
Érable de Lobel	Lobel's maple	**Acer lobelii**
Érable macrophyllum	Oregon maple	**Acer macrophyllum**
Érable de Montpellier	Montpelier maple	**Acer monspessulanum**
Érable negundo	Ash-leaved maple / Box elder	**Acer negundo**
Érable nikoense	Nikko maple	**Acer nikoense**
Érable palmatum 'Senkaki'	Cork bark maple	**Acer palmatum 'Senkaki'**
Érable plane	Norway maple	**Acer plantanoides**
Érable sycomore	Sycamore	**Acer pseudoplatanus**
Érable rouge	Red maple	**Acer rubrum**
Érable rufinerve	Snake-bark maple	**Acer rufinerve**

Érable à sucre	Sugar maple	**Acer saccharum**
Érable velutinum vanvolxemii	Van Volxem's maple	
		Acer velutinum vanvolxemi
Éranthe	Winter aconite	**Eranthis hyemalis**
Eremurus	Foxtail lily / King's spear	**Eremurus**
Erinacea anthyllis	Hedgehog broom	**Erinacea anthyllis**
Érine des Alpes	Fairy foxglove	**Erinus alpinus**
Eriogonum	Wild buckwheat	**Eriogonum**
Eriogonum giganteum	St. Catherine's lace	**Eriogonum giganteum**
Eriophorum angustifolium	Common cotton-grass	
		Eriophorum angustifolium
Érythrine	Erythrina	**Erythrina**
Érythrine coralloides	Flame coral tree / Naked coral tree	
		Erythrina coralloides
Érythrine crête de coq	Cockspur coral-tree	**Erythrina crista-galli**
Escholtzia stauntonii	Mint bush	**Escholtzia stauntonii**
Esparcette	Sanfoin	**Onobrychis viciifolia**
Espostosa lanata	Cotton ball	**Espostosa lanata**
Estragon	Tarragon	**Artemisia dracunculus**
Étoile de Bethléhem	Nodding star of Bethlehem	**Ornithogalum nutans**
Étoile de Bethléem	Campanula isophylla	**Campanula isophylla**
Étoile de Bethléem	Star-of-Bethleham orchid	
		Angraecum sesquipedale
Étoile de Marie	Campanula isophylla	**Campanula isophylla**
Eucalyptus	Gum tree	**Eucalyptus**
Eucalyptus camaldulensis	Murray river gum / River red gum	
		Eucalyptus camaldulensis
Eucalyptus coccifera	Tasmanian snow gum	**Eucalyptus coccifera**
Eucalyptus dalrympleana	Mountain gum	**Eucalyptus dalrympleana**
Eucalyptus ficifolia	Flowering gum	**Eucalyptus ficifolia**
Eucalyptus glaucescens	Tigiringi gum	**Eucalyptus glaucescens**
Eucalyptus gunnii	Cider gum	**Eucalyptus de Gunn**
Eucalyptus niphophila	Snow gum	**Eucalyptus niphophila**
Eucalyptus pauciflora	White Sally	**Eucalyptus pauciflora**
Eucalyptus perriniana	Spinning gum	**Eucalyptus perriniana**
Eucalyptus à feuilles d'osier	Manna gum / Ribbon gum	
		Eucalyptus viminalis
Eucomis	Pineapple flower	**Eucomis**
Eucomis pallidiflora	Giant pineapple flower / Giant pineapple lily	
		Eucomis pallidiflora
Eucommia ulnoides	Gutta-percha tree	**Eucommia ulnoides**

Eucryphia cordifolia	Ulmo	**Eucryphia cordifolia**
Eupatoire à feuilles de chanvre	Hemp agrimony	
		Eupatorium cannabinum
Eupatoire purpureum	Joe Pye weed	**Eupatorium purpureum**
Eupatoire rugeua	Hardy age / Mist flower / White snakeroot	
		Eupatorium rugosum
Euphorbe	Milkweed / Spurge	**Euphorbia**
Euphorbe des bois	Wood spurge	**Euphorbia amygdaloides**
Euphorbe fulgens	Scarlet plume	**Euphorbia fulgens**
Euphorbia gorgonensis	Gorgon's head	**Euphorbia gorgonensis**
Euphorbia obesa	Gingham golf ball	**Euphorbia obesa**
Euphraise officinal	Eyebright	**Euphrasia officinalis**
Euphorbe panaché	Snow-on-the-mountain / Snow-in-summer	
		Euphorbia marginata
Euphraise rouge	Red bartsia	**Odontites verna**
Exacum affine	Persian violet	**Exacum affine**
Expostoa lanata	Peruvian old man cactus	**Expostoa lanata**

F

Falcaria commun	Longleaf	**Falcaria vulgaris**
Fallugia paradoxa	Apache plume	**Fallugia paradoxa**
Farouch.	Crimson clover.	**Trifolium incarnatum**
Fatshedera lizei	Tree ivy	**Fatshedera lizei**
Fatsia japonica	Japanese aralia	**Fatsia japonica**
Fausse camomile	Corn chamomile	**Anthemis arvensis**
Fausse capillaire	Maidenhair spleenwort	**Asplenium**
		trichomanes
Fausse roquette de France	Hairy rocket	**Erucastrum gallicum**
Fausse sanguenitte	Cotton lavender	**Santolina**
		chamaecyparissus
Faux-cassis	Flowering currant	**Ribes sanguineum**
Faux cyprès	False cypress	**Chamaecyparis**
Faux-cyprès de Lawson	Lawson Cypres	**Chamaecyparis**
		lawsoniana
Faux-ébénier	Common laburnum	**Laburnum anagyroides**
Faux indigo	False indigo	**Baptisia australis**
Faux narcisse	Wild daffodil	**Narcissus pseudonarcissus**
Faux orme de Sibérie.	Caucasian elm.	**Zelkova carpinifolia**
Faux pistachier	Bladder nut	**Staphylea**
Faux poivrier	Californian pepper tree / Peruvian mastic tree / Peruvian pepper tree	
		Schinus molle

Faux-tremble	Quaking aspen	Populus tremuloides
Faux-Vernis du Japon	Tree of heaven	Ailanthus altissima
Feijoa sellowiana	Pineapple guava	Feijoa sellowiana
Felicia bergeriana	Kingfisher daisy	Felicia bergeriana
Fenasse	False oat grass	Arrhenatherum elatius
Fenestraria aurantiaca rhopalophylla	Baby's toes	Fenestraria aurantiaca var. rhopalophylla
Fenouil des Alpes	Spignel-meu	Meum athamanticum
Fenouil des chevaux	Pepper saxifrage	Silaum silaus
Fenouil commun	Fennel	Foeniculum vulgare
Fénugrec.	Fenugreek.	Trigolella foenum-graecum
Fer-à-cheval	Horseshoe vetch	Hippocrepis comosa
Ferocactus	Barrel cactus	Ferocactus
Féroner	Elephant apple	Feronia
Férule	Giant fennel	Ferula
Festuca glauca	Blue fescue	Festuca glauca
Février d'Amérique	Honey locust	Gleditsia triacanthas
Février caspica	Caspian locust	Gleditsia caspica
Février du Japon	Japanese locust	Gleditsia japonica
Ficaire	Lesser celandine	Ranunculus ficaria
Ficoïde	Ice plant / Livingstone daisy	Dorotheanthus belliformis
Ficus benjamina	Weeping fig	Ficus benjamina
Ficus deltoides	Mistletoe fig	Ficus deltoides
Ficus lyrata	Fiddle-leaf fig	Ficus lyrata
Ficus macrophylla	Australian banyan / Moreton Bay fig	Ficus macrophylla
Ficus pumila	Creeping fig	Ficus pumila
Ficus rubiginosa	Port Jackson fig / Rusty-leaved fig	Ficus rubiginosa
Figue des Hottentots	Hottentot fig / Kaffir fig	Carpobrotus edulis
Figuier	Fig	Ficus
Figuier des Banyans	Banyan	Ficus benghalensis
Figuier de Barbarie	Edible prickly pear / Indian fig	Opuntia ficus-indica
Figuier des pagodes	Bo / Peepul / Sacred fig tree	Ficus religiosa
Filipendule à 6 petales	Dropwort	Filipendula vulgaris
Fille de l'air	Spanish moss	Tillandsia usneoides
Fittonia verschaffeltii	Painted net leaf / Silver net-leaf	Fittonia verschaffeltii
Flamboyant	Barbados pride	Caesalpinia pulcherrima
Flammule	Clematis flammula	Clematis flammula

131

Flèche d'eau américaine	American arrowhead / Duck potato	
		Sagittaria latifolia
Flèche d'eau américaine	Japanese arrowhead	Sagittaria sagittifolia
		'Flore pleno'
Fleur de coucou	Ragged Robin	Lychnis flos-cuculi
Fleur des dames	Heliotrope arborescens	Heliotrope arborescens
Fleur des dieux	Shamrock pea	Parochetus communis
Fleur de Jupiter	Ragged Robin	Lychnis flos-cuculi
Fleur de léopard	Belamcanda	Belamcanda
Fleur de mai	May lily	Maianthemum bifolium
Fleur de passion	Passion flower	Passiflora
Fleur de la Passion bleu	Blue passion flower	Passiflora caerulea
Flûteau	Water plantain	Alisma plantago-aquatica
fausse-renoncule	Lesser water plantain	
		Baldellia ranunculoides
Flûteau à feuilles de graminée	Ribbon-leaved water plantain	
		Alisma gramineum
Flûteau nageant	Floating water plantain	Luronium natans
Fontinale	Water moss / Willow moss	
		Fontinalis antipyretica
Fothergilla gardenii	Witch alder	Fothergilla gardenii
Fougère carthusiana	Narrow buckler fern	Dryopteris carthusiana
Fougère dilatata	Broad buckler fern	Dryopteris dilatata
Fougère erythrosora	Japanese shield fern	Dryopteris erythrosora
Fougère femelle	Lady fern	Athyrium filix-femina
Fougère femelle	Painted fern	Athyrium nipponicum
Fougère goldiana	Giant wood fern	Dryopteris goldiana
Fougère mâle	Male fern	Dryopteris filix-mas
Fougère pectinée	Hard fern	Blechnum spicant
Fougère royale	Royal fern	Osmunda regalis
Fragon piquant	Butcher's broom	Ruscus aculeatus
Fraisier commun	Wild strawberry	Fragaria vesca
Framboisir	Raspberry	Rubus idaeus
Francoa appendiculata	Bridal wreath	Francoa appendiculata
Frangipanier	Frangipani	Plumeria rubra
Frankenénie lisse	Sea heath	Frankenia laevis
Fraxinelle	Burning bush	Dictamnus albus
Frêne	Ash	Fraxinus
Frêne de l'Arizona	Arizona ash	Fraxinus velutina
Frêne blanc	White ash	Fraxinus americana
Frêne oxyphylle	Narrow leafed ash	Fraxinus angustifolia
Frêne à fleurs	Manna ash	Fraxinus ornus

Frêne oxyphylle	Claret ash	**Fraxinus oxycarpa**
Frêne pleureur	Weeping ash	**Fraxinus excelsior 'Pendula'**
Frêne vert	Green ash / Red ash	**Fraxinus pennsylvanica**
Fritillaire pintade	Fritillary	**Fritillaria meleagris**
Fritillaire pudica	Yellow fritillary	**Fritillaria pudica**
Fritillaire recurva	Scarlet Fritillary	**Fritillaria recurva**
Fremontodendron	Flannel flower	**Fremontodendron**
Fromental	False oat grass	**Arrhenatherum elatius**
Fuchsia arborescent	Tree fuchsia	**Fuchsia arborescens**
Fuchsia du Cap	Cape figwort	**Phygelius capensis**
Fuchsia magellanica	Lady's eardrops	**Fuchsia magellanica**
Fumeterre officinale	Fumitory	**Fumaria oficinalis**
Funkie	Funkia / Plantain lily	**Hosta**
Fusain ailé	Winged spindle	**Euonymus alatus**
Fusain d'Europe	Spindle tree	**Euonymus europaeus**
Fusain du Japon	Japanese spindle	**Euonymus japonicus**

G

Gagée jaune	Yellow star of Bethlehem	**Gagea lutea**
Gaillardia	Blanket flower	**Gaillardia**
Gaillet	Bedstraw	**Galium**
Gaillet	Woodruff	**Galium odoratum**
Gaillet commun	Hedge bedstraw	**Galium mollugo**
Gaillet fangeux	Fen bedstraw	**Galium uliginosum**
Gaillet jaune	Lady's bedstraw	**Galium verum**
Gaillet gratteron	Goosegrass	**Galium aparine**
Gaillet des marais	Marsh bedstraw	**Galium palustre**
Gaillet du nord	Northern bedstraw	**Galium boreale**
Gaillet de Paris	Wall bedstraw	**Galium Parisiense**
Gaillet des rochers	Heath bedstraw	**Galium saxatile**
Gaillet à trois cornes	Small goosegrass	**Galium tricornutum**
Gainier	Redbud	**Cercis**
Gainier du Canada	Eastern redbud	**Cercis canadensis**
Galane	Turtle-head	**Chelone**
Galantine	Snowdrop	**Galanthus nivalis**
Galé odorante	Bog myrtle	**Myrica gale**
Galéga officinal	Goat's rue	**Galega officinalis**
Galópsis à feuilles étroites	Red hemp-nettle	**Galeopsis angustifolia**
Galópsis orné	Large hemp-nettle	**Galeopsis speciosa**

Galinsoga à petites fleurs	Gallant soldier	**Galinsoga parviflora**
Gandasuli	Ginger lily	**Hedychium**
Gant de Notre-Dame	Foxglove	**Digitalis purpurea**
Gantelée	Nettle leaved bellflower	**Campanula trachelium**
Garance voyageuse	Wild madder	**Rubia peregrina**
Garrya elliptica	Silk-tassel bush	**Garrya elliptica**
Gattillier commun	Chastity bush / Monk's pepper	**Vitex agnus castus**
Gaude	Weld	**Reseda luteola**
Gaultheria shallon	Shallon	**Gaultheria shallon**
Gaylussacia	Huckleberry	**Gaylussacia**
Gaylussacie baccata	Black huckleberry	**Gaylussacia baccata**
Gazon blanc	Venus's navelwort	**Omphalodes linifolia**
Gelsemium sempervirens	Carolina jasmine / False jasmine	
		Gelsemium sempervirens
Genestrolle	Dyers' greenweed	**Genista tinctoria**
Genévrier	Juniper	**Juniperus**
Genêt	Broom	**Genista / Cytisus**
Genêt d'Angleterre	Petty whin	**Genista anglica**
Genêt à balais	Broom	**Cytisus scoparius**
Genêt blanc	White broom	**Cytisus albus**
Genêt d'Espagne	Spanish broom	**Spartium junceum**
Genêt de l'Etna	Mount Etna broom	**Genista aetnensis**
Genêt d'Espagne	Spanish gorse	**Genista hispanica**
Genêt poilu	Hairy greenweed	**Genista pilosa**
Genêt précoce	Warminster broom	**Cytisus x praecox**
Genêt pourpré	Purple broom	**Cytisus purpureus**
Genêt des teinturiers	Dyers' greenweed	**Genista tinctoria**
Genévrier de Chine	Chinese juniper	**Juniperus chinensis**
Genévrier davurica	Dahurian junipe	**Juniperus davurica**
Genévrier procumbens	Bonin Isles juniper	**Juniperus procumbens**
Genévrier rampante	Creeping juniper	**Juniperus horizontalis**
Genévrier recurva	Drooping juniper / Himalayan weeping juniper	
		Juniperus recurva
Genévrier rigida	Temple juniper	**Juniperus rigida**
Genévrier des rivages	Shore juniper	**Juniperus conferta**
Genévrier Sabine	Savin	**Juniperus sabina**
Genévrier scopulorum	Rocky mountain juniper	**Juniperus scopulorum**
Genévrier de Syrie	Syrian juniper	**Juniperus drupacea**
Genévrier de Virginie	Pencil cedar	**Juniperus virginiana**
Gentiane	Gentian	**Gentiana**
Gentiana acaulis	Stemless gentian	**Gentiana acaulis**
Gentiane d'Allemagne	Chiltern gentian	**Gentiana germanica**

Gentiane amère	Felwort gentian	**Gentiana amarella**
Gentiane d'Angleterre	Early gentian	**Gentiana anglica**
Gentiane asclepiadea	Willow gentian	**Gentiana asclepiadea**
Gentiane champêtre	Field gentian	**Gentiana campestris**
Gentiane clusii	Trumpet gentian	**Gentiana clusii**
Gentiana jaune	Great yellow gentian	**Gentiana lutea**
Gentiane des marais	Welsh gentian	**Gentiana uliginosa**
Gentiane pneumonanthe	Marsh gentian	**Gentiana pneumonanthe**
Gentiane printanière	Spring gentian	**Gentiana verna**
Géranium	Geranium	**Pelargonium**
Géranium des bois	Wood cranesbill	**Geranium sylvaticum**
Géranium brun	Dusky cranesbill	**Geraniuphaeum**
Géranium changeant	Pencilled cranesbill	**Geranium versicolor**
Géranium des colombes	Long stalked cranesbill	**Geranium columbinum**
Géranium découpé	Cut-leaved cranesbill	**Geranium dissectum**
Géranium d'endresse	French craniesbill	**Geranium endressi**
Géranium à feuilles rondes	Round-leaved cranesbill	
		Geranium rotundifolium
Géranium fluet	Small flowered cranesbill	**Geranium pusillum**
Géranium luisant	Shining cranesbill	**Geranium lucidum**
Géranium noueux	Knotted cranesbill	**Geranium nodosum**
Géranium pourpré	Little robin	**Geranium purpureum**
Géranium des prés	Meadow cranesbill	**Geranium pratense**
Géranium des Pyrénées	Pyrenean cranesbill	**Geranium pyrenaicum**
Géranium sanguin	Bloody cranesbill	**Geranium sanguineum**
Gerbera jamesonii	Barberton daisy	**Gerbera jamesonii**
Germandrée	Wood-sage	**Teucrium scorodonia**
Germandrée fruticans	Shrubby germander / Tree germander	
		Teucrium fruticans
Germandrée petit-chêne	Wall germander	**Teucrium chamaedrys**
Germandrée scordium	Water germander	**Teucrium scordium**
Gesse aphylle	Yellow vetchling	**Lathyruus aphaca**
Gesse à grandes fleurs	Everlasting pea	**Lathyrus grandiflorus**
Gesse hérissée	Hairy pea	**Lathyrus hirsutus**
Gesse à larges feuilles	Everlasting pea	**Lathyrus latifolius**
Gesse des marais	Marsh pea	**Lathyrus palustris**
Gesse maritime	Sea pea	**Lathyrus japonicus**
Gesse de montagne	Bitter vetch	**Lathyrus montanus**
Gesse nervosus	Lord Anson's blue pea	**Lathyrus nervosus**
Gesse des prés	Meadow pea	**Lathyrus pratensis**
Gesse sans vrille	Grass vetchling	**Lathyrus nissolia**
Giroflée	Wallflower	**Cheiranthus cheiri**

Giroflée des dunes	Great sea stock	**Matthiola sinuata**
Giroflée jaune	Wallflower	**Cheiranthus cheiri**
Giroflée de Mahon	Virginia stock	**Malcolmia maritima**
Giroflée quarantaine	Stock	**Matthiola**
Glaïeul	Gladiolus	**Gladiolus**
Glaïeul d'Illurie	Gladiolus illyricus	**Gladiolus illyricus**
Glaucière jaune	Horned poppy / Yellow horned poppy	**Glaucium flavum**
Glauce	Sea milkwort	**Glaux maritima**
Globulaire	Globularia	**Globularia**
Gloire de neige	Glory-of-the-snow	**Chionodoxa**
Gloxinia	Gloxinia	**Sinningia speciosa**
Glycérie aquatique	Glyceria	**Glyceria maxima**
Glycine.	Wisteria.	**Wistaria**
Glycine du Japon.	Japanese wisteria.	**Wisteria floribunda**
Glycine de Chine.	Chinese wisteria.	**Wisteria sinensis**
Glycine venusta .	Silky wisteria.	**Wisteria venusta**
Gnaphale blanc-jaunâtre	Jersey cudweed	**Gnaphalium luteoalbum**
Gnaphale des forêts	Heath cudweed	**Gnaphalium undulatum**
Gnaphale nain	Dwarf cudweed	**Gnaphalium supinum**
Gnaphale de Norvège	Highland cudweed	**Gnaphalium norvegicum**
Gnaphale ondulé	Cape cudweed	**Gnaphalium undulatum**
Gnavelle annuelle	Knawel	**Scleranthus annuus**
Gnavelle vivace	Perennial knawel	**Scleranthus perennis**
Gommier bleu	Blue gum / Tasmanian blue gum	**Eucalyptus globulus**
Goodyère rampante	Creeping lady's tresses	**Goodyera repens**
Gordonia à feuilles glabrées	Loblolly bay	**Gordonia lasianthus**
Graceline	Nipplewort	**Lapsana communis**
Grande astrance	Pink masterwort	**Astrantia major**
Grande aunée	Elecampane	**Inula helenium**
Grande bardane	Great burdock	**Arctium lappa**
Grand boucage	Greater burnet-saxifrage	**Pimpinella major**
Grande brize	Greater quaking grass	**Briza maxima**
Grande camomille	Feverfew	**Tanacetum parthenium**
Grande capucine.	Garden nasturtium.	**Tropaeolum majus**
Grande chélidoine	Greater celandine	**Chelidonium majus**
Grande ciguë	Hemlock	**Conium maculatum**
Grand coudriier	Filbert	**Corylus maxima**
Grande consoude	Common comfrey	**Symphytum officinale**
Grande douve	Greater spearwort	**Ranunculus lingua**
Grande éclaire	Celandine	**Chelidonium**
Grande gentiane	Great yellow gentian	**Gentiana lutea**
Grande marguerite	Ox-eye-daisy	**Chrysanthemum leucanthemum**

136

Grande mauve	Common mallow	**Malva sylvestris**
Grand muflier	Common snapdragon	**Antirrhinum majus**
Grand orme	Common elm	**Ulmus procera**
Grande ortie	Stinging nettle	**Urtica dioica**
Grande pervenche	Greater periwinkle / Quater	**Vinca major**
Grande pimpernelle	Grass burnet	**Sanguisorba officinalis**
Grand plantain	Rat's tail plantain	**Plantago major**
Grande tayove	Giant elephant's ear / Taro	**Alocasia macrorrhiza**
Graptopetalum paraguayense	Mother of pearl plant	
		Graptopetalum paraguayense
Graptophyllum pictum	Caricature plant	**Graptophyllum pictum**
Graou	Mezereon	**Daphne mezereum**
Grassette commune	Common butterwort	**Pinguicula vulgaris**
Grassette à grandes fleurs	Giant butterwort	**Pinguicula grandiflora**
Grassette du Portugal	Pale butterwort	**Pinguicula lusitanica**
Grattau	Hedge parsley	**Torilis japonica**
Grémil	Lithospermum	**Lithospermum**
Grémil officinal	Common gromwell	**Lithospermum officinale**
Grémil pourpre-violet	Purple gromwell	**Lithospermum purpuro-caerulea**
Grenadier	Pomegranite	**Punica granatum**
Grenadier nain	Dwarf pomegranate	**Punica granatum nana**
Grevillea robusta	Silky oak	**Grevillea robusta**
Grisard	Grey poplar	**Populus canescens**
Griselinia littoralis	Broadleaf	**Griselinia littoralis**
Groseillier	Currant	**Ribes**
Groseillier des Alpes	Mountain currant	**Ribes rubrum**
Groseilleir doré	Buffalo currant	**Ribes odoratum**
Grosseillier de Barbades	Barbados gooseberry / Lemon vine	
		Pereskia aculeata
Groseillier à fleurs	Flowering currant	**Ribes sanguineum**
Groseillier à maquereau	Gooseberry currant	**Ribes uva-crispa**
Groseillier rouge	Red currant	**Ribes rubrum**
Groseillier sanguin	Flowering currant	**Ribes sanguineum**
Gros ail	Wild leek	**Allium ampeloprasum**
Gros minet	Hare's tail grass	**Lagurus ovatus**
Guele-de-loup	Common snapdragon /Snapdragon	**Antirrhinum majus**
Guele de tigre	Tiger-jaws	**Faucaria tigrina**
Guet maculé	Cuckoo pint / Lords and Ladies	**Arum maculatum**
Gui	Mistletoe	**Viscum album**
Guimauve hérisée	Rough mallow	**Althaea hirsuta**
Guimauve officinale	Marsh-mallow	**Althaea officinalis**
Guzmania monostachia	Striped torch	**Guzmania monostachia**

Gymnadénia a long éperon	Scented orchid	**Gymnadenia canopsea**
Gynure	Velvet plant	**Gynura aurantiaca**
Gypsophile	Gypsophila	**Gypsophila**
Gyroselle	Shooting stars	**Dodecatheon**

H

Habenaria à fleurs denses	Dense-flowered orchid	**Neotinea intacta**
Haemanthus albiflos	Paintbrush	**Haemanthus albiflos**
Haemanthus coccineus	Blood lily	**Haemanthus coccineus**
Hamamélide japonais	Japanese witch hazel	**Hamamelis japonicua**
Hamamélide velouté	Chinese witch hazel	**Hamamelis mollis**
Hamamélide virginiana	Virginia witch hazel	**Hamamelis virginiana**
Hardenbergia violacea	Australian sarsparilla / Coral pea / Vine lilac	
		Hardenbergia violacea
Hatiora salicornoides	Bottle plant / Drunkard's dream	**Hatiora salicornoides**
Hebe pinguifolia	Disk-leaved hebe	**Hebe pinguifolia**
Hédychie	Ginger lily	**Hedychium**
Hedychium coronarium	White ginger lily	**Hedychium coronarium**
Hélénie	Sneezewort	**Helenium**
Hélianthème	Rock rose	**Helianthemum**
Hélianthème des Appennines	White rock-rose	
		Helianthemum apenninum
Hélianthème blanchâtre	Hoary rock-rose	**Helianthemum canum**
Hélianthème commun	Common rock-rose	
		Helianthemum nummularium
Hélianthème à gouttes.	Annual rock-rose.	**Tuberaria guttata**
Helianthus salicifolius	Willow-leaved sunflower	**Helianthus salicifolius**
Helichrysum italicum	Curry plant	**Helichrysum italicum**
Heliconia	Lobster claws	**Heliconia**
Heliconia psittacorum	Parrot's flower	**Heliconia psittacorum**
Helictotrichon sempervirens	Blue oat grass	
		Helictotrichon sempervirens
Héliotrope d'hiver	Winter heliotrope	**Petasites fragrans**
Héliotrope de Pérou	Heliotrope arborescens	**Heliotrope arborescens**
Helonias bullata	Swamp pink	**Helonias bullata**
Hémérocalle	Day lily	**Hemerocallis**
Hémérocalle jaune	Yellow day lily	**Hemerocallis lilio-asphodelus**
Hemerocallis minor	Grass leaved daylily	**Hemerocallis minor**
Herbe à la bosse	Green hellebore	**Helleborus viridis**
Herbe aux chantres	Hedge mustard	**Sisymbrium officinale**
Herbe aux chats	Cat's valerian / Common valerian	**Valeriana officinalis**

138

Herbe aux chats	Catmint / Wild catmint	**Nephrolepis cordifolia**
Herbe aux écus	Moneywort	**Lysimachia nummularia aurea**
Herbe aux écus	Honesty	**Lunaria annua**
Herbe à l'esquinancie	Squinancywort	**Asperula cynanchia**
Herbe aux goutteux	Goat weed	**Aegopodium**
Herbe aux goutteux	Ground elder / Bishop's weed (In Scotland)	
		Aegopodium podagraria
Herbe aux goutteux panaché	Variegated Bishop's weed	
		Aegopodium podagraria 'Variegatum'
Harbe aux goutteux à feuilles panachées	Variegated gout weed	
		Aegopodium podagraria 'Variegatum'
Herbe de Guinée	Old witch grass	**Panicum capillare**
Herbe de grace	Herb of grace	**Ruta graveolens**
Herbe à mille trous Common	St. John's wort	**Hypericum perforatum**
Herbe aux mites	Moth mullein	**Verbascum blattaria**
Herbe aux mouches	Ploughman's spikenard	**Inula conyza**
Herbe de pampas	Pampass grass	**Cortaderia selloana**
Herbe de Parnasse	Grass of Parnassus	**Parnassia palustris**
Herbe aux perles Common	gromwell	**Lithospermum officinale**
Herbe à Robert	Herb Robert	**Geranium robertianum**
Herbe de Sainte-Barbe	Common winter-cress	**Barbarea vulgaris**
Herbe de St. Christophe	Baneberry	**Actaea**
Herbe de Saint-Fiacre	Heliotrope arborescens	**Heliotrope arborescens**
Herbe à la taupe Angels'	trumpets / Thorn-apple	**Datura stramonium**
Herbe aux turquoises	Japanese hyacinth	**Ophiopogon japonicus**
Herbe aux verrues	Celandine	**Chelidonium**
Herminium à un bulbe	Musk orchid	**Herminium monarchis**
Hermodactylus tuberosus	Widow iris	
		Hermodactylus tuberosus
Herniaire ciliée	Rupture-wort	**Herniaria ciliata**
Herniaire glabre	Smooth rupture-wort	**Herniaria glabra**
Herschfeldie grisâtre	Hoary mustard	**Hirschfeldia incana**
Heteromeles arbutifolia	Christmas berry / Toyo	
		Heteromeles arbutifolia
Hêtre	Beech	**Fagus sylvatica**
Hêtre d'Amérique	American beech	**Fagus grandifolia**
Hêtre antarctica	Antarctic beech / Nirre	**Nothofagus antarctica**
Hêtre d'Orient	Oriental beech	**Fagus orientalis**
Hêtre pleureur	Weeping beech	**Fagus sylvatica pendula**
Hêtre pourpré	Copper beech	**Fagus sylvatica purpurea**
Heuchera	Alum root	**Heuchera**
Hibiscus mutabilis	Confederate rose / Cotton rose	**Hibiscus mutabilis**

Hibiscus trionum	Flower of the hour	**Hibiscus trionum**
Hickory	Hickory	**Carya**
Hidalgoa	Climbing dahlia	**Hidalgoa**
Hièble	Dwarf elder	**Sambucus ebulus**
Hinoki	Hinoki cypress	**Chamaecyparis obtusa**
Hippocrépis à toupet	Horseshoe vetch	**Hippocrepis comosa**
Hoheria populnea	Lace-bark	**Hoheria populnea**
Hoheria sexstylosa	Ribbon wood	**Hoheria sexstylosa**
Holcus mollis	Creeping soft grass	**Holcus mollis**
Holcus mollis variegatus	Variegated creeping soft grass	

Holcus mollis 'Variegatus'

Holmskioldia sanguinea   Chinese hat plant / Mandarin's hat plant

Holmskioldia sanguinea

Homogyne des Alpes   Alpine coltsfoot / Purple coltsfoot

Homogyne alpina

Hortensia	Hydrangea	**Hydrangea**
Hortensia grimpant Climbing hydrangea		**Hydrangea anomala petiolaris**
Hortensia à feuilles de chêne Oak leafed hydrangea		**Hydrangea quercifolia**
Horminum pyrenaicum	Dragon's mouth	**Horminum pyrenaicum**
Hosta hypoleuca	White-backed hosta	**Hosta hypoleuca**
Hosta plantaginea	August lily	**Hosta plantaginea**
Hottonie des marais	Water violet	**Hottonia palustris**
Houblon	Hop	**Humulus lupulus**
Houx	Holly	**Ilex aquifolium**
Houx d'Amérique	American holly	**Ilex opaca**
Houx aquiflium flavescens	Moonlight holly	**Ilex aquiflium flavescens**
Houx aquifolium 'Watereriana'	Waterer's gold holly	

‘   **Ilex aquiflium 'Wateriana'**

Houx aquifolium 'Argentea Marginata'   Silver margin holly

Ilex aquifolium 'Argentea Marginata'

Houx cornu	Horned holly	**Ilex cornuta**
Houx crenata	Box-leafed holly / Japanese holly	**Ilex crenata**
Houx dipyrena	Himalayan holly	**Ilex dipyrena**
Houx frelon	Butcher's broom	**Ruscus aculeatus**
Houx glabra	Inkberry	**Ilex glabra**
Houx des hérissons	Hedgehog holly	**Ilex aquifolium 'Ferox'**
Houx des hérissons argenté	Silver hedgehog holly	

Ilex aquifolium 'Ferox argentea'

Houx laevigata	Smooth winterberry	**Ilex laevigata**
Houx latifolia	Tarajo holly	**Ilex latifolia**
Houx x meserveae	Blue holly	**Ilex x meserveae**
Houx verticillata	Winterberry	**Ilex verticillata**

Howeée Sentry palm / Thatch-leaf plant / Paradise palm		**Howea forsteriana**
Hoya carnosa	Wax plant	**Hoya carnosa**
Huernia zebrina	Owl eyes	**Huernia zebrina**
Humea elegans	Incense plant	**Humea elegans**
Hunnemannia fumariifolia	Mexican tulip poppy	
		Hunnemannia fumariifolia
Hutchinsie des pierres	Hutchinsia	**Hornungia peteraea**
Hydrocharis des Grenouilles	Frog-bit	**Hydrocharis morsus-ranae**
Hydrocléis nymphoides	Water poppy	**Hydrocleys nymphoides**
Hylocereus undatus	Queen-of-the-night	**Hylocereus undatus**
Hymenocallis narcissiflora	Peruvian daffodil	
		Hymenocallis narcissiflora
Hymenosporum flavum	Native Australian frangipani	
		Hymenosporum flavum
Hypoestes phyllostachya	Freckle face / Polka-dot plant	
		Hypoestes phyllostachya
Hysope officinale	Hyssop	**Hyssopus officinalis**

I

Iberis amer	Wild candytuft	**Iberis amara**
If	Yew	**Taxus baccata**
If d'Irlande	Irish yew	**Taxus baccata fastigiata**
If du Japon	Japanese yew	**Taxus cuspidata**
Igname	Ornamental yam	**Dioscorea discolor**
llécèbre verticillé	Coral necklace	**Illecebrum verticillatum**
Illicium floridanum	Purple anise	**Illicium floridanum**
Immortelle	Garland flower	**Helichrysum**
Immortelle annuelle	Immortelle	**Xeranthemum annuum**
Immortelle blanche	Pearl everlasting	**Annaphalis margaritacea**
Immortelle bleue	Sea lavender / Statice	**Limonium vulgare**
Immortelle à bractées	Everlasting flower / Strawflower	
		Helichrysum bracteatum
Immortelle de Virginia	Pearl everlasting	**Annaphalis margaritace**
Impatiente	Balsam	**Impatiens balsamina**
Impatiente	Touch -me-not	**Impatiens noli-tangere**
Indigotier	Indigofera	**Indigofera**
Inule aunée	Elecampane	**Inula helenium**
Inule faux-crithmum	Golden samphire	**Inula crithmoides**
Inule à feuilles de saule	Irish fleabane	**Inula salicina**
Inule squarreuse	Ploughman's spikenard	**Inula conyza**

141

Ionopsidium acaule	Violet cress	**Ionopsidium acaule**
Ipomée	Ipomoea	**Ipomoea**
Ipomoea alba	Moon flower	**Ipomoea alba**
Ipomoea coccinea	Red morning glory / Star ipomoea	
		Ipomoea coccinea
Ipomoea x mulitfida	Cardinal climber / Hearts-and-honey vine	
		Ipomoea x multifida
Ipomoea quamoclit	Cupid flower / Cypress vine	**Ipomoea quamoclit**
Iresine herbistii	Beefsteak plant	**Iresine herbistii**
Iresine lindenii	Blood leaf	**Iresine lindenii**
Iris	Iris	**Iris**
Iris d'Angleterre	English iris	**Iris latifolia**
Iris bâtard	Butterfly iris	**Iris spuria**
Iris discolor	Willd iris	**Iris discolor**
Iris ensata	Japanese flag	**Iris ensata**
Iris evansia	Japanese roof iris	**Iris tectorum**
Iris faux-acore	Yellow flag	**Iris pseudacorus**
Iris fétide	Gladwin	**Iris foetidissima**
Iris fétide	Roast-beef plant	**Iris foetidissima**
Iris de Florence	Dalmatian iris	**Iris pallida**
Iris gigot	Stinking iris	**Iris foetidissima**
Iris des marais	Yellow flag	**Iris pseudacorus**
Iris missouriensis	Missouri flag	**Iris missouriensis**
Iris à parfum	Dalmatian iris	**Iris pallida**
Iris pumila	Dwarf bearded iris	**Iris pumila**
Iris setosa	Bristle pointed iris	**Iris setosa**
Iris de Sibérie	Siberian flag	**Iris sibirica**
Iris susiana	Mourning widow	**Iris de Suse**
Iris tigré	Belamcanda	**Belamcanda**
Iris unguicularis	Algerian iris / Algerian winter iris / Winter iris	
		Iris unguicularis
Iris variegata	Variegated iris	**Iris variegata**
Iris versicolore	Blue flag /Purple water flag	**Iris versicolor**

J

Jacinthe	Hyacinth	**Hyacinthus**
Jacinthe des bois	Bluebell / English bluebell	**Hyacinthoides non-scripta**
Jacinthe du Cap	Summer hyacinth	**Galtonia candicans**
Jacinthe d'eau	Water hyacinth	**Eichornia crassipes**
Jacinthe d'Espagne	Spanish bluebell	**Hyacinthoides hispanica**
Jacinthe d'Espagne	Spanish bluebell	**Brimeura amethystina**

Jacinthe des pyrénées	Spanish bluebell	**Brimeura amethystina**
Jalousie	Sweet William	**Dianthus barbatus**
Jaquier noir	Black Jack oak	**Quercus marilandica**
Jasione des montagnes	Sheep's bit	**Jasione montana**
Jasmin	Jasmine	**Jasminium**
Jasmin du Cap	Cape jasmine	**Gardenia jasminoides**
Jasmin commun	Jessamine	**Jasminium officinale**
Jasmin d'Espagne	Royal jasmine / Spanish jasmine	**Jasminium grandiflorum**
Jasmin étoilé	Confederate jasmine / Star jasmine	**Trachelospermum jasminoides**
Jasmin d'hiver	Winter jasmine	**Jasminium nudiflorum**
Jasmin d'Italie	Yellow jasmine	**Jasminium humile**
Jasmin trompette	Trumpet vine / Trumpet creeper	**Campsis radicans**
Jasminium mesneyi	Primrose jasmine	**Jasminium mesneyi**
Jeannette	Callous-fruited water dropwort	**Oenanthe pimpinelloidesa**
Jeannette	Poet's daffodil	**Narcissus poeticus**
Jonc épars	Corkscrew rush	**Juncus effusus spiralis**
Jonc fleuri	Flowering rush	**Butomus umbellatus**
Joncinelle	Pipewort	**Eriocaulon aquaticum**
Jonquille	Lent Lily	**Narcissus pseudonarcissus**
Jonquine	Bullrush	**Scirpus**
Joubarbe	Houseleek	**Sempervivum**
Joubarbe toile d'araigné	Cobweb houseleek / Spider web houseleek	**Sempervivum arachnoideum**
Joubarbe des toits	Common houseleek / Roof houseleek	**Sempervivum tectorum**
Julienne des dames	Dame's violet / Sweet rocket	**Hesperis matronalis**
Julienne des jardins	Dame's violet / Sweet rocket	**Hesperis matronalis**
Julienne de Mahon	Virginia stock	**Malcolmia maritima**
Jusquiame noire	Henbane	**Hyoscyamus niger**
Justicia	Snake bush	**Justicia**

K

Kaki	Kaki / Persimmon	**Diospyros kaki**
Kalanchoe blossfeldiana	Flaming Katy	**Kalanchoe blossfeldiana**
Kalanchoe diagremontiana	Mexican hat plant	**Kalanchoe diagremontiana**
Kalanchoe fedtschenkoi	South American air plant	**Kalanchoe fedtschenko**
Kennedia nigricans	Black bean	**Kennedia nigricans**
Kickxie	Fluellin	**Kicksia**
Kigélie	Sausage tree	**Kigelia pinnata**

Knautie des champs	Field scabious	**Knautia arvensis**
Knightia excelsa	New Zealand honeysuckle / Rewarewa	
		Knightia excelsa
Kniphofia / Tritome	Red-hot poker / Torch lily	**Kniphofia**
Kochie	Burning bush / Summer cypress	**Kochia scoparia trichophylla**
Kiwi	Chinese gooseberry / Kiwi fruit	**Actinidia chinensis**
Koenigia d'Islande	Iceland purslane	**Koenigia islandica**
Kolkwitzia amabilis	Beauty bush	**Kolkwitzia amabilis**

L

Laburnum x wartereii 'Vossii'	Voss's laburnum	
		Laburnum x warterei 'Vossii'
Lagerstoemia speciosa	Queen's crape myrtle	
		Lagerstroemia speciosa
Lagunaria patersonii	Norfolk Island hibiscus / Queensland pyramidial tree	
		Lagunaria patersonii
Laîche buchananii	Leatherleaf sedge	**Carex buchananii**
Laîche en Gazon	Tufted sedge	**Carex elata**
Laîche grayi	Mace sedge	**Carex grayi**
Laîche pendante	Pendulous sedge	**Carex pendula**
Laiteron	Sow thistle	**Sonchus**
Laiteron des champs	Corn sow-thistle	**Sonchus arvensis**
Laiteron rude	Prickly sow-thistle	**Sonchus asper**
Laiteron potager	Smooth sow-thistle	**Sonchus oleraceus**
Laiteron des marais	Marsh sow-thistle	**Sonchus palustris**
Laitue des Alpes	Alpine sow-thistle / Mountain sow thistle	
		Cicerbita alpina
Laitue d'eau	Water lettuce	**Pistia stratiotes**
Laitue à feuilles de saulle	Least lettuce	**Lactuca saligna**
Laitue à grandes feuilles	Blue sow-thistle	**Cicerbita macrophylla**
Laitue des murs	Wall lettuce	**Mycelis muralis**
Laitue scariole	Prickly lettuce	**Lactuca serriola**
Laitue vireuse	Greater prickly lettuce	**Lactuca virosa**
Lamarckie	Golden top	**Lamarckia aurea**
Lamier	Dead nettle	**Lamium**
Lamier blanc	White dead-nettle	**Lamium album**
Lamier amplexicaule	Henbit	**Lamium amplexicaule**
Lamier hybride	Cut-leaved dead-nettle	**Lamium hybridum**
Lamier maculé	Spotted dead-nettle	**Lamium maculatum**
Lamier pourpre	Red dead-nettle	**Lamium purpureum**

Lampourde épineuse.	Spiny cocklebur.	**Xanthium spinosum**
Langue de bœuf	Hart's tongue fern	**Phyllitis scolopendrium**
Langue de cerf	Hart's tongue fern	**Phyllitis scolopendrium**
Langue de chien	Great hound's tongue	**Cynoglossum germanicum**
Langue-de-chien	Hound's tongue	**Cynoglossum officinale**
Lanterne japonais	Winter cherry	**Physalis alkekengi**
Lanterne japonaise	Strawberry tomato	**Physalis peruviana**
Lapageria rosea	Chilean bellflower / Copihue	**Lapageria rosea**
Lapsane commune	Nipplewort	**Lapsana communis**
Larmes de Job	Job's tears	**Coix lachryma-jobi**
Larée	Creosote bush	**Larrea**
Laurelia serrata	Chilean laurel	**Laurelia serrata**
Laurier	Bay tree / Laurel	**Laurus**
Laurier d'Alexandrie	Alexandrian laurel	**Danae racemosa**
Laurier américain	Calico bush	**Kalmia latifolia**
Laurier benzoin	Benjamin / Spiceberry	**Lindera benzoin**
Lauréole des bois	Spurge laurel	**Daphne laureola**
Laurier cerise	Cherry laurel	**Prunus laureocerasus**
Laurier des montagnes	Calico bush	**Kalmia latifolia**
Laurier des moutons	Sheep laurel	**Kalmia angustifolia**
Laurier noble	Bay laurel	**Laurus nobilis**
Laurier du Portugal	Portugal laurel	**Prunus lusitanica**
Laurier rose	Oleander	**Nerium oleander**
Laurier de Staint- Antoine	Rose-bay willow-herb	

Chamaenerion angustifolium

Laurier de Saint-Antoine album   White rosebay

Epilobium angustifolium album

Lauirer-sauce	Sweet bay	**Laurus nobilis**
Laurier rose à fleurs jaune	Yellow oleander	**Thevetia peruviana**
Laurier-tin,	Laurustinus.	**Viburnum tinus**
Lavande	Lavender	**Lavandula**
Lavande dentata	French lavender	**Lavendula dentata**
Lavande de mer	Sea lavender / Statice	**Limonium vulgare**
Lavande stoechas	French lavender	**Lavendula stoechas**
Lavatère arborescente	Tree mallow	**Lavatera arborea**
Lavatère de crète	Cornish mallow	**Lavatera cretica**
Lavatère à grandes fleurs	Lavatera trimestris	**Lavatera trimestris**
Lavatère d'Hyères	Lavatera olbia	**Lavatera olbia**
Layie platyglossa	Tidy tips	**Layia platyglossa**
Lemaireocereus marginatus	Organ pipe cactus	

Lemaireocereus marginatus

Lenticule	Duck weed	**Lemna**

145

Lentille d'eau bossue	Fat duckweed	**Lemna gibba**
Lentille d'eau trilobée	Ivy duckweed	**Lemna trisulca**
Lentisque	Mastic tree	**Pistacia lentiscus**
Leptospermum scoparium	Manuka / New Zealand tea tree	
		Leptospermum scoparium
Leucocoryne ixiodes	Glory-of-the-sun	**Leucocoryne ixiodes**
Lewisia rediviva	Bitter root	**Lewisia rediviva**
Leycesteria formosa	Himalayan honeysuckle	**Leycesteria formosa**
Liardier	Black poplar	**Populus nigra**
Liatride	Gay feathers	**Liatris**
Liatris pycnostachya	Kansas gay feather	**Liatris pycnostachya**
Libertia grandiflora	New Zealand satin flower	**Libertia grandiflora**
Libocedrus decurrens	Incense cedar	**Calocedrus decurrens**
Lierre	Ivy	**Hedera**
Lierre des Canaries	Canary Island Ivy	**Hedera canariensis**
Lierre colchica 'Sulphur Heart'	Paddy's pride	
		Hedera colchica 'Sulphur Heart'
Lierre helix deltoides	Shield ivy / Sweetheart ivy	**Hedera helix 'Deltoides'**
Lierre helix digitata	Finger-leafed ivy	**Hedera helix digitata**
Lierre helix pedata	Bird's foot ivy	**Hedera helix pedata**
Lierre d'Irlande	Irish ivy	**Hedera helix var.hibernica**
Lierre japonais	Boston ivy / Japanese ivy	**Parthenocissus tricuspidata**
Lierre de Japon	Japanese ivy	**Hedera rhombea**
Lierre nepalensis	Nepalese ivy	**Hedera nepalensis**
Lierre de Perse	Persian ivy	**Hedera colchica**
Lierre de Perse	Elephant's ears	**Hedera colchica 'Dentata'**
Lierre terrestre	Ground ivy	**Glechoma hederacea**
Lierre terrestre panachée	Variegated ground ivy	
		Glechoma hederacea 'Variegata'
Lilas	Lilac	**Syringa**
Lilas Varin	Rouen lilac	**Syringa x chinensis**
Lilas d'Espagne	Goat's rue	**Galega officinalis**
Lilas d'été	Crape myrtle	**Lagerstroemia indica**
Lilas de l'Himalaya	Himalayan lilac	**Syringa emodi**
Lilas des Indes	Pride of India	**Lagerstroemia speciosa**
Lilas de Perse	Persian lilac	**Syringa persica**
Limnanthe douglasii	Poached egg plant / Meadow foam	
		Limnanthes douglasii
Limnanthème faux-nénuphar	Fringed water lily / Water fringe	
		Nymphoides peltata
Limoselle aquatique	Common mudwort	**Limosella aquatica**
Lin	Flax	**Linum**

Lin cultivé	Cultivated flax	**Linum usitatissimum**
Lin à feuilles étroites	Pale flax	**Linum bienne**
Lin jaune	Golden flax / Yellow flax	**Linum flavum**
Lin de Nouvelle-Zélande	New Zealand flax	**Phormium tenax**
Lin purgatif	Fairy flax	**Linum catharticum**
Lin vivace	Perennial flax	**Linum perenne**
Linaire	Toadflax	**Linaria**
Linaire des Alpes	Alpine toadflax	**Linaria alpina**
Linaire bâtarde velvote	Round-leaved fluellen	**Kickxia spuria**
Linaire commune	Common toadflax	**Linaria vulgaris**
Linaire couchée	Prostrate toadflax	**Linaria supina**
Linaire cymbalaire	Ivy-leafed toadflax / Kenilworth ivy	**Cymbalaria muralis**
Linaire dalmatica	Dalmatian toadflax	**Linaria genistifolia dalmatica**
Linaire élatine	Sharp-leaved fluellen	**Kickxia elatine**
Linaire de Pellisier	Jersey toadflax	**Linaria pelisseriana**
Linaire pourprée	Purple toadflax	**Linaria purpurea**
Linaire rampante	Pale toadflax	**Linaria repens**
Linaire des sables	French toadflax	**Linaria arenaria**
Lindheimera texana	Star daisy	**Lindheimera texana**
Linée boréale	Twin flower	**Linnaea borealis**
Liondent d'automne	Autumn hawkbit	**Leontodon autumnalis**
Liondent hispide	Greater hawkbit	**Leontodon hispidus**
Liparis de Loesel	Fen orchid	**Liparis loeselii**
Liquidambar orientalis	Oriental sweet gum	**Liriodendron tulipifera**
Liriope	Lilyturf	**Liriope**
Lis	Lily	**Lilium**
Lis blanc	Madonna lily	**Lilium candidum**
Lis bulbiferum	Fire lily / Orange lily	**Lilium bulbiferum**
Lis canadense	Canada lily / Meadow lily / Wild yellow lily	**Lilium canadense**
Lis chalcedonicum	Scarlet turk's cap lily	**Lilium chalcedonicum**
Lis doré du Japon	Golden-rayed lily of Japan	**Lilium auratum**
Lis d'eau	Water lily	**Nymphaea**
Lis de Guernsey	Guernsey lily	**Nerine sarniensis**
Lis jaune	Yellow day lily	**Hemerocallis lilio-asphodelus**
Lis jaune	Fulvous day lily / Tawny day lily	**Hemerocallis fulva**
Lis à longues fleurs	Bermuda lily / Easter lily / White trumpet lily	**Lilium longiflorum**
Lis mackliniae	Manipur lily	**Lilium mackliniae**
Lis de la Madone	Madonna lily	**Lilium candidum**
Lis martagon	Martagon lily / Turkscap lily	**Lilium martagon**
Lis matthiola	Sea daffodil	**Pancratium maritimum**

Lis narcisse	Sea daffodil	**Pancratium maritimum**
Lis pardalinum	Leopard Lily / Panther lily	**Lilium pardalinum**
Lis des Pyrénées	Pyrenean lily / Yellow turkscap lily	
		Lilium pyrenaicum
Lis royal	Regal lily	**Lilium regale**
Lis de Saint-Bruno	St. Bruno's lily	**Paradisea liliastrum**
Lis de la Saint-Jean	Madonna lily	**Lilium candidum**
Lis superbum	Swamp lily	**Lilium superbum**
Lis x testaceum	Nankeen lily	**Lilium couleur Isabelle**
Lis tigré	Tiger lily	**Lilium lancifolium**
Liseron d'Amérique	American bindweed	**Calystegia silvatica**
Liseron des champs	Field bindweed	**Convolvulus arvensis**
Liseron des haies	Great bindweed	**Calystegia sepium**
Liseron de mer	Sea bindweed	**Calystegia soldanella**
Listère	Twayblades	**Listera**
Listère à feuilles cordées	Lesser twayblades	**Listera cordata**
Listère à feuilles ovales	Common twayblades	**Listera ovata**
Lithocarpus densiflorus	Tanbark oak	**Lithocarpus densiflorus**
Littorelle uniflore	Shore-weed	**Littorella uniflora**
Livèche d'Écosse	Lovage	**Ligusticum scoticum**
Livistona australis	Australian cabbage palm / Gippsland fountain palm	
		Livistona australis
Lloydie tardive	Snowdon lily	**Lloydia serotina**
Lobélie brûlante	Heath lobelia	**Lobelia urens**
Lobélie cardinalis	Cardinal flower	**Lobelia cardinalis**
Lobélie de Dortmann	Water lobelia	**Lobelia dortmanna**
Lomatium nudicaule	Pestle parsnip	**Lomatium nudicaule**
Loquat	Loquat	**Eriobotrya japonica**
Lotier berthelotii	Coral gem	**Lotus berthelotii**
Lotier corniculé	Common birdsfoot trefoil	**Lotus corniculatus**
Lotus	Lotus	**Nelumbo**
Lotus des Indes	Sacred lotus	**Nelumbo nucifera**
Lotus jaune d'Amérique	American lotus	**Nelumbo lutea**
Ludwigia des marais	Hampshire purslane	**Ludwigia palustris**
Lupin	Lupin	**Lupinus**
Lupin arborescent	Tree lupin	**Lupinus arboreus**
Lupin d'Écosse	Scottish lupin	**Lupinus nootkatensis**
Luzerne d'Arabie	Spotted medick	**Medicago arabica**
Luzerne arborescente	Moon trefoil / Tree medick	**Medicago arborea**
Luzerne cultivée	Lucerne	**Medicago sativa**
Luzerne lupuline	Black medick	**Medicago lupulina**
Luzerne naine	Bur medick	**Medicago minima**

Luzule	Woodrush	**Luzula**
Luzule nivea	Snowy woodrush	**Luzula nivea**
Luzule sylvatica	Greater woodrush	**Luzula sylvatica**
Lyciet jasminoïdes	Duke of Argyll's tea tree / Chinese box thorn	
		Lycium barbarum
Lycope d'Europe	Gipsywort	**Lycopus europaeus**
Lycoris aurea	Golden spider lily	**Lycoris aurea**
Lycoris radiata	Red spider lily	**Lycoris radiata**
Lygodium japonicum	Japanese climbing fern	**Lygodium japonicum**
Lyonothamnus floribundus	Catalina ironwood	**Lyonothamnus floribundus**
Lycopode du jardinier	Selaginella kraussiana	**Selaginella kraussiana**
Lysichiton americanus	Yellow skunk cabbage	**Lysichiton americanus**
Lysimaque des bois	Yellow pimpernel	**Lysimachia nemorum**
Lysimaque commune	Yellow loosestrife	**Lysimachia vulgaris**
Lysimaque nummulaire	Creeping Jenny	**Lysimachia nummularia**
Lysimaque punctata	Garden loosestrife	**Lysimachia punctata**
Lysimaque rouge	Purple loosestrife	**Lythrum salicaria**

M

Macadamia integrifolia	Macadamia nut / Queensland nut	
		Macadamia integrifolia
Maceron cultivé	Alexanders	**Smyrnium olusatrum**
Macfadyena unguis-cati	Cat's claw	**Macfadyena unguis-cati**
Mâche doucette.	Cornsalad.	**Valerianella locusta**
Macre.	Jesuit's nut / Water Chestnut.	**Trapa natans**
Macusson	Fyfield pea	**Lathyrus tuberosus**
Madère	Taro	**Colocasia esculenta**
Magnolia étoilé	Star magnolia	**Magnolia stellata**
Magnolia à feuilles acuminées	Cucumber tree	**Magnolia acuminata**
Magnolia à grandea fleurs	Bull bay	**Magnolia grandiflora**
Magnolia hypoleuca	Japanese big leaf magnolia	**Magnolia hypoleuca**
Magnolia parasol	Magnolia tripetala	**Magnolia tripetala**
Magnolia salicilfolia	Willow-leaved magnolia	**Magnolia salicilfolia**
Magnolia de Virginie	Sweet bay magnoliia	**Magnolia virginiana**
Magnolia de Yulan	Lily / Yulan	**Magnolia denudata**
Mahonia à feuilles de houx	Oregon grape	**Mahonia aquifolium**
Mahonille	Virginia stock	**Malcolmia maritima**
Mai	Thorn	**Crataegus**
Maianthème à deux feuilles	May lily	**Maianthemum bifolium**
Maïs	Indian corn / Maize.	**Zea mays**

Maïs	Ornamental maize / Sweet corn.	**Zea mays**
Malaxis des marais	Bog orchid	**Hammarbya paludosa**
Malus hupehensis	Hupeh crab	**Malus hupehensis**
Malus x purpurea	Purple crab	**Malus x purpurea**
Malvaviscus arboreus	Sleepy mallow	**Malvaviscus arboreus**
Mammillaria	Pincushion cactus	**Mammillaria**
Mammillaria boscasana	Powder-puff cactus	**Mammillaria boscasana**
Mammillaria candida	Snowball pincushion	**Mammillaria candida**
Mammillaria elongata	Lace cactus	**Mammillaria elongata**
Mammillaria hahniana	Old lady cactus	**Mammillaria hahniana**
Mammillaria prolifera	Strawberry cactus	**Mammillaria prolifera**
Mammillaria zeilmanniana	Rose pincushion	**Mammillaria zeilmanniana**
Mandevilla laxa	Chilean jasmine	**Mandevilla laxa**
Mandragore	Mandrake	**Mandragora**
Manettia cordifolia	Firecracker vine	**Manettia cordifolia**
Manettia inflata	Brazilian firecracker	**Manettia inflata**
Maranta leuconeura 'Erythroneura'	Herringbone plant	**Maranta leuconeura 'Erythroneura'**
Maranta leuconeura kerchoviana	Rabbit tracks	**Maranta leuconeura kerchoviana**
Maranta leuconeura	Prayer plant	**Maranta leuconeura**
Margousier azedarach	Bead tree / Persian lilac	**Melia azedarach**
Margueritte d'automne	Chrysanthemum rubellum	**Chrysanthemum rubellum**
Margueritte du Cap	Blue margueritte	**Felicia amelloides**
Marguerite dorée	Corn marigold	**Chrysanthemum segetum**
Margyricarpus pinnatus	Pearl berry	**Margyricarpus pinnatus**
Marjolaine	Marjoram	**Origanum vulgare**
Marjolaine bâtarde	Marjoram	**Origanum vulgare**
Marjolaine origan	Marjoram	**Origanum vulgare**
Marronnier	Buckeye / Chestnut	**Aesculus**
Marronnier	Horse chestnut	**Aesculus hippocastanum**
Marronier de Californie	California nutmeg	**Aesculus californica**
Marronnier de Chine	Chinese horse chestnut	**Aesculus chinensis**
Marronnier à fleurs rouges	Red horsechestnut	**Aesculus x carnea**
Marronnier à fruit turbiné	Japanese horse chestnut	**Aesculus turbinata**
Marronnier jaune	Sweet buckeye / Yellow buckeye	**Aesculus flava**
Marronnier glabra	Ohio buckeye	**Aesculus glabra**
Marronnier d'Inde	Indian horse chestnut	**Aesculus indica**
Marronnier paviflora	Bottlebrush buckeye	**Aesculus parviflora**
Marrube commun	White horehound	**Marrubium vulgare**
Martynia annua	Unicorn plant	**Martynia annua**

Marsault	Pussy willow	**Salix caprea**
Marsault Kilmarnock	Kilmarnock willow	**Salix caprea Kilmarnock**
Marrube	Hoarhound	**Marrubium**
Massette à feuilles étroites	Lesser bulrush	**Typha angustifolia**
Massette à larges feuilles	False bulrush	**Typha latifolia**
Matricaire maritime	Scentless mayweed.	**Matricaria inodora**
Matteuccia struthiopteris	Ostrich fern / Ostrich feather fern	
		Matteuccia struthiopteris
Mauve	Mallow	**Malva**
Mauve du jardin	Tree mallow	**Lavatera arborea**
Mauve musquée	Musk mallow	**Malva moschata**
Mauve sylvestre	Common mallow	**Malva sylvestris**
Maytenus boaria	Maiten	**Maytenus boaria**
Meconopsis napaulensis	Satin poppy	**Meconopsis napaulensis**
Méconopsis du pays de Galles	Welsh poppy	**Meconopsis cambrica**
Mélampyre des champs	Field cow-wheat	**Melampyrum arvense**
Mélampyre des prés	Crested cow-wheat	**Melampyrum cristatum**
Mélampyre des bois	Small cow-wheat	**Melampyrum sylvaticum**
Melaneuca amarillaris	Bracelet honey myrtle	**Melaneuca amarillaris**
Melaleuca elliptica	Granite bottlebrush	**Melaleuca elliptica**
Melaleuca nesophylla	Western tea-myrtle	**Melaleuca nesophylla**
Melaleuca quinquenervia	Paper bark tree	**Melaleuca quinquenervia**
Melaleuca squarrosa	Scented paper-bark	**Melaleuca squarrosa**
Méléagre	Snake's head fritillery	**Fritillaria meleagris**
Mélèze de Europe	European larch	**Larix decidua**
Mélèze du Japon	Japanese larch	**Larix kaempferi**
Mélianthe	Honey bush	**Melianthus major**
Melica altissima	Tall melic	**Melica altissima**
Melicytus ramiflorus	Mahoe / Whiteywood	**Melicytus ramiflorus**
Mélèze doré	Golden larch	**Pseudolarix amabilis**
Mélilot blanc	White melilot	**Melilotus alba**
Mélilot élevé	Golden melilot	**Melilotus altissima**
Mélilot des Indes	Small-flowered melilot	**Melilotus indica**
Mélilot officinal	Common melilot	**Melilotus officinalis**
Mélique	Siberian melic	**Melica altissima**
Mélisse officinale	Balm	**Melissa officinalis**
Mélitte	Bastard balm	**Melittis**
Menisperme	Moonseed	**Menispermum**
Menispermum canadense	Canada moonseed / Yellow parilla	
		Menispermum canadense
Menthe	Mint	**Mentha**
Menthe aquatique	Water mint	**Mentha aquatica**

Menthe de Corse	Corsican mint	**Mentha requienii**
Menthe en épi	Spear-mint	**Mentha spicata**
Menthe à feuilles rondes	Apple mint	**Mentha suavolens**
Menthe poivrée	Peppermint	**Mentha x piperita**
Menthe poivrée	Eau-de-Cologne mint	**Mentha piperita 'Citrata'**
Menthe pouliot	Pennyroyal	**Mentha pulegium**
Mentha suavolens varieg.	Variegated apple mint	**Mentha suavolens varieg.**
Mercuriale annuelle	Annual mercury	**Mercurialis annua**
Mercuriale des bois	Dog's mercury	**Mercurialis perennis**
Merremia tuberosa	Wood rose / Yellow morning glory	
		Merremia tuberosa
Meryta sinclairii	Puka	**Meryta sinclairii**
Metassequoia glyptostroboides	Dawn redwood	
		Metassequoia glyptostroboides
Metrosiderus excelsa	New Zealand Christmas tree / Pohutukawa	
		Metrosiderus excelsa
Méon	Baldmoney	**Meum athamanticum**
Milium effusum	Wood millet	**Milium effusum**
Miltonia	Pansy orchid	**Miltonopsis**
Merisier des oiseaux	Gean / Wild cherry	**Prunus avium**
Mignonette	Mignonette	**Reseda**
Millepertuis	St John's-wort	**Hypericum**
Millepertuis couché	Trailing St. John's wort	**Hypericum humifusum**
Millepertuis élégant	Elegant St. John's wort	**Hypericum pulchrum**
Millepertuis à grandes fleurs	Aaron's beard / Rose of Sharon	
		Hypericum calycinum
Millepertuis de montagne	Pale St. John's wort	**Hypericum montanum**
Millepertuis perforé	Common St. John's wort	**Hypericum perforatum**
Millepertuis à quatre ailes	Square St. John's wort	**Hypericum tetrapterum**
Millepertuis velu	Hairy St. John's wort	**Hypericum hirsutum**
Millet à grappes	Foxtail millet	**Setaria italica**
Millet d'Italie	Foxtail millet	**Setaria italica**
Mimosa.	Mimosa.	**Acacia**
Mimosa couteau	Knife-leaf wattle	**Acacia cultriformis**
Mimosa	Silver wattle	**Acacia dealbata**
Mimulus	Monkey musk	**Mimulus**
Mimulus luteus	Yellow musk	**Mimulus luteus**
Mimulus musqué	Musk	**Mimulus moschatus**
Mimule tacheté	Monkey flower	**Mimulus guttatus**
Minette	Black medick	**Medicago minima**
Minuartia rougeâtre	Red sandwort	**Minuartia rubella**
Minuartia raide	Teesdale sandwort	**Minuartia stricta**

Minuartia du printemps	Spring sandwort	**Minuartia verna**
Miroir de Vénus	Venus's looking-glass	**Legousia hybrida**
Miscanthus saccharifolia	Amur silver grass	**Miscanthus saccharifolia**
Micocoulier de Provence	Nettle tree	**Celtis australis**
Micocoulier de Virginie	Hackberry	**Celtis occidentalis**
Misère	Silver inch plant	**Tradescantia zebrina**
Mitchella repens	Partridge berry	**Mitchella repens**
Mitre d'évêque	Bishop's cap / Bishop's mitre	**Astrophytum myriostigma**
Moehringie à troisnervures	Three-veined sandwort	**Moehringia triniveria**
Moenchia dresé	Dwarf chickweed	**Moenchia erecta**
Molène	Mullein	**Verbascum**
Molène blattaire	Moth mullein	**Verbascum blattaria**
Molène fausse-blattaire	Large flowered mullein	**Verbascum virgatum**
Molène faux-phlomide	Orange mullein	**Verbascum phlomoides**
Molène lychnide	White mullein	**Verbascum lychnitis**
Molène noire	Dark mullein	**Verbascum nigrum**
Molène pulvérulente	Hoary mullein.	**Verbascum pulverolentum**
Molinia caerulea 'Variegata'	Variegated purple moor grass	**Molinia caerulea 'Varieg.**
Monarde	Bergamot	**Monarda**
Monarde pourprea	Bee Balm	**Monarda didyma**
Monnayère	Honesty	**Lunaria annua**
Monnai du Pape	Honesty	**Lunaria annua**
Monotrope sucepin	Yellow birdsnest	**Monotropa hypopitys**
Monstera acuminata	Shingle plant	**Monstera acuminata**
Monstera deliciosa	Swiss cheese plant	**Monstera deliciosa**
Montbretia	Montbretia	**Crocosmia x crocosmiflora**
Montie des fontaines	Blinks	**Montia fontana**
Montie perfolée	Spring beauty	**Claytonia virginica / perfiolata**
Montie de Sibérie	Pink purslane	**Claytonia sibirica**
Morina	Whorl flower	**Morina**
Morelle noire	Black nightshade	**Solanum nigrum**
Morelle verte	Green nightshade	**Solanum physalifolium**
Moschatelline	Moschatel	**Adoxa moschatellina**
Mouron aquatique.	Water speedwell.	**Veronica anagallis-aquatica**
Mouron bleu	Blue pimpernal	**Anagallis foemina**
Mouron délicat	Bog pimpernel	**Anagallis tenella**
Mouron des marécages	Bog pimpernel	**Anagallis tenella**
Mouron des oiseaux	Common chickweed	**Stellaria media**

Mouron rouge	Scarlet pimpernel	**Anagallis arvenis**
Mousse espagnol	Spanish moss	**Tillandsia usneoides**
Moutarde blanche	White mustard	**Sinapis alba**
Moutarde des champs	Charlock	**Sinapis arvensis**
Moutarde giroflée	Dune cabbage	**Rhynchosinapis monensis**
Moutarde noire	Black mustard	**Brassica nigra**
Muflier	Snapdragon	**Antirrhinum**
Muflier des champs	Lesser snapdragon	**Misopates orontium**
Muguet	Lily of the valley	**Convallaria majalis**
Mûrier	Mulberry	**Morus**
Mûrier blanc	White mulberry	**Morus alba**
Mûrier noir	Black mulberry	**Morus nigra**
Mûrier à papier	Paper mulberry	**Broussonetia papyrifera**
Murraya paniculata	Orange jasmine	**Murraya paniculata**
Muscari à grappes	Grape hyacinth	**Muscari neglectum**
Muscari à toupet	Tassel grape hyacinth	**Muscari comosum**
Myosotidium hortensia	Chatham Island forget-me-not	
		Myosotidium hortensia
Myosotis	Forget-me-not	**Myosotis**
Myosotis des Alpes	Alpine forget-me-not	**Myosotis alpestris**
Myosotis bicolore	Changing forget-me-not	**Myosotis discolor**
Myosotis dea bois	Wood forget-me-not	**Myosotis sylvatica**
Myosotis des champs	Common forget-me-not	**Myosotis arvensis**
Myosotis des marais	Water forget-me-not	**Myosotis scorpioides**
Myosotis de Sicile	Jersey forget-me-not	**Myosotis sicula**
Myriophylle aquaticum	Parrot's feather	**Myriophylle aquaticum**
Myriophylle à épis	Spiked water-milfoil	**Myriophyllum spicatum**
Myriophylle à feuilles alternes	Alternate water-milfoil	
		Myriophyllum alternifolium
Myriophylle verticille	Whorled water-milfoil	**Myriophyllum verticillatum**
Myrsine africana	Cape myrtle	**Myrsine africana**
Myrte d'Australie	Australian brush cherry	**Eugenia myrtifolia**
Myrtillocactus geometrizans	Blue candle	**Myrtillocactus geometrizans**
Myrtille	Bilberry	**Vaccinium myrtillus**
Myrtillier commun.	Whortleberry	**Vaccinium myrtillus**
Myrte	Myrtle	**Myrtus**

N

Naiade flexible	Slender naid	**Najas flexilis**
Nandine fruitière	Heavenly bamboo / Sacred bamboo	**Nandina domestica**
Napel	Monkshood	**Napellus**
Narcisse	Daffodil	**Narcissus**
Narcissus bulbocodium	Hoop pettcoat daffodil	**Narcissus bulbocodium**
Narcisse campernellii	Campernelle jonquil	**Narcissus x odorus**
Narcisse de Constantinople	Bunch flowered daffodil	**Narcissus tazetta**
Narcissus eystenensis	Queen Anne's double daffodil	**Narcissus eystenensis**
Narcisse jaune	Lent Lily	**Narcissus pseudonarcissus**
Narcissus jonquilla florepleno	Queen Anne's jonquil	**Narcissus jonquilla florepleno**
Narcissus obvallaris	Tenby daffodil	**Narcissus obvallaris**
Narcisse des poètes	Pheasant's eye / Poet's narcissus	**Narcissus poeticus**
Narcissus triandrus	Angel's tears	**Narcissus triandrus**
Narthèce	Bog asphodel	**Narthecium ossifragum**
Néflier	Medlar	**Mespilus germanica**
Néflier du Japon	Loquat	**Eriobotrya japonica**
Nélumbium	Lotus	**Nelumbo**
Némésie	Nemesia	**Nemesia**
Ne-me-touchez-pas	Touch -me-not	**Impatiens noli-tangere**
Némophile	Baby blue-eyes	**Nemophila menziesii**
Némophile maculata	Five-spot baby	**Nemophila maculata**
Nénuphar	Water lily	**Nymphaea**
Nénuphar advena	American spatterdock / Yellow pond lily	**Nuphar advena**
Nénuphar blanc	White water lily	**Nymphaea alba**
Nénuphar bleu du Cap	Cape blue water lily	**Nymphaea capensis**
Nénuphar jaune	Brandy Bottle / Yellow water lily	**Nuphar lutea**
Neoregalia carolinae	Blushing bromeliad	**Neoregalia carolinae**
Néottie nid-d'oiseau	Bird's nest orchid	**Neottia nidus-avis**
Nepenthes	Pitcher plant	**Nepenthes**
Nepeta aux chats	Catmint / Wild catmint	**Nepeta cataria**
Néphrolépis cordifolia	Ladder fern	**Nephrolepis cordifolia**
Néphrolépis exaltata	Sword fern	**Nephrolepis exaltata**
Nerprun	Common buckthorn	**Rhamnus cathartica**
Neprun alaterne	Italian buckthorn	**Rhamnus alaternus**
Nertera grandensis	Bead plant	**Nertera grandensis**
Nicandra physalodes	Apple of Peru / Shoofly	**Nicandra physalodes**
Nidularium fulgens	Blushing bromeliad	**Nidularium fulgens**
Nidularium innocentii	Bird's nest bromeliad	**Nidularium innocentii**
Nielle des blés	Corn cockle	**Agrostemma githago**

Nigelle de Damas	Love-in-a-mist	**Nigella damascena**
Nivéole	Snowdrop	**Galanthus nivalis**
Nivéole d'été	Summer snowflake	**Leucojum aestivum**
Nivéole automnale	Autumn snowflake	**Leucojum autumnale**
Nivéole d'été	Loddon lily	**Leucojum aestivum**
Nivéole perce-neige	Spring snowflake	**Leucojum vernum**
Nivéole du printemps	Snowflake	**Leucojum**
Noisettier	Cobnut / Hazel	**Corylus avellana**
Noisetier du Chili	Chilean hazel	**Gevuina avellana**
Noisetier de Constantinople	Turkish hazel	**Corylus colurna**
Noisetier de sorcière	Witch hazel	**Hamamelis**
Noisetier tortueux	Corkscrew nut	**Corylus avellana contorta**
Nombril-de-Venus	Venus's navelwort	**Omphalodes linifolia**
Nombril-de-Vénus	Blue-eyed Mary	**Omphalodes verna**
Nopal	Opuntia / Prickly pear	**Opuntia**
Nopalxochia ackermannii	Red orchid cactus	**Nopalxochia ackermannii**
Nothofagus	False beech	**Nothogagus**
Nothofagus menziesii	Silver beech	**Nothofagus menziesii**
Nothofagus obliqua	Roble	**Nothofagus obliqua**
Nothofagus procera	Rauli	**Nothofagus procera**
Notocactus haselbergii	Scarlet ball cactus	**Notocactus haselbergii**
Notocactus leninghausii	Golden ball cactus	**Notocactus leninghausii**
Notocactus scopa	Silver ball cactus	**Notospartium carmichaelia**
Notospartium carmichaeliae carmichaeliae	Pink broom	**Notospartium**
Noyer	Walnut	**Juglans**
Noyer ailantifolia	Japanese walnut	**Juglans ailantifolia**
Noyer d'Amérique	Hickory	**Carya**
Noyer d'Amérique	Bitternut hickory	**Carya cordiformis**
Noyer à balais	Pignut / Pignut hickory	**Carya glabra**
Noyer blanc d'Amérique	Shag-bark hickory	**Carya ovata**
Noyer de Chine	Chinese walnut	**Juglans cathayensis**
Noyer cendré	Butternut	**Juglans cinera**
Noyer des marais	Bitternut	**Carya cordiformis**
Noyer noir	Black walnut	**Juglans nigra**
Noyer des pourceaux	Pignut / Pignut hickory	**Carya glabra**
Noyer des rochers	Little walnut / Texan walnut	**Juglans microcarpa**
Nyssa sylvatica	Black gum	**Nyssa sylvatica**

O

Ochna serrulata	Mickey mouse plant	**Odontites verna**
Œil de Christ	Aster amellus	**Aster amellus**
Œil de paon	Peacock flower / Tiger flower	**Tigridia pavonia**
Œillet	Carnation	**Dianthus**
Œillet mignardise	Pink	**Dianthus**
Œillet des Alpes	Alpine pink	**Dianthus alpinus**
Œillet bleuatre	Cheddar pink	**Dianthus gratianopolitanus**
Œillet des bois	Deptford pink	**Dianthus armeria**
Œillet de Chine	Indian pink	**Dianthus chinensis**
Œillet couché	Maiden pink	**Dianthus deltoides**
Œillet d'Inde	French marigold	**Tagetes patula**
Œillet marin	Thrift / Sea pink	**Armeria maritima**
Œillet de poète	Sweet William	**Dianthus barbatus**
Œillet velu	Deptford pink	**Dianthus armeria**
Œmleria cerasiformis	Indian plum / Oso berry	**Oemleria cerasiformis**
Œnanthe aquatique	Fine-leafed water dropwort	**Oenanthe aquatica**
Œnanthe fistuleuse	Tubular water dropwort	**Oenanthe fistulosa**
Œnanthe de lachenal	Parsley water dropwort	**Oenanthe lachenalii**
Œnothère	Evening primrose	**Oenothera**
Œuf de pintade	Snake's head fritillery	**Fritillaria meleagris**
Œuf de vanneau	Snake's head fritillery	**Fritillaria meleagris**
Oignon	Onion	**Allium**
Oiseau de Paradis	Bird-of-paradise flower	**Strelitzia**
Oiseau de Paradis	Caesalpinia gilliesii	**Caesalpinia gilliesii**
Oléaire	Daisy bush	**Olearia**
Olivier	Olive	**Olea europaea**
Olivier de Bohême	Oleaster	**Elaeagnus angustifolia**
Olivier odorant	Fragrant olive	**Osmanthus fragrans**
Ombilic.	Wall pennywort.	**Umbilicus rupestris**
Ombilic	Navelwort	**Cotyledon umbilicus**
Onagre	Evening primrose	**Oenothera**
Onagre bisannuelle	Lesser evening primrose	**Oenothera biennis**
Onagre de Lamarck	Large evening primrose	**Oenothera lamarkiana**
Onagre odorante	Fragrant evening primrose	**Oenothera stricta**
Oncidium flexuosum	Dancing doll orchid	**Oncidium flexuosum**
Oncidium papillon	Butterfly orchid	**Oncidium papilio**
Onocléa délicat	Sensitive fern	**Onoclea sensibilis**
Onopordon faux-acanthe	Scotch thistle	**Onopordum acanthium**
Ophrys abeille	Bee orchid	**Ophrys apifera**
Ophrys araignée	Spider orchid	**Ophrys sphegodes**

Ophrys bourdon	Late spider orchid	**Ophrys fuciflora**
Ophrys mouche	Fly orchid	**Ophrys insectifera**
Ophrys tenthredinifera	Sawfly orchid	**Ophrys tenthredinifera**
Opilismenus hirtellus	Basket grass	**Opilismenus hirtellus**
Orangier des osages	Osage orange	**Maclura pomifera**
Orangier du Mexique	Mexican orange blossom	**Choisya ternata**
Orangier de savetier	Jerusalem cherry	**Solanum pseudocapsicum**
Orcanette	Dyer's alkanette	**Alkanna tinctoria**
Orchis bouc	Lizard orchid	**Himantoglossum hircinum**
Orchis bouffon	Gandergoose / Green veined orchid / Green-winged orchid	**Orchis morio**
Orchis brulé	Burnt-tip orchid	**Orchis ustulata**
Orchis à deux feuilles	Lesser butterfly orchid	**Platanthera bifolia**
Orchis d'Ecosse	Northern marsh orchid	**Dactylorhiza purpurella**
Orchis à feuilles larges	Irish marsh orchid	**Dactylorhiza majalis**
Orchis à fleurs laches	Loose-flowered orchid	**Orchis laxiflora**
Orchis de Fuchs	Common spotted orchid	**Dactylorhiza fuchsii**
Orchis grenouille	Frog orchid	**Coeloglossum viride**
Orchis Homme-pendu.	Man orchid.	**Aceras anthropophorum**
Orchis incarnat	Early marsh orchid	**Dactylorhiza incarnata**
Orchis male	Early purple orchid	**Orchis mascula**
Orchis militaire	Soldier orchid	**Orchis militaris**
Orchis négligé	Southern marsh orchid	**Dactylorhiza praetermissa**
Orchis des pentecôtes	Jersey orchid	**Orchis laxiflora**
Orchis pourpre	Lady orchid	**Orchis purpurea**
Orchis pyramidial	Pyramidial orchid	**Anacamptis pyramidalis**
Orchis singe	Monkey orchid	**Orchis simia**
Orchis à tubercules digités	Heath spotted orchid	**Dactylorhiza maculata**
Orchis verdante	Butterfly orchid	**Planthera chlorantha**
Oreille d'âne	Field scabious	**Knautia arvensis**
Oreille de chat	Lamb's tongue	**Stachys byzantina**
Oreille-de-lapin	Bunny ears	**Opuntia microdasys**
Oreille-de-lièvre	Shrubby hare's ear	**Bupleurum fruticosum**
Oreille d'ours	Auricula	**Primula auricula**
Orge barbue	Foxtail barley / Squirrel tail grass	**Hordeum jubatum**
Origan commun	Marjoram / Wild marjoram	**Origanum vulgare**
Origan dictamnus	Cretan dittany	**Origanum dictamnus**
Orme	Elm	**Ulmus**
Orme d'Amérique	American white elm / White elm	**Ulmus americana**
Orme d'Angleterre	English elm	**Ulmus procera**
Orme angustifolia	Goodyer's elm	**Ulmus angustifolia**
Orme blanc	Wych elm	**Ulmus glabra**

Orme de Chine	Chinese elm	**Ulmus parvifolia**
Orme de Cornouaillea	Cornish elm	**Ulmus angustifoliua cornubiensis**
Orme doré	Cornish golden elm / Dickson's golden elm	**Ulmus dicksonii**
Orme à feuilles de charme	Smooth-leaved elm	**Ulmus carpinifolia**
Orme x Hollandica	Dutch elm	**Ulmus x Hollandica**
Orme de Jersey	Jersey elm / Wheatley elm	**Ulmus 'Sarniensis'**
Orme à larges feuilles	American white elm / White elm	**Ulmus americana**
Orme de montagne fastigié	Exeter elm	**Ulmus glabra exoniensis**
Orme à petites feuilles	Chinese elm	**Ulmus parvifolia**
Orme de Samarie	Hop tree	**Ptelea trifoliata**
Orme de Sibérie	Siberian elm	**Ulmus pumila**
Orme 'Vegeta'	Huntingdon elm	**Ulmus 'Vegeta'**
Ornithogale	Chincherinchee	**Ornithogalum thyrsoides**
Ornithope penné	Orange birdsfoot	**Ornithopus pinnatus**
Ornithope délicat	Common birdsfoot	**Ornithopus perpusillus**
Orobanche blanche	Thyme broomrape	**Orobanche alba**
Orobanche du thym	Thyme broomrape	**Orobanche alba**
Orobanche giroflée	Clove-scented broomrape	**Orobanche caryophyllacea**
Orobanche élevée	Knapweed broomrape	**Orobanche elatior**
Orobanche pourprée	Yarrow broomrape	**Orobanche purpurea**
Orobanche des genêts	Great broomrape	**Orobanche rapum-genistae**
Oronce	Golden club	**Orontium aquaticum**
Orpin	Stonecrop	**Sedum**
Orpin blanc	White stonecrop	**Sedum album**
Orpin d'Angleterre	Engish stonecrop	**Sedum anglicum**
Orpin à feuilles épaisses	Thick-leaved stonecrop	**Sedum dasyphyllum**
Orpin de Forster	Rock stonecrop	**Sedum forsteranum**
Orpin réfléchi	Large yellow stonecrop / Reflexed stonecrop	**Sedum reflexum**
Orpin reprise	Orpine	**Sedum telephium**
Orpin rose	Roseroot	**Sedum rosea**
Orpin velu	Pink stonecrop	**Sedum villosum**
Ortie blanche	White dead-nettle	**Lamium album**
Ortie brûlante.	Small nettle.	**Urtica urens**
Ortie rouge	Red dead-nettle	**Lamium purpureum**
Orvale	Clary sage	**Salvia sclarea**
Osmunda cinnamonea	Cinnamon fern	**Osmunda cinnamonea**
Osmunda claytoniana	Interrupted fern	**Osmunda claytoniana**
Osmonde royale	Royal fern	**Osmunda regalis**
Oseille des prés	Common sorrel	**Rumex acetosa**

Osier rouge	Purple osier	**Salix purpurea**
Ossifrage	Bog asphodel	**Narthecium ossifragum**
Ostryer de Virginie	American hop hornbeam / Ironwood	**Ostrya virginiana**
Otanthe maritime	Cottonweed	**Otanthus maritimus**
Oxalis corniculé	Sleeping beauty	**Oxalis corniculata**
Oxalis des Bermudes	Bermuda buttercup	**Oxalis pes-caprae**
Oxydendron en arbre	Sorrel tree	**Oxydendron arboreum**
Oxyria à deux styles	Mountain sorrel	**Oxyria digyna**
Oxytropis champêtre	Yellow milk-vetch	**Oxytropis campestris**
Oxytropis de Haller	Purple mountain milk-vetch	**Oxytropis halleri**

P

Pachyphytum oviferum	Moonstones / Sugar-almond plum	
		Pachyphytum oviferum
Pachystachys coccinea	Cardinal's guard	**Pachystachys coccinea**
Pachysatchys lutea	Lollipop plant	**Pachysatchys lutea**
Pain de coucou	Wood sorrel	**Oxalis acetosella**
Palma Christi	Castor oil plant	**Ricinus communis**
Palmier de Chine	Chusan palm	**Trachycarpus fortunei**
Palmier èvental de Chine	Chinese fan palm / Chinese fountain palm	
		Livistona chinensis
Palmier nain	Dwarf palmeto	**Sabal minor**
Panais cultivé	Wild parsnip	**Pastinaca sativa**
Pancrais maritime	Sea daffodil / Sea lily	**Pancratium maritimum**
Pandanus veitchii	Veitch's screw pine	**Pandanus veitchii**
Panicaut champêtre	Watling street thistle	**Eryngium campestre**
Panicaut de mer	Sea holly	**Eryngium maritimum**
Pâquerette	Blue margueritte	**Felicia amelloides**
Pâquerette	Daisy	**Bellis**
Pâquerette vivace	Double daisy	**Bellis Perennis**
Parasol chinois	Chinese parasol tree	**Firmiana simplex**
Parisette à quatre feuilles	Herb Paris	**Paris quadrifolia**
Parkinsonia aculeata	Jerusalem thorn / Mexican palo verde	
		Parkinsonia aculeata
Parnassie des marais	Grass of Parnassus	**Parnassia palustris**
Parrotia persica	Persian ironwood	**Parrotia persica**
Pas-d'âne	Coltsfoot	**Tussilago farfara**
Passe-rose	Hollyhock	**Alcea**
Passe-velours	Fairy fountain	**Celosia cristata**
Passerage champêtre	Common pepperwort	**Lepidium campestre**
Passerage des décombres	Narrow leafed pepperwort	**Lepidium ruderale**

Passerage à feuilles large	Dittander	**Lepidium latifolium**
Passiflore	Passion flower	**Passiflora**
Passiflora antioquensis	Banana passion fruit	**Passiflora antioquensis**
Passiflore bleu	Blue passion flower	**Passiflora caerulea**
Passiflore rouge	Red passion flower	**Passiflora coccinea**
Pastel des teinturiers	Woad	**Isatis tinctoria**
Patience des Alpes	Monk's Rhubarb	**Rumex alpinus**
Patience agglomérée	Clustered dock	**Rumex conglomeratus**
Patience crépue	Curled dock	**Rumex crispus**
Patience d'eau	Great water dock	**Rumex hydrolapathum**
Patience élégante	Fiddle dock	**Rumex pulcher**
Patience à feuilles longues	Butter dock	**Rumex longifolius**
Patience à feuilles obtuses	Broad dock	**Rumex obtusifolius**
Patience des marais	Marsh dock	**Rumex palustris**
Patience maritime	Golden dock	**Rumex maritimus**
Patience des rochers	Shore dock	**Rumex rupestris**
Patience sanguine	Wood or Red-veined dock	**Rumex sanguineus**
Patole.	Snake gourd.	**Trichosanthes anguina**
Patte d'ours	Hogweed	**Heracleum sphondylium**
Paulownia impérial	Foxglove tree / Princess tree	**Paulownia tomentosa**
Pavier	Horse chestnut	**Aesculus hippocastanum**
Pavier blanc	Bottlebrush buckeye	**Aesculus parviflora**
Pavier rouge	Red buckeye	**Aesculus pavia**
Pavot	Poppy	**Papaver**
Pavot des Alpes	Alpine poppy	**Papaver burseri**
Pavot argémone	Pale poppy	**Papaver argemone**
Pavot bleu	Blue poppy	**Meconopsis grandis**
Pavot bleu de l'Himalaya	Meconopsis betonicifolia	
		Meconopsis betonicifolia
Pavot douteux	Long-headed poppy	**Papaver dubium**
Pavot hybride	Bristly poppy	**Papaver hybridum**
Pavot d'Islande	Iceland poppy	**Papaver nudicaule**
Pavot grande	Harebell poppy	**Meconopsis quintuplinervia**
Pavot jaune	Lampshade poppy	**Meconopsis integrifolia**
Pavot d'Orient	Oriental poppy	**Papaver orientale**
Pavot somnifère	Opium poppy	**Papaver somniferum**
Pavot de Tournefort	Oriental poppy	**Papaver orientale**
Pêcher	Peach	**Prunus persica**
Pécher de David	David's peach	**Prunus davidiana**
Pédiculaire des marais	Red rattle	**Pedicularis palustris**
Pédiculaire des bois	Lousewort	**Pedicularis sylvatica**

Pedilanthus tithymaloides Varieg.	Redbird flower	
		Pedilanthus tithymaloides Varieg.
Pelargonium tomentosum	Peppermint geranium	
		Pelargonium tomentosum
Pellaea atropurpurea	Purple stemmed cliff brake	**Pellaea atropurpurea**
Pellaea atropurpurea	Purple rock brake	**Pellaea atropurpurea**
Pellaea rotundifolia	Button fern	**Pellaea rotundifolia**
Pellionia daveauana	Watermelon begonia	**Pellionia daveauana**
Peltiphyllum peltatum	Umbrella plant	**Peltiphyllum peltatum**
Pennisetum alopecuroides	Chinese fountain grass	
		Pennisetum alopecuroides
Pennisetum setaccum	African fountain grass	**Pennisetum setaccum**
Pennisetum villosum	Feather-top	**Pennisetum villosum**
Pensée.	Pansy.	**Viola wittrockliana**
Pensée des champs.	Field pansy.	**Viola arvensis**
Pensée des vosgess.	Mountain pansy.	**Viola lutea**
Pensée sauvage.	Heartsease / Wild pansy.	**Viola tricolor**
Penstemon newberryi	Mountain pride	**Penstemon newberryi**
Pentas lanceolata	Star-cluster /Egyptian star	**Pentas lanceolata**
Peperomia argyreia	Watermelon plant	**Peperomia argyreia**
Peperomia caperata	Emerald ripple	**Peperomia caperata**
Peperomia clusiifolia	Baby rubber plant	**Peperomia clusiifolia**
Peperomia glabella	Wax privet	**Peperomia glabella**
Peperomia griseoargenta	Ivy peperomia / Silver-leaf peperomia	
		Peperomia griseoargentea
Peperomia magnoliifolia	Desert privet	**Peperomia magnoliifolia**
Peperomia marmorata	Silver heart	**Peperomia marmorata**
Peperomia scandens	Cupid peperomia	**Peperomia scandens**
Perce-neige	Snowdrop	**Galanthus nivalis**
Perce-neige 'Flore Pleno'	Double Common snowdrop	
		Galanthus nivalis 'Flore Pleno'
Perce-pierre	Rock samphire	**Crithmum maritimum**
Pereskia grandiflora	Rose cactus	**Pereskia grandiflora**
Périploque	Silk vine	**Periploca graeca**
Persil	Parsley	**Petroselinum crispum**
Persil des moissons	Corn parsley	**Petroselinum segetum**
Persil de montagne	Moon carrot	**Seseli libanotis**
Pesse d'eau	Marestail	**Hippuris vulgaris**
Pétasite blanc	White butterbur	**Petasites albus**
Pétasite hybride	Butterbur	**Petasites hybridus**
Pétasite du Japon	Creamy butterbur	**Petasites japonicus**
Petit boucage	Burnet-saxifrage	**Pimpinella saxifraga**

Petite bourache	Blue-eyed Mary	**Omphalodes verna**
Petite centaurée commune	Common centaury	**Centaurium erythraea**
Petite centaurée délicat	Slender centaury	**Centaurea nemoralis**
Petite centaurée fauss-scille	Perennial centaury	**Centaurium scilloides**
Petite centauré a fleurs ténues	Channel centaury	
		Centaurium tenuiflorum
Petite centaurée du littoral	Seaside centaury	**Centaurium littorale**
Petite ciguë	Fool's parsley	**Aethusa cynapium**
Petit cocriste	Yellow rattle	**Rhinanthus crista-galli**
Petite douve	Lesser spearwort	**Ranunculus flammula**
Petit houx	Butcher's broom	**Ruscus aculeatus**
Petite jonquille	Jonquil	**Narcissus jonquilla**
Petite lentille d'eau	Common duckweed	**Lemna minor**
Petite linaire	Small toadflax	**Chaenorhinum minus**
Petite mauve	Dwarf mallow	**Malva neglecta**
Petit muguet	May lily	Maianthemum bifolium
Petit muguet	Woodruff	**Galium odoratum**
Petite oseille	Sheep's sorrel	**Rumex acetosella**
Petite pervenche.	Lesser periwinkle.	**Vinca minor**
Petit pigamon	Lesser meadow rue	**Thalictrum minus**
Petite pimpernelle	Burnet	**Sanguisorba**
Petite pyrole	Common wintergreen	**Pyrola minor**
Petteria ramantacea	Dalmatian laburnum	**Petteria ramantacea**
Pétunia	Petunia	**Petunia**
Peucédan officinal	Hog's fennel	**Peucedanum officinale**
Peucédan impératoire	Masterwort	Peucedanum ostruthium
Peucédan des marais	Milk parsley	**Peucedanum palustre**
Pervenche.	Periwinkle.	**Vinca**
Pervenche de Madagascar.	Madagascar periwinkle.	**Vinca rosea**
Pet-d'âne	Scotch thistle	**Onopordum acanthium**
Peuplier	Poplar	**Populus**
Peuplier blanc	Abele / White poplar	**Populus alba**
Peuplier baumier	Balsam Poplar / Tacamahac	**Populus balsamifera**
Peuplier de Berlin	Berlin poplar	**Populus x berolinensis**
Peuplier x candicans	Balm of Gilead / Black Italian poplar	
		Populus x candicans
Peuplier euroaméricains	Canadian poplar	**Populus x canadensis**
Peuplier grisard	Grey poplar	**Populus canescens**
Peuplier d'Italie	Lombardy poplar	**Populus nigra "Italica"**
Peuplier lasiocarpa	Chinese necklace poplar	**Populus lasiocarpa**
Peuplier noir	Black poplar	**Populus nigra**

Peuplier noir d'Amérique	Cottonwood / Eastern cottonwood /Necklace poplar	**Populus deltoides**
Peuplier d'Ontario	Ontario poplar	**Populus candicans**
Peuplier tremble d'Amérique	American aspen	**Populus tremuloides**
Peyote	Dumpling cactus	**Lophophora williamsii**
Phacelia campanularia	California bluebell	**Phacelia campanularia**
Phalangère à fleur de lis	St. Bernard's lily	**Anthericum liliago**
Phalaris arundinacea picta	Gardener's garters	**Phalaris arundinacea picta**
Phegopteris connectilis	Beech fern	**Phegopteris connectilis**
Phellodendron amurense	Amur cork tree	**Phellodendron amurense**
Philodendron cordatum	Heart leaf	**Philodendron cordatum**
Philodendron domesticum	Elephant's ears / Spade leaf	**Philodendron domesticum**
Philodendron erubescens	Blushing philodendron	**Philodendron erubescens**
Phlox annuel	Annual phlox	**Phlox drummondii**
Phlox bifida	Sand phlox	**Phlox bifida**
Phlox stolonifera	Creeping phlox	**Phlox stolonifera**
Phoenix roebelenii	Miniature date palm / Pygmy date palm	**Phoenix roebelenii**
Phormium cookianum	Mountain flax	**Phormium cookianum**
Phyllocladus aspleniifolius	Tasman celery pine	**Phyllocladus aspleniifolius**
Phyllodoce bleuatre	Menziesia	**Phyllodoce caerulea**
Physocarpe opulifolius	Ninebark	**Physocarpus opulifolius**
Physosperme de cornouailles	Bladder seed	**Physospermum cornubiense**
Physostegia	Obedient plant	**Physostegia**
Phytolacca americana	Red-ink plant / Virginia pokeweed	**Phytolacca americana**
Picride vipérine	Bristly ox-tongue	**Picris echioides**
Picride épervière	Hawkweed ox-tongue	**Picris hieracioides**
Pieris floribunda	Fetterbush / Mountain fetterbush	**Pieris floribunda**
Pied d'alouette	Delphinium	**Delphinium**
Pied d'alouette annuel	Larkspur	**Consolida**
Pied-d'alouette des jardins	Giant larkspur	**Consolida ambigua**
Pied-de-chat dioïque	Mountain everlasting	**Antennaria dioica**
Pied-de-corbeau	Buckshorn plantain	**Plantago coronopus**
Pied-d'éléphant	Elephant's foot	**Dioscorea elephantipes**
Pied-de-griffon	Stinking hellebore	**Helleborus foetidus**
Pied-d'oiseau	Common birdsfoot	**Ornithopus perpusillus**
Pied-de-pigeon	Long stalked cranesbill	**Geranium columbinum**
Pied-de-poule	Common birdsfoot trefoi	**Lotus corniculatus**

Pied-de-pigeon	Long stalked cranesbill	**Geranium columbinum**
Pied-de-poule	Common birdsfoot trefoi	**Lotus corniculatus**
Pierre vivante	Living stones / Stone plant	**Lithops**
Pigamon des Alpes	Alpine meadow rue	**Thalictrum alpinum**
Pigamon jaune	Common meadow-rue / Meadow rue	**Thalictrum flavum**
Pilea involucrata	Friendship plant	**Pilea involucrata**
Pilea numulariifolia	Creeping Charlie	**Pilea numulariifolia**
Piment commun	Ornamental pepper	**Capsicum annuum**
Pin	Pine	**Pinus**
Pin d'Alep	Aleppo pine	**Pinus halpensis**
Pin d'Anthony	Bishop pine	**Pinus muricata**
Pin aristata	Bristle cone pine	**Pinus aristata**
Pin de Banks	Jack pine	**Pinus banksiana**
Pin de Bosnie	Bosnian pine	**Pinus leucodermis**
Pin cembro	Arolla pine	**Pinus cembra**
Pin cembro	Mexican stone pine / Pinyon	**Pinus cembroides**
Pin vrillé	Beach pine / Big-cone pine / Coulter pine / Shore pine	**Pinus contorta**
Pin contorta latifolia	Lodgepole pine	**Pinus contorta latifolia**
Pin x holfordiana	Holford's pine	**Pinus x holfordiana**
Pin jaune	Western yellow pine	**Pinus ponderosa**
Pin de Jeffrey	Black pine / Jeffrey pine	**Pinus jeffreyi**
Pin de Jersey	Virginia pine	**Pinus virginiana**
Pin d'e Jerusalem	Aleppo pine	**Pinus halpensis**
Pin des landes	Cluster pine / Maritime Pine	**Pinus pinaster**
Pin de Macédoine	Macedonian pine	**Pinus peuce**
Pin maritime	Cluster pine / Maritime Pine	**Pinus pinaster**
Pin de montagne	Dwarf pine / Mountain pine / Swiss mountain pine	**Pinus mugo**
Pin de Monterey	Monterey pine	**Pinus radiata**
Pin de Montezuma	Montezuma pine / Rough-barked Mexican pine	**Pinus montzumae**
Pin noir d'Autriche	Black pine	**Pinus nigra**
Pin noir de Corse	Austrian pine / Corsican pine	**Pinus nigra laricio**
Pin noir du Japon	Japanese black pine	**Pinus thunbergii**
Pin parasol	Stone pine / Umbrella pine	**Pinus pinea**
Pin parasol du Japon	Japanese umbrella pine / Umbrella pine	**Sciadopitys verticillata**
Pin parviflora	Japanese white pine	**Pinus parviflora**
Pin de père Armand David	Armand pine /David's pine	**Pinus armandii**
Pin pleuereur de l'Himalaya	Bhutan pine / Himalayan pine	**Pinus wallichiana**

Pin pumila	Dwarf Siberian pine	**Pinus pumila**
Pin rigida	Northern pitch pine	**Pinus rigida**
Pin rouge du Japon	Japanese red pine	**Pin densiflora**
Pin sylvestre	Scots pine	**Pinus sylvestris**
Pin de Virginie	Virginia pine	**Pinus virginiana**
Pin Weymouth	Eastern white pine / Weymouth pine	**Pinus strobus**
Pisonia umbellifera	Bird-catcher tree / Para para	**Pisonia umbellifera**
Pissenlit	Dandelion	**Taraxacum officinale**
Pittosporum crassifolium	Karo	**Pittosporum crassifolium**
Pittosporum tobira	Japanese pittosporum / Mock orange	
		Pittosporum tobira
Pittosporum undulatum	Victorian box	**Pittosporum undulatum**
Pivoine	Peony	**Paeonia**
Pivoine de Majorca	Majorcan poppy	**Paeonia cambessedesii**
Pivoine en arbre	Moutan	**Paeonia suffruticosa**
Plaine blanche.	Silver maple.	**Acer saccherinum**
Plaine rouge.	Red maple.	**Acer rubrum**
Plantain corne-de bœuf	Buckshorn plantain	**Plantago coronopus**
Plantain d'eau commun	Common water plantain	
		Alisma plantago-aquatica
Plantain d'eau lancéolé	Narrow water plantain	**Alisma lanceolatum**
Plantain lancéolé	Ribwort plantain	**Plantago lanceolata**
Plantain majeur	Rat's tail plantain	**Plantago major**
Plantain maritime	Sea plantain	**Plantago maritima**
Plantain moyen	Hoary plantain	**Plantago media**
Plante aluminium	Aluminium plant	**Pilea cadierei**
Plante boussole	Compass plant	**Silphium laciniatum**
Plante-caillou	Livingstones / Stone plant	**Lithops**
Plante chandelle	Candle plant	**Senecio articulans**
Plante corail	Coral plant	**Russelia equisetiformis**
Plante panda	Panda plant / Pussy ears	**Kalanchoe tomentosa**
Plante qui fait les yeux émerveillés	Dumpling cactus	
		Lophophora williamsii
Plaqueminier kaki	Kaki / Persimmon	**Diospyros kaki**
Plaqueminier faux lotier	Date plum	**Diospyros lotus**
Platane	Plane	**Platanus**
Platane de Londres	London plane	**Platanus acerifolia**
Platane d'Orient	Oriental plane	**Platanus orientalis**
Platycérium	Stag's horn fern	**Platycerium**
Platycodon	Baloon flower	**Platycodon**
Platystemon californicus	Cream cups	**Platystemon californicus**
Plectranthus australis	Swedish ivy	**Plectranthus australis**

Plectranthus oertendahlii	Prostrate coleus / Swedish ivy	
		Plectranthus oertendahlii
Pleioblastus variegatus	Dwarf white stripe bamboo	
		Pleioblastus variegatus
Pleomele bolusii	Living rock / Mimicry plant	**Pleiospilos bolusii**
Plumeria alba	West Indian jasmine	**Plumeria alba**
Podocarpe montagnard	Tasmanian podocarp	**Podocarpus alpinus**
Podocarpus andinus	Plum yew	**Podocarpus andinus**
Podocarpus macrophyllus	Kusamaki	**Podocarpus macrophyllus**
Podocarpus nivalis	Alpine totara	**Podocarpus nivalis**
Podophylle Indien	Himalayan May apple	**Podophyllum emodi**
Podophyllum peltatum	May apple	**Podophyllum peltatum**
Poinsettia	Poinsettia	**Euphorbia pulcherrima**
Poireau roux	Tassel grape hyacinth	**Muscari comosum**
Poirier	Pear	**Pyrus**
Poirier calleryana	Callery pear	**Pyrus calleryana**
Poirier pleureur à feuilles de saule	Weeping willow pear	
		Pyrus salicifolia pendula
Pois de cœur	Baloon vine / Heart pea / Winter cherry	
		Cardiospermum grandiflorum
Pois de senteur	Sweet pea	**Lathyrus odoratus**
Pois rotundifolia	Persian everlasting pea	**Lathyrus rotundifolia**
Pois vivace	Everlasting pea	**Lathyrus sylvestris**
Pois vivace	Perennial pea	**Lathyrus latifolius**
Poivre de muraille	Biting stonecrop / Wall-pepper	**Sedum acre**
Poivrier du Japon	Japan pepper	**Zanthoxylum piperitum**
Polémoine blue	Jacob's ladder	**Polemonium caeruleum**
Polycarpon à quatre feuilles	Four-leaved allseed	**Polycarpon tetraphyllum**
Polygala des sols calcaires	Chalk milkwort	**Polygala calcaria**
Polygale faux-buis	Polygala chamaebuxus	**Polygala chamaebuxus**
Polygala à feuilles de serpolet	Heath milkwort	**Polygala serpyllifolia**
Polygala commun	Common milkwort	**Polygala vulgaris**
Polypode commun	Polypody	**Polypodium vulgare**
Polypodium glycyrrhiza	Liquorice fern	**Polypodium glycyrrhiza**
Polypodium virginianum	American wall fern	**Polypodium virginianum**
Polyscias filicifolia	Fern-leaf aralia	**Polyscias filicifolia**
Polyscias guilfoylei	Wild coffee	**Polyscias guilfoylei**
Polystic	Christmas fern	
		Polystichum acrostchoides
Polystic aculeatum	Hard shield fern / Prickly shield fern	
		Polystichum aculeatum
Polystic lonchitis	Holly fern	**Polystichum lonchitis**

167

Polystic munitum	Giant holly fern	**Polystichum munitum**
Polystic setiferum	Soft shield fern	**Polystichum setiferum**
Pomme épineause	Angels' trumpets / Thorn-apple	**Datura stramonium**
Pomme de terre	Potato	**Solanum tuberosum**
Pommier	Apple	**Malus**
Pommier d'amour	Jerusalem cherry	**Solanum pseudocapsicum**
Pommier à baies	Siberian crab	**Malus baccata**
Pommier sauvage	Crab apple	**Malus sylvestris**
Poncirus trifoliatta	Japanese bitter orange	**Poncirus trifoliatta**
Pontédérie à feuilles en cœur	Pickerel weed	**Pontederis cordata**
Calycanthe	Calycanthus	**Calycanthus**
Porana panicultata	Bridal bouquet / Snow creeper	**Porana panicultata**
Porcelle glabre	Smooth catsear	**Hypochoeris glabra**
Porcelle maculée	Spotted catsear	**Hypochoeris maculata**
Porcelle enracinée	Common catsear	**Hypochoeris radicata**
Porillon	Poet's narcissus	**Narcissus poeticus**
Potamot allongé	Long stalked pondweed	**Potamogeton praelongus**
Potamot alpin	Reddish pondweed	**Potamogeton alpinus**
Potamot de Berchtold	Slender pondweed	**Potamogeton berchtoldii**
Potamot capillaire	Hairlike pondweed	**Potamogeton trichoides**
Potamot coloratus	Plantain-leaved pondweed	**Potamogeton coloratus**
Potamot comprimé	Wrack-like pondweed	**Potamogeton compressus**
Potamot crépu	Curly pondweed	**Potamogeton crispus**
Potamot dense	Opposite pondweed	**Groenlandia densa**
Potamot epihydrus	American pondweed	**Potamogeton epihydrus**
Potamot à feuilles aiguës	Sharp-leafed pondweed	**Potamogeton acutifolius**
Potamot à feuilles de graminée	Various leaved pondweed	**Potamogeton gramineus**
Potamot à feuilles obtuses	Blunt-leaved pondweed	**Potamogeton obtusifolius**
Potamot à feuilles de renouée	Bog pondweed	**Potamogeton polygonifolius**
Potamot filiforme	Slender leafed pondweed	**Potamogeton filiformis**
Potamot fluet	Lesser pondweed	**Potamogeton pusillus**
Potamot luisant	Shining pondweed	**Potamogeton lucens**
Potamot nageant	Broad-leaved pondweed	**Potamogeton natans**
Potamot noueux	Loddon pondweed	**Potamogeton nodosus**
Potamot pectiné	Fennel pondweed	**Potamogeton pectinatus**
Potamot perfolié	Perfiolate pondweed	**Potamogeton perfiolatus**
Potentille des Alpes	Alpine cinquefoil	**Potentilla crantzii**
Potentille argentée	Hoary cinquefoil	**Potentilla argentea**
Potentille dressée	Sulpher cinquefoil	**Potentilla recta**

Potentille faux-fraisier	Barren strawberry	**Potentilla sterilis**
Potentille ligneuse	Shrubby cinquefoil	**Potentilla fruticosa**
Potentille rampante	Creeping cinquefoil	**Potentilla reptans**
Potentille des rochers	White cinquefoil	**Potentilla rupestris**
Potentille dressée	Tormentil	**Potentilla erecta**
Pourpier en arbre	Elephant bush	**Portulacaria afra**
Pourpier de mer	Sea sandwort	**Honkenya peploides**
Pourpier de mer	Tree purslane	**Atriplex halimus**
Primevère acaule	Primrose	**Primula vulgaris**
Primevère denticulata	Drumstick primula	**Primula denticulata**
Primevère élevée	Oxlip	**Primula elatior**
Primevère farineuse	Bird's eye primrose	**Primula farinosa**
Primevère florindae	Giant cowslip	**Primula florindae**
Primevère d'Ecosse	Scots primrose	**Primula scotica**
Primevère officinale	Cowslip	**Primula veris**
Primevère polyanthe	Polyanthus	**Primula polyanthus**
Prostanthera	Mint bush	**Prostanthera**
Prostanthera rotundifolia	Round-leaved mint-bush	**Prostanthera rotundifolia**
Protea cynaroides	King protea	**Protea cynaroides**
Protea repens	Sugar bush	**Protea repens**
Pruche	Canada hemlock/ Eastern hremlock	**Tsuga canadensis**
Prunellier	Sloe	**Prunus spinosa**
Prunier myrobolan	Cherry plum / Myrobalan	**Prunus cerasifera**
Prunier de Pennsylvanie	Pin cherry	**Prunus pensylvanica**
Prunus campanulata	Bellflowered cherry / Taiwan cherry	
		Prunus campanulata
Prunus incisa	Fuji cherry	**Prunus incisa**
Prunus sargentii	Sargent cherry	**Prunus sargentii**
Prunus serrula	Hill cherry	**Prunus serrulata var. spontanea**
Prunus subhirtella	Rosebud cherry	**Prunus subhirtella**
Prunus 'Tai Haku'	Great white cherry	**Prunus 'Tai Haku'**
Prunus virginiana	Virginia bird cherry	**Prunus virginiana**
Prunus x yedoensis	Yoshino cherry	**Prunus x yedoensis**
Pseudopanax arboreus	Five fingers	**Pseudopanax arboreus**
Pseudopanax crassifolius	Lancewood	**Pseudopanax crassifolius**
Pseudosasa japonica	Arrow bamboo / Metake	**Pseudosasa japonica**
Pseudowintera axillaris	Heropito / Pepper tree	**Pseudowintera axillaris**
Ptélée	Hop tree	**Ptelea trifoliata**
Pteris cretica	Cretan brake	**Pteris cretica**
Pteris ensiformis	Snow brake	**Pteris ensiformis**

Pteris multifida	Spider fern	**Pteris multifida**
Pterocarya	Wing nut	**Pterocarya**
Pterocarya frazinifolia	Caucasian wing nut	**Pterocarya frazinifolia**
Pterocarya stenoptera	Chinese wing nut	**Pterocarya stenoptera**
Pterostyrax hispida	Epaulette tree	**Pterostyrax hispida**
Pueraria lobata	Kadzu vine	**Pueraria lobata**
Pulicaire dysentérique	Common fleabane	**Pulcaria dysenterica**
Pulicaire commune	Small fleabane	**Pulcaria vulgaris**
Pulmonaire a feuilles longues	Joseph & Mary	**Pulmonaria longifolia**
Pulmonaire officinale	Lungwort	**Pulmonaria officinalis**
Puschkinia scilloides	Striped squill	**Puschkinia scilloides**
Pyrèrthre	Pyrethrum	**Tanacetum coccineum**
Pyrole	Wintergreen	**Pyrola**
Pyrole à feuilles rondes	Wild lily of the valley / Round-leaved wintergreen **Pyrola rotundifolia**
Pyrole moyenne	Greater wintergreen	**Pyrola media**
Pyrole uniflore	St. Olaf's candlestick	**Moneses uniflora**
Pyrole unilatérale	Yavering bells	**Orthilia secunda**
Pyrostegia venusta	Flame flower / Flame vine / Golden shower **Pyrostegia venusta**

Q

Quamash	Quamash	**Camassia**
Quarantaine	Brompton stock / Sea stock	**Matthiola incana**
Quercitron	Black oak	**Quercus velutina**
Queue de lézard	Lizard's tail / Swamp lily / Water dragon	**Saururus cernuus**
Queue de lièvre	Hare's tail grass	**Lagurus ovatus**
Queue de lion	Lion's ear	**Leonotis leonorus**
Queue-de-porc	Hog's fennel	**Peucedanum officinale**
Queue de renard	Love-lies-bleeding / Tassel flower	**Amaranthus caudatus**
Queue de souris	Mousetail	**Myosurus minimus**
Quisqualis indica	Rangoon creeper	**Quisqualis indica**

R

Racine-de-corail	Coral-root orchid	**Corallorhiza trifida**
Radiare	Pink masterwort	**Astrantia major**
Radiole faux-lin	Flax-seed	**Radiola linoides**
Raifort	Horse radish	**Armoracia rusticana**
Raiponce en épi	Spiked rampion	**Phyteuma spicatum**
Raiponce orbiculaire	Round-headed rampion	**Phyteuma orbiculare**

Raisin des Alpes	Black bearberry	**Arctostaphylos alpinus**
Raisin d'ours	Bearberry	**Arctostaphylos uva-ursi**
Rameau d'or	Wallflower	**Cheiranthus cheiri**
Rapette couchée	Madwort	**Asperugo procumbens**
Raquette	Opuntia / Prickly pear	**Opuntia**
Réglisse	Liquorice	**Glycyrrhiza glabra**
Réglisse bâtarde	Wild liquorice	**Astragalus glycyphyllos**
Reine des bois	Goat's beard	**Aruncus dioicus**
Reine-margueritte	China aster	**Callistephus**
Reine des prés	Meadowsweet	**Filipendula ulmaria**
Renoncule	Buttercup	**Ranunculus**
Renoncle âcre flore pleno	Double meadow buttercup	
		Ranunculus acris flore pleno
Renoncule des Alpes	Alpine buttercup	**Ranunculus alpestris**
Renoncule bulbeuse	Bulbous buttercup	**Ranunculus bulbosa**
Renoncule des champs	Corn buttercup	**Ranunculus arvensis**
Renoncule flamette	Lesser spearwort	**Ranunculus flammula**
Renoncule des fleuristes	Persian buttercup	**Ranunculus asiaticus**
Renoncule des jardins	Persian buttercup	**Ranunculus asiaticus**
Renoncule lyallii	Giant buttercup	**Ranunculus lyallii**
Renoncule à peites fleurs	Small flowered buttercup	
		Ranunculus parviflorus
Renoncule rampante	Creeping buttercup	**Ranunculus repens**
Renoncule sarde	Hairy buttercup	**Ranunculus sardous**
Renoncule scélérate	Celery leafed buttercup	**Ranunculus sceleratus**
Renonclue à tête d'or	Goldilocks / Wood goldilocks	**Ranunculus auricomus**
Renoncule à tige rampante	Creeping spearwort	**Ranunculus reptans**
Renouée	Knotweed	**Polygonum**
Renouée	Mile a minute plant / Russian vine	**Polygonum baldschuanicum**
Renouée amphibe	Amphibious bistort	**Persicaria amphibium**
Renouée aubertii	Mile a minute plant / Russian vine	**Polygonum aubertii**
Renouée maritime	Sea knotgrass	**Polygonum maritimum**
Renouée des oiseaux	Knotgrass	**Polygonum aviculare**
Ravenelle	Wild radish	**Raphanus raphanistrum**
Radis cultivé	Radish	**Raphanus sativus**
Ravenala madegascariensis	Traveller's tree	**Ravenala madegascariensis**
Reinwardtia indica	Yellow flax	**Reinwardtia indica**
Réséda blanc	White mignonette	**Reseda alba**
Réséda jaune	Wild mignonette	**Reseda lutea**
Réséda raiponce	Corn mignonette	**Reseda phyteuma**
Réséda dea teinturiers	Weld	**Reseda luteola**
Rhaphiolepis indica	Indian hawthorn	**Rhaphiolepis indica**

Rhapis excelsa	Bamboo Palm / Slender lady palm	**Rhapis excelsa**
Rhipsalis	Mistletoe cactus	**Rhipsalis**
Rhipsalis cereuscula	Coral cactus	**Rhipsalis cereuscula**
Rhipsalis paradoxa	Chain cactus	**Rhipsalis paradoxa**
Rhodiole rose	Roseroot	**Sedum rosea**
Rhododendron calendulaceum	Flame azalea	**Rhododendron calendulaceum**
Rhoicissus capensis	Cape grape	**Rhoicissus capensis**
Rhubarbe	Rhubarb	**Rheum**
Rhus copallina	Dwarf sumach	**Rhus copallina**
Rhynchelytrum repens	Natal grass / Ruby grass	**Rhynchelytrum repens**
Ribes speciosum	Fuchsia flowered currant	**Ribes speciosum**
Ricin commun	Castor oil plant	**Ricinus communis**
Ricinelle	Jacob's coat / Copperleaf	**Acalypha wilkesiana**
Robinier faux-acacia	False acacia / Locust	**Robinia pseudoacacia**
Roi des Alpes	Eritrichium nanum	**Eritrichium nanum**
Roi des palmiers	Cuban royal palm	**Roystonea regia**
Romarin	Rosemary	**Rosmarinus officinalis**
Romneya coulteri	Californian poppy	**Romneya coulteri**
Romulée à petites fleurs	Sand crocus	**Romulea columnae**
Ronce	Blackberry / Bramble (in Scotland)	**Rubus**
Ronce bleuâtre	Dewberry	**Rubus caesius**
Ronce commune	Bramble	**Rubus fruticosus**
Ronce odorante	Flowering raspberry / Thimbleberry	**Rubus odoratus**
Ronce des rochers	Stone bramble	**Rubus saxatilis**
Ronce des tourbières	Cloudberry	**Rubus chamaemorus**
Roquette de mer	Sea rocket	**Cakile maritima**
Rorippa amphibie	Greater yellow cress	**Rorippa amphibia**
Rorippa des forêts	Creeping yellow cress	**Rorippa sylvestris**
Rorippa d'Islande	Marsh yellow cress	**Rorippa islandica**
Rose	Rose	**Rosa**
Rose à bâton	Hollyhock	**Alcea**
Rose du désert	Desert rose	**Adenium**
Rose d'Inde	African marigold / Aztec marigold	**Tagetes erecta**
Rose de Noël	Christmas rose	**Helleborus niger**
Rose primula	Incense rose	**Rosa primula**
Rose trémière	Hollyhock	**Alcea**
Rosier de Banks	Banksia rose	**Rosa banksiae**
Rosier jaune de Banks	Yellow banksia	**Rosa banksiae lutea**
Rosier Dupontii	Snowbush tree	**Rosa 'Dupontii'**
Rosier gallica versicolor	Rosa mundi	**Rosa gallica versicolor**
Rosier pimpernelle	Burnet rose / Scotch rose	**Rosa pimpinellifolia**
Rosier multiflore	Hedgehog rose / Japanese rose	**Rosa multiflora**

Rosier 'Zéphirine Drouhin'	Thornless rose	**Rosa 'Zéphirine Drouhin'**
Rossolis	Sundew	**Drosera**
Rossolis d' Angleterre	Great sundew	**Drosera anglica**
Rossolis du Cap	Cape sundew	**Drosera capensis**
Rossolis à feuilles rondes	Common sundew	**Drosera rotundifolia**
Rossolis intermédiaire	Long-leaved sundew	**Drosera intermedia**
Rouget	Shining cranesbill	**Geranium lucidum**
Roystonea	Royal palm	**Roystonea**
Rubanier	Bur reed	**Sparganium**
Rubanie à feuilles étroites	Floating bur-reed	**Sparganium angustifolium**
Rubanier dressé	Branched bur reed	**Sparganium erectum**
Rubanier nain	Least bur-reed	**Sparganium minimum**
Rubéole des champs	Field madder	**Sherardia arvensis**
Rubiacées	Creeping bluets	**Hedyotis michauxii**
Rudbeckia	Coneflower	**Rudbeckia**
Rudbeckie hérissée	Black-eyed Susan	**Rudbeckia hirta**
Rue de chèvre	Goat's rue	**Galega officinalis**
Ruine-de-Rome	Ivy-leafed toadflax / Kenilworth ivy	**Cymbalaria muralis**
Ruppia maritime	Tassel pondweed	**Ruppia maritima**
Ruppia spiralée	Coiled pondweed	**Ruppia spiralis**
Rue	Rue	**Ruta**
Rue fétide	Herb of grace	**Ruta graveolens**
Rue de prés	Alpine meadow rue	**Thalictrum alpinum**

S

Sabline	Sandwort	**Arenaria**
Sabline de Norvège	Scottish sandwort	**Arenaria norvegica**
Sabline à feuilles de serpolet	Thyme-leaved sandwort	**Arenaria serpyllifolia**
Sabot de Vénus	Lady's slipper orchid / Slipper orchid	**Cypripedium calceolus**
Safran d'automne	Saffron crocus	**Crocus sativus**
Sagine	Pearlwort / Sagina	**Sagina**
Sagine des Alpes	Alpine pearlwort	**Sagina saginoides**
Sagine apétale	Annual pearlwort	**Sagina apetala**
Sagine couchée	Mossy pearlwort	**Sagina procumbens**
Sagine maritime	Sea pearlwort	**Sagina maritima**
Sagine noueuse	Knotted pearlwort	**Sagina nodosa**
Sagine subulée	Heath pearlwort	**Sagina subulata**
Sagittaire à feuilles en flèche	Arrow-head	**Sagittaria sagittifolia**
Sainfoin	Sanfoin	**Onobrychis viciifolia**
Sainfoin à bouquets	French honeysuckle	**Hedysarum coronarium**

Sainfoin d'Espagns	French honeysuckle	**Hedysarum coronarium**
Saladelle	Sea lavender	**Limonium vulgare**
Salicaire commune	Purple loosestrife	**Lythrum salicaria**
Salicaire à feuilles d'hysoppe	Hyssop-leaved loostrife	
		Lythrum hyssopifolia
Salicorne d'Europe	Glasswort	**Salicornia europaea**
Salsifis cultivé.	Salsify	**Tragopogon porrifolius**
Salsifis des prés Goat's beard	/ Jack-go-to-bed-at-noon	**Tragopogon pratensis**
Samole de valérand	Brookweed	**Samolus valerandi**
Sandersonia aurantiaca	Chinese lantern lily	**Sandersonia aurantiaca**
Sanguinaria canadensis	Bloodroot	**Sanguinaria canadensis**
Sanguisorbe	Burnet	**Sanguisorba**
Sanguisorba canadensis	Canadian burnet	**Sanguisorba canadensis**
Sanguisorbe officinale	Grass burnet	**Sanguisorba officinalis**
Sanicle d'Europe	Sanicle	**Sanicula europaea**
Sansiviera trifasciata	Mother-in-law's-tongue	**Sansiviera trifasciata**
Santoline	Lavender cotton	**Santolina**
Santoline / Santoline blanche	Cotton lavender	
		Santolina chamaecyparissus
Santolina rosmarinifolia	Holy flax	**Santolina rosmarinifolia**
Sanvitalia procumbens	Creeping zinnia	**Sanvitalia procumbens**
Sapin de Douglas	Douglas fir	**Pseudotsuga menziesii**
Sapin de Douglas bleu	Blue Douglas fir	**Pseudotsuga menzieii 'Glauca'**
Sapin de l'Oregon	Douglas fir	**Pseudotsuga menziesii**
Sapium sebiferum	Chinese tallow tree	**Sapium sebiferum**
Saponaire ocymoides	Tumbing Ted	**Saponaria ocymoides**
Saponaire officinale	Soapwort	**Saponaria officinalis**
Sarcococca	Christmas box / Sweet box	**Sarcococca**
Sarracène à fleurs jaunes	Trumpets / Yellow pitcher plant	**Sarracenia flava**
Sarracène pourpre	Huntsman's cap / Pitcher plant	
		Sarracenia purpurea
Sarriette	Savory	**Satureja**
Sarriette vivace	Winter savory	**Satureja montana**
Sapin amabilis	Pacifc fir	**Abies amabilis**
Sapin argenté	Silver fir	**Abies alba**
Sapin Baumier	Balsam fir	**Abies balsamea**
Sapin de Céphalonie	Greek fir	**Abies cephalonica**
Sapin chinois	Chinese fir	**Cunninghamia lanceolata**
Sapin commun	Silver fir	**Abies alba**
Sapin concolor	White fir	**Abies concolor**
Sapin de Corée	Korean fir	**Abies koreana**
Sapin delaveyi	Delavay fir	**Abies delavayi**

174

Sapin homolepis	Nikko fir	**Abies homolepis**
Sapin lasiocarpa	Subalpine fir	**Abies lasiocarpa**
Sapin noble	Noble fir	**Abies procera**
Sapin de Nordmann	Caucasian fir	**Abies nordmanniana**
Sapin de Norvège	Norway spruce	**Picea abies**
Sapin rouge	Norway spruce	**Picea abies**
Sapin de Vancouver	Giant fir / Grand fir	**Abies grandis**
Sapin de Veitch	Veitch fir	**Abies veitchii**
Sapin des Vosges	Silver fir	**Abies alba**
Sapinette blanche	White spruce	**Picea glauca**
Sapinette noir	Black spruce	**Picea mariana**
Sapinette d'Orient	Caucasian spruce	**Picea orientalis**
Sarrasin	Buckwheat	**Fagopyrum esculentum**
Sarrette	Sawwort	**Serratula tinctoria**
Sarriette commune	Wild basil	**Clinopodium vulgare**
Saucissonier	Sausage tree	**Kigelia pinnata**
Sauge	Sage	**Salvia**
Sauge argentée	Salvia argentea	**Salvia argentea**
Sauge des bois	Wood-sage	**Teucrium scorodonia**
Sauge éclatante	Scarlet sage	**Salvia splendens**
Sauge faux-horminum	Clary	**Salvia sclarea**
Sauge de Jérusalem	Jerusalem sage	**Phlomis fruticosa**
Sauge leucantha	Mexican bush sage	**Salvia leucantha**
Sauge des prés	Meadow sage	**Salvia pratensis**
Sauge sclarée	Clary sage	**Salvia sclarea**
Sauge uliginosa	Bog sage	**Salvia uliginosa**
Saule	Willow	**Salix**
Saule aegyptiaca	Musk willow	**Salix aegyptiaca**
Saule alba vitellina	Golden willow	**Salix alba vitellina**
Saule d'Amérique	Black willow	**Salix 'Melanostachys'**
Saule arbuscula	Mountain willow	**Salix arbuscula**
Saule argenté	Silver willow / White willow	**Salix alba**
Saule blanc	Silver willow / White willow	**Salix alba**
Saule blanc var coerulea	Cricket bat willow	**Salix alba caerulea**
Saule chrysocoma	Golden weeping willow	**Salix chrysocoma**
Saule daphné	Violet willow	**Salix daphnoides**
Saule elaeagnos	Hoary willow	**Salix elaeagnos**
Saule fragilis	Crack willow	**Salix fragilis**
Saule herbacea	Dwarf willow / Least willow	**Salix herbacea**
Saule lanata	Woolly willow	**Salix lanata**
Saule laurier	Bay willow	**Salix pentandra**
Saule marsault	Goat willow	**Salix caprea**

Saule matsudana 'Tortuosa'	Dragon's claw willow	
		Salix matsudana 'Tortuosa'
Saule noir	Black willow	**Salix 'Melanostachys'**
Saule noir	Violet willow	**Salx daphnoides**
Saule pleureur	Weeping willow	**Salix babylonica**
Saule rampant	Creeping willow	**Salix repens**
Saule reticulé	Net veined willow	**Salix reticulata**
Saule vivier	Silver willow / White willow	**Salix alba**
Saussurée des Alpes	Purple hawkweed	**Saussurea alpina**
Savonnier	Golden-rain tree / Pride of India	**Koelreuteria paniculata**
Sawara	Sawara cypress	**Chamaecyparis pisifera**
Saxegothaea conspicua	Prince Albert's yew	**Saxegothaea conspicua**
Saxifrage	Saxifrage	**Saxifraga**
Saxifrage arctique	Arctic saxifrage	**Saxifraga nivalis**
Saxifrage benoîte	Saxifraga x geum	**Saxifraga x geum**
Saxifrage gazonnante	Tufted saxifrage	**Saxifraga caespitosa**
Saxifrage etoile	Starry saxifrage	**Saxifraga stellaris**
Saxifrage faux hypne	Mossy saxifrage	**Saxifraga hypnoides**
Saxifrage à feuilles opposées	Purple saxifrage	**Saxifraga oppositifolia**
Saxifrage granulée	Fair maids of France / Meadow saxifrage	
		Saxifraga granulata
Saxifrage herissée	Kidney saxifrage	**Saxifraga hirsuta**
Saxifrage jaune des montagnes	Yellow mountain saxifrage	
		Saxifraga aizoides
Saxifrage œil de bouc	Yellow marsh saxifrage	**Saxifraga hirculus**
Saxifrage penchée	Drooping saxifrage	**Saxifraga cernua**
Saxifrage des Pyrénées	Pyrenean saxifrage	**Saxifraga umbrosa**
Saxifrage des ruisseaux	Highland saxifrage	**Saxifraga rivularis**
Saxifrage spathulée	St. Patrick's cabbage	**Saxifraga spathularis**
Saxifraga stolonifera	Mother of thousands	**Saxifraga stolonifera**
Saxifraga stolonifera 'Tricolor'	Strawberry geranium	
		Saxifraga stolonifera 'Tricolor'
Saxifrage à trois doigis	Fingered saxifrage	**Saxifraga tridactylites**
Saxifraga urbium	London pride	**Saxifraga urbium**
Sauromatum venosum	Monarch of the East / Voodoo lily	
		Sauromatum venosum
Savonnière	Soapwort	**Saponaria officinalis**
Scabieuse	Scabious	**Knautia arvensis / Scabiosa**
Scabieuse colombaire	Small scabious	**Scabiosa columbaria**
Scabieuse des jardins	Sweet scabious	**Scabiosa atropurpurea**

Scadoxus multiflorus katherinae	Blood flower	
		Scadoxus multiflorus katherinae
Scadoxus puniceus	Royal paintbrush	**Scadoxus puniceus**
Scandix peigne-de-Vénus	Shepherd's needle	**Scandix pecten-veneris**
Sceau-de-Salomon	Solomon's seal	**Polygonatum**
Sceau-de-Salomon	Great Solomon's seal	
		Polygonatum commutatum
Scaeu de Salomon multiflore	Common Solomon's seal	**Polygonatum multiflorum**
Sceau de Salomon odorant	Angled Solomon's seal	
		Polygonatum odoratum
Sceau de Salomon verticillé	Whorled Solomon's seal	
		Polygonatum verticillatum
Scheuchzérie des marais	Rannoch rush	**Scheuchzeria palustris**
Schizanthus	Butterfly flower / Poor man's orchid	**Schizanthus**
Schizophragma hydrangeoides	Japanese hydrangea vine	
		Schizophragma hydrangeoides
Schlumbergera bridgesii	Christmas cactus	**Schlumbergera bridgesii**
Schizostylis	Kaffir Lily	**Schizostylis**
Scille d'automne	Autumn squill	**Scilla autumnalis**
Scilla du Pérou	Peruvian scilla	**Scilla peruviana**
Scille printanière	Spring squill	**Scilla verna**
Scille de Sibérie	Siberian squill	**Scilla sibirica**
Scirpe	Bull rush	**Scirpus**
Scirpe épingle	Needle spike rush	**Eleocharis acicularis**
Scirpe à tête ronde	Round headed club-root	**Scirpus holoschoenus**
Scorzonère basse	Viper's grass	**Scorzonera humilis**
Scrofulaire	Figwort	**Scrophularia**
Scrofulaire aquatique	Water figwort	**Scrophularia auriculata**
Scrofulaire noueuse	Common figwort	**Scrophularia nodosa**
Scrofulaire du Cap	Cape figwort	**Phygelius capensis**
Scrofulaire à feuilles de germandrée	Balm-leaved figwort	**Scrophularia scorddonia**
Scrofulaire du printemps	Yellow figwort	**Scrophularia vernalis**
Scutellaire	Skullcap	**Scutellaria**
Scutellaire casquée	Common skullcap	**Scutellaria galericulata**
Sedum morganianum	Burro's tail / Donkey-tail	**Sedum morganianum**
Sedum spectabile	Ice plant	**Sedum spectabile**
Selaginella lepidophylla	Resurrection plant / Rose of Jericho	
		Selaganella lepidophylla
Sélinum à feuilles de carvi	Cambridge parsley	**Selinum carvifolia**
Semele andrgyna	Climbing butcher's broom	**Semele andrgyna**

Semiarundinaria fastuosa	Narihira bamboo	**Semiarundinaria fastuosa**
Sénebière corne-de-cerf	Common wart cress	**Coronopus squamatus**
Sénebière didyme	Slender wart cress	**Coronopus didymus**
Séneçon aquatique	Marsh ragwort	**Senecio aquaticus**
Séneçon en arbre	Bush groundsel	**Baccharis halimifolia**
Séneçon des bois	Heath groundsel	**Senecio sylvaticus**
Séneçon confusus	Mexican flame vine	**Senecio confusus**
Séneçon à feuilles de roquette	Hoary ragwort	**Senecio erucifolius**
Séneçon à feuilles entières	Field fleawort	**Senecio integrifolius**
Séneçon jacobée	Common ragwort	**Senecio jacobaea**
Séneçon macroglossus	Natal ivy / Wax vine	**Senecio macroglossus**
Séneçon négligé	Oxford ragwort	**Senecio squalidus**
Séneçon des rivières	Saracen's woundwort	**Senecio fluviatilis**
Séneçon rowleyanus	String-of-beads	**Senecio rowleyanus**
Séneçon smithii	Magellan ragwort	**Senecio smithii**
Séneçon visqueux	Sticky groundsel	**Senecio viscosus**
Sénevé	Charlock	**Sinapis arvensis**
Senné didymobotrya	Golden wonder	**Cassia didymobotrya**
Sensitive pudique	Humble plant / Sensitive plant	**Mimosa pudica**
Serpent végétal.	Snake gourd.	**Trichosanthes anguina**
Sequoia sempervirens	Coast redwood / Redwood	**Sequoia sempervirens**
Sequoiadendron giganteum	Big tree / Giant redwood / Wellintonia	**Sequoiadendron giganteum**
Serenoa repens	Saw palmetto / Scrub palmetto	**Serenoa repens**
Seringat	Mock orange	**Philadelphus coronarius**
Serpentaire	Dragon tree	**Dracunculus vulgaris**
Serratule des teinturiers	Sawwort	**Serratula tinctoria**
Sesleria heufleriana	Balkan blue grass	**Sesleria heufleriana**
Sétaire d'Italie	Italian millet	**Setaria italica**
Shepherdia argentea	Buffalo Berry	**Shepherdia argentea**
Shérarde des champs	Field madder	**Sherardia arvensis**
Shortia galacifolia	Oconee bells	**Shortia galacifolia**
Sibbaldie couchée	Least cinquefoil	**Sibbaldia procumbens**
Sibthorpie d'Europe	Cornish moneywort	**Sibthorpia europaea**
Silène	Campion / Catchfly	**Silene**
Silène acaule	Moss campion	**Silene acaulis**
Silène conique	Sand catchfly	**Silene conica**
Silène de Crète	Nodding catchfly	**Silene pendula**
Silène du nuit	Night-scented catchfly	**Silene noctiflora**
Silène penché	Nottingham catchfly	**Silene nutans**
Silène à petites fleurs	Breckland catchfly	**Silene otites**

Silène maritime	Sea campion	**Silene vulgaris maritima**
Silène maritime double	Double sea campion	**Silene vulgaris maritima flore pleno**
Simathis à feuilles plates	Kerry lily	**Simethis planifolia**
Sison amome	Stone parsley	**Sison amomum**
Sisymbre fausse-moutarde	Tumbling mustard	**Sisymbrium altissimum**
Sisymbre sagesse	Flixweed	**Descurainia sophia**
Sisyrinchium californicum	Golden-eyed grass	**Sisyrinchium californicum**
Sisyrinchium douglasii	Grass widow / Spring bell	**Sisyrinchium douglasii**
Smilacina racemosa	False spikenard	**Smilacina racemosa**
Smithiantha cinnabarina	Temple bells	**Smithiantha cinnabarina**
Solandra maxima	Capa de oro / Golden chalice tree	**Solandra maxima**
Solanum jasminoides	Potato vine	**Solanum jasminoides**
Soldanelle des montagnes	Mountain tassel	**Soldanella montana**
Solanum rantonnetii	Blue potato bush	**Solanum rantonnetii**
Solanum seaforthianum	Potato creeper	**Solanum seaforthianum**
Soldanelle	Snowbell	**Soldanella**
Soldanelle des Alpes	Alpine snowbell	**Soldanella alpina**
Soldanella minima	Least snowbell	**Soldanella minima**
Soleil	Sunflower	**Helianthus**
Soleil annuel	Annual sunflower	**Helianthus annuus**
Soleil de Californie	Mexican sunflower	**Tiphonia rotundifolia**
Soleirolia	Baby's tears / Mind your own business / Mother of thousands	**Soleirolia**
Sophora tetraptera	Kowhai	**Sophora**
Sophora du Japon	Pagoda tree	**Sophora japonica**
Sorbier des oiseleurs	Mountain ash / Rowan	**Sorbus aucuparia**
Sorbier à feuilles d'aune	Korean mountain ash	**Sorbus alnifolia**
Sorbier d'Amérique	American mountain ash	**Sorbus americana**
Sorbier domestique	Service tree	**Sorbus domestica**
Sorbus hupehensis	Hupeh rowan	**Sorbus hupehensis**
Sorbus intermedia	Swedish whitebeam	**Sorbus intermedia**
Sorbus sargentiana	Sargent's rowan	**Sorbus sargentiana**
Souchet	Galingale	**Cyperus longus**
Souchet à papier	Papyrus	**Cyperus papyrus**
Souci	African daisy / Cape marigold	**Dimorphotheca**
Souci	Marigold	**Calendula**
Souci des jardins	Pot marigold	**Calendula officinalis**
Souci pluvial	Rain daisy	**Dimorphotheca pluvialis**
Soude maritime	Common seablite	**Suaeda maritima**

Soude salsovie	Saltwort	**Salsola kali**
Souris végétale	Kiwi fruit / Chinese gooseberry	
		Actinidia chinensis
Sparaxis	Harlequin flower	**Sparaxis**
Sparmannia africana	African Hemp	**Sparmannia africana**
Spathiphyllum wallisii	Peace lily / White sails	
		Spathiphyllum wallisii
Spathodea campanulata	African tulip tree / Flame-of-the-forest	
		Spathodea campanulata
Spergulaire bocconei	Greek sand spurrey	**Spergularia bocconi**
Spergulaire marginée	Greater sea spurrey	**Spergularia media**
Spergulaire marine	Sea spurrey	**Spergularia marina**
Spergulaire rouge	Sand spurrey	**Spergularia rubra**
Spergulaire des rochers	Cliff spurry	**Spergularia rupicola**
Spirée 'Arguta'	Bridal wreath / Foam of May	**Spiraea 'Arguta'**
Spirée ulmaire	Meadowsweet	**Filipendula ulmaria**
Spirée x vanhouttei	Bridal wreath	**Spiraea x vanhouttei**
Spiranthe d'Irlande	American lady's tresses	
		Spiranthes romanzoffiana
Spiranthe contourné	Autumn lady's tresses	**Spiranthes spiralis**
Stapelia variegata	Star flower	**Stapelia variegata**
Statice	Statice	**Limonium**
Statice à deux nervures	Rock sea-lavender	**Limonium binervosum**
Statice à feuilles de paquerette	Matted sea-lavender	
		Limonium bellidifolium
Statice nain	Lax sea-lavender	**Limonium humile**
Stellaire aquatique	Water chickweed	**Myosoton aquaticum**
Stellaire des bois	Wood chickweed	**Stellaria nemorum**
Stellaire graminé	Lesser stitchwort	**Stellaria graminea**
Stellaire holostée	Greater stitchwort	**Stellaria holostea**
Stellaire des marais	Marsh stitchwort	**Stellaria palustris**
Stellaire négligé	Greater chickweed	**Stellaria neglecta**
Stellaire pâle	Lesser chickweed	**Stellaria pallida**
Stenocarpus sinuatu	Australian firewheel tree	**Stenocarpus sinuatu**
Stenotaphrium secundatum	St. Augustine's grass	
		Stenotaphrium secundatum
Stephanotis floribunda	Madagascar jasmine / Wax flower	
		Stephanotis floribunda
Stipa arundinacea	Pheasant grass	**Stipa arundinacea**
Stipa gigantea	Golden oats	**Stipa gigantea**
Stramoine odorante	Angels' trumpets / Thorn-apple	**Datura**
Stratiote faux-aloès	Water soldier	**Stratiotes aloides**

Streptocarpus rexii	Cape primrose	**Streptocarpus rexii**
Streptosolen jamesonii	Marmalade bush	**Streptosolen jamesonii**
Strongylodon macrobotrys	Jade vine	**Strongylodon macrobotrys**
Stylidium graminifolium	Trigger plant	**Stylidium graminifolium**
Styrax obassia	Fragrant snowbel	**Styrax obassia**
Subulaire aquatique	Awlwort	**Subularia aquatica**
Succise des prés	Devil's bit scabious	**Succisa pratensis**
Sugi	Japanese cedar	**Cryptomeria japonica**
Sumac	Sumach	**Rhus**
Sumac à bois glabre	Smooth sumach	**Rhus glabra**
Sumac amarante	Stag's horn sumach	**Rhus typhina**
Sumac fustet	Smoke tree / Venetian sumach	**Cotinus coggygria**
Sumac faux vernis	Wax tree	**Rhus succedanea**
Sumac verniciflua	Varnish tree	**Rhus verniciflua**
Sumac de Virginie	Stag's horn sumach	**Rhus typhina**
Sureau	Elder	**Sambucus**
Sureau du Canada	American elder	**Sambucus canadensis**
Sureau à grappes	Red-berried elder	**Sambucus racemosa**
Sureau noir aurea	Golden elder	**Sambucus nigra aurea**
Sureau rouge	Red-berried elder	**Sambucus racemosa**
Swainsonia galegifolia	Darling pea	**Swainsonia galegifolia**
Symphorine	Snowberry	**Symphoricarpus albus**
Symphorine orbiculata	Indian currant	**Symphoricarpos orbiculata**
Symplocarpe	Skunk cabbage	**Symplocarpus**
Symplocos paniculata	Sapphira berry	**Symplocos paniculata**
Synadenium grantii	African milkbush	**Synadenium grantii**
Syngonium auritum	Five fingers	**Syngonium auritum**

T

Tabac blanc odorant	Nicotiana alata	**Nicotiana alata**
Tabac sylvestris	Flowering tobacco	**Nicotiana sylvestris**
Tabebuia chrysotricha	Golden trumpet tree	**Tabebuia chrysotricha**
Tabebuia rosea	Pink trumpet	**Tabebuia rosea**
Tabouret des champs	Common penny-cress	**Thlaspi arvense**
Tacca chantrieri	Bat flower	**Tacca chantrieri**
Tacca leontopetaloides	South sea arrowroot	**Tacca leontopetaloides**
Tamarin	Tamarind	**Tamarindus indica**
Tamarinier	Tamarind	**Tamarindus indica**
Tamaris	Tamarisk	**Tamarix gallica**
Tamaris de France	Tamarisk	**Tamarix gallica**
Tamier commun	Black bryony	**Tamus communis**

Tanaisie commune	Tansy	**Tanacetum vulgare**
Taro	Taro	**Colocasia esculenta**
Taro	Giant elephant's ear / Taro	**Alocasia macrorrhiza**
Tecoma stans	Yellow bells / Yellow elder	**Tecoma stans**
Teesdalie à tige nue	Shepherd's cress	**Teesdalia nudicaulis**
Telopea speciosissima	Waratah	**Telopea speciosissima**
Telopea truncata	Tasmanian waratah	**Telopea truncata**
Templetonia retusa	Coral bush	**Templetonia retusa**
Térébinthe	Cyprus turpentine / Terebinth tree	
		Pistachia terebintha
Tétragonolobe siliqueeux	Dragon's teeth	**Tetragonolobus maritimus**
Tetranema roseum	Mexican foxglove / Mexican violet	
		Tetranema roseum
Tetrapanax papyriferus	Rice-paper plant	**Tetrapanax papyriferus**
Tetrastigma voinerianum	Chestnut vine	**Tetrastigma voinerianum**
Thamnocalamus spathaceus	Muriel bamboo	**Thamnocalamus spathaceus**
Thé du Labrador Labrador tea		**Ledum groenlandicus / Ledum palustre**
Thelypteris hexagonoptera	Broad beech fern	**Thelypteris hexagonoptera**
Thelypteris oreopteris	Mountain wood fern / Mountain fern	
		Thelypteris oreopteris
Thelypteris palustirs	Marsh buckler fern	**Thelypteris palustirs**
Thésium couché	Bastard toadflax	**Thesium humifusum**
Thespesia populnea	Mahoe / Portia oil nut	**Thespesia populnea**
Thlaspi des Alpes	Alpine penny-cress	**Thlaspi alpinum**
Thuya du Canada	American arbor-vitae / Eastern white cedar	
		Thuja occidentalis
Thuya de Corée	Korean thuja	**Thuja koraiensis**
Thuya d'Orient Biota / Chinese arbor-vitae / Chinese thuja		**Thuja orientalis**
Thuja plicata	Western red cedar	**Thuja plicata**
Tujopsis dolabrata	Hiba	**Thujopsis dolabrata**
Thunbergia alata	Black-eyed Susan	**Thunbergia alata**
Thunbergia grandiflora	Blue trumpet vine	**Thunbergia grandiflora**
Thym	Thyme	**Thymus**
Thym herba-barona	Caraway thyme	**Thymus herba-barona**
Thymélée des Alpes	Daphne cneorum	**Daphne cneorum**
Tiarella	Foamflower	**Tiarella**
Tibouchina urvelleana	Glory bush	**Tibouchina urvelleana**
Tigride	Peacock flower / Tiger flower	**Tigridia pavonia**
Tillée mousse	Mossy stonecrop	**Crassula tillaea**
Tilleul	Lime / Linden	**Tilia**
Tilleul d'Amèrique	American lime / Basswood	**Tilia american**
Tilleul argenté	European white lime /Silver lime	**Tilia tomentosa**

Tilleul de Crimée	Caucasian lime / Crimean lime	**Tilia x euchlora**
Tilleul à feuille de vigne	Mongolian Lime	**Tilia mongolica**
Tilleul à grandes feuille	Broad-leaved lime / Large leafed lime	
		Tilia platyphyllos
Tilleul de Hollande	Large leafed lime	**Tilia platyphylos**
Tilleul de Hongrie	European white lime	**Tilia tomentosa**
Tilleul petiolaris	Pendent silver lime	**Tilia petiolaris**
Tilleul de Mongolie	Mongolian Lime	**Tilia mongolica**
Tilleul à petites feuilles	Small leaved lime	**Tilia cordata**
Tillandsia ionantha	Sky plant	**Tillandsia ionantha**
Tillandsia lindenii	Blue flowered torch	**Tillandsia lindenii**
Tipuana tipu	Tipa tree / Pride of Bolivia	**Tipuana tipu**
Tofieldie fluette	Scottish asphodel	**Tolmiea menziesii**
Tolmiea menziesii	Pick-a-back plant / Youth and age	**Tolmiea menziesii**
Tomate en arbre	Tree tomato	**Cyphomandra betacea**
Topinambour	Jerusalem artichoke	**Helianthus tuberosus**
Toque en casque	Common skullcap	**Scutellaria galericulata**
Toque mineur	Lesser skullcap	**Scutellaria minor**
Tordyle majeur	Hartwort	**Tordylium maximum**
Torenia fournieri	Wish-bone flower	**Torenia fournieri**
Torilis des champs	Spreading bur parsley	**Torilis arvensis**
Torilis faux-cherfeuil	Hedge parsley	**Torilis japonica**
Torilis à feuilles glomérulées	Knotted bur parsley	**Torilis nodosa**
Toque	Skullcap	**Scutellaria**
Torreya californica	California buckeye	**Torreya californica**
Tournesol	Annual sunflower	**Helianthus annuus**
Toute-bonne	Salvia sclarea	**Salvia sclarea**
Toute-bonne	Tutsan	**Hypericum androsaemum**
Trachélie	Throatwort	**Trachelium caeruleum**
Trachycarpus fortunei	Windmill palm	**Trachycarpus fortunei**
Trachymene caerulea	Blue lace flower	**Trachymene caerulea**
Trachystème d'Orient	Abraham, Isaac & Jacob.	
		Trachystemon orientalis
Tradescantia	Spiderwort	**Tradescantia**
Tradescantia fluminensis	Wandering Jew	**Tradescantia fluminensis**
Tradescantia spathacea	Boat lily.	**Tradescantia spathacea**
Trèfle	Clover	**Trifolium**
Trèfle aggloméré	Clustered clover	**Trifolium glomeratum**
Trèfle blanc	White clover	**Trifolium repens**
Trèfle des champs	Hare's foot clover	**Trifolium arvense**
Trèfle d'eau	Bog bean / Buckbean	**Menyanthes trifoliata**

Trèfle douteux	Common yellow trefoil	**Trifolium dubium**
Trèfle étouffé	Suffocated clover	**Trifolium suffocatum**
Trèfle flexueux	Zigzag clover	**Trifolium medium**
Trèfle fraisier	Strawberry clover	**Trifolium fraggiferum**
Trèfle hybride	Alsike clover	**Trifolium hybridum**
Trèfle incarnat	Crimson clover	**Trifolium incarnatum**
Trèfle jaune	Hop trefoil	**Trifolium campestre**
Trèfle jaunâtre	Sulphur clover	**Trifolium ochroleucon**
Trèfle maritime	Sea clover	**Trifolium squamosum**
Trèfle des prés	Red clover	**Trifolium pratense**
Trèfle rampant	White clover	**Trifolium repens**
Trèfle strié	Soft clover	**Trifolium striatum**
Tremble	Aspen	**Populus tremula**
Tremble pleureur	Weeping aspen	**Populus tremula 'Pendula'**
Tremblotte	Quaking grass	**Briza**
Trichocereus spachianus	Torch cactus	**Trichocereus spachianus**
Tricyrtis	Toad lily	**Tricyrtis**
Trientalis d'Europe	Chickweed willow-herb	**Trientalis europaea**
Trigonelle	Fenugreek	**Trigoella foenum-graecum**
Trillie	Trinity flower / Wood lily	**Trillium**
Trillie erectum	Birthroot / Squawroot	**Trillium erectum**
Trillie	Wake-robin	**Trillium grandiflorum**
Trillie nivale	Dwarf white wood lily / Snow trillium	**Trillium nivale**
Trillie sessile	Toadshade / Wake-robin	**Trillium sessile**
Trillie undulatum	Painted trillium / Painted wood lily	**Trillium undulatum**
Trinia glauque	Honewort	**Trinia glauca**
Tristania conferta	Brush-box tree	**Tristania conferta**
Troène	Privet	**Ligustrum vulgare**
Troène du Japon	Japanese privet	**Ligustrum japonicum**
Troène de Chine	Chinese privet	**Ligustrum lucidum**
Trolle	Globe flower	**Trollius europaeus**
Troscart des marais	Marsh arrow-grass	**Triglochin palustris**
Troscart maritime	Sea arrow-grass	**Triglochin maritima**
Tsuga de Californie	Western hemlock	**Tsuga heterophylla**
Tsuga du Canada	Canada hemlock / Eastern hemlock	**Tsuga canadensis**
Tsuga de Caroline	Carolina hemlock	**Tsuga caroliniana**
Tsuga de Japon	Japanese hemlock / Northern Japanese hemlock	**Tsuga diversifolia**
Tsuga de Japon	Japanese hemlock / Southern Japanese hemlock	**Tsuga sieboldii**
Tsuga mertensiana	Mountain hemlock	**Tsuga mertensiana**
Tubéreuse	Tuberose	**Polianthes tuberosa**
Tue-chien	Autumn crocus	**Colchicum autumnale**

Tulip	Tulip	**Tulipa**
Tulipe cornue	Horned tulip	**Tulipa acuminata**
Tulipe de l'Écluse	Lady tulip	**Tulipa clusiana**
Tulipa kaufmaniana	Water lily tulip	**Tulipa kaufmaniana**
Tulipe de Mormons	Golden fairy lantern / Golden globe tulip	
		Calochortus amabilis
Tulipe radis	Lady tulip	**Tulipa clusiana**
Tulipe sauvage	Wild tulip	**Tulipa sylvestris**
Tulipe turque	Horned tulip	**Tulipa acuminata**
Tulipier	Tulip tree	**Liriodendron tulipifera**
Tulipier de Chine	Chinese tulip tree	**Liriodendron chinense**
Tunique	Tunic flower	**Petrorhagia saxifraga**
Tupélo	Tupelo	**Nyssa**
Tylecodon paniculata	Butter tree	**Tylecodon paniculata**
Tylecodon reticulata	Barbed wire plant	**Tylecodon reticulata**

U

Urginea maritima	Crusaders' spears / Sea onion / Sea onion	**Urginea maritima**
Utricularia intermedia	Irish bladderwort	**Utricularia intermedia**
Utriculaire fluette	Small bladderwort	**Utricularia minor**
Utriculaire commune	Greater bladderwort	**Utricularis vulgaris**
Uvularia grandiflora	Bellwort / Merry-bells	**Uvularia grandiflora**

V

Vaccineum arctastaphylos	Caucasian whortleberry	**Vaccineum arctastaphylos**
Vacoua	Screw pine	**Pandanus**
Valériane	Valerian	**Valeriana**
Valériane dioïque	Marsh valerian	**Valeriana dioica**
Valériane Grecque	Jacob's ladder	**Polemonium caeruleum**
Valériane officinalis	Cat's valerian / Common valerian	
		Valeriana officinalis
Valériane des Pyrénées	Giant valerian	**Valeriana pyrenaica**
Valériane rouge	Red valerian	**Centranthus ruber**
Vallisnérie spiraliée	Tape grass	**Vallisneria spiralis**
Veillote	Autumn crocus	**Colchicum autumnale**
Vélar	Siberian wallflower	**Erysimum hieraciifolium**
Vélar fause-giroflée	Treacle mustard	**Erysimum cheiranthoides**
Vératre blanc	White false hellebore	**Veratrum album**
Vératre noir	Black false hellebore	**Veratrum nigrum**
Verge d'or	Golden-rod	**Solidago virgaurea**

Verge d'or du Canada	Canadian golden-rod	**Solidago canadensis**
Vergerette	Fleabane	**Erigeron**
Vergerette acre	Blue fleabane	**Erigeron acer**
Vergerette dea Alpes	Alpine fleabane	**Erigeron alpinus**
Vergerette dea Alpes	Highland fleabane	**Erigeron borealis**
Vergerette du Canada	Canadian fleabane	**Conyza canadenis**
Verne	Alder	**Alnus glutinosa**
Vernouiller	Dogwood	**Cornus sanguinea**
Véronique	Speedwell	**Veronica**
Véronique agreste	Green field speedwell	**Veronica agrestis**
Véronique aquatique	Pink water speedwell	**Veronica catenata**
Véronique des champs	Wall speedwell	**Veronica arvensis**
Véronique couchée	Prostrate speedwell	**Veronica prostrata**
Véronique à Écusson	Marsh speedwell	**Veronica scutellata**
Véronique en épi	Spiked speedwell	**Veronica spicata**
Véronique luisante	Grey field speedwell	**Veronica persica**
Véronique à feuilles de lierre	Ivy speedwell	**Veronica hederifolia**
Véronique digitée	Fingered speedwell	**Veronica triphyllos**
Véronique perfoliata	Digger speedwell	**Veronica perfoliata**
Véronique de Perse	Common field speedwell	**Veronica persica**
Véronique précoce	Breck speedwell	**Veronica praecox**
Véronique printanière	Spring speedwell	**Veronica verna**
Véronique des rochers	Rock speedwell	**Veronica fruticans**
Véronique voyageuse	American speedwell	**Veronica peregrina**
Verveine officinale	Vervain	**Verbena officinalis**
Verveine ruguese	Verbena rigida	**Verbena rigida**
Verveine veineuse	Verbena rigida	**Verbena rigida**
Vesce	Vetch	**Vicia**
Vesce de Bithynie	Bithynian vetch	**Vicia bithynica**
Vesce cracca	Tufted vetch	**Vicia cracca**
Vesce cultivée	Common vetch	**Vicia sativa**
Vesce des forêts	Wood vetch	**Vicia sylvatica**
Vesce des haies	Bush vetch	**Vicia sepium**
Vesce hérissée	Hairy tare	**Vicia hirsuta**
Vesce jaune	Yellow vetch	**Vicia lutea**
Vesce printanière	Spring vetch	**Vicia lathyroides**
Vesce orobe	Upright vetch	**Vicia orobus**
Vesce à quatre graines	Smooth tare	**Vicia tetrasperma**
Vigna caracalla	Snail flower	**Vigna caracalla**
Vigne	Vine	**Vitis**
Vigne de l'Amur	Amur grape	**Vitis amurensis**
Vigne du Mont Ida	Cowberry	**Vaccinium vitis-idaea**

Vigne vrai	Grape vine	**Vriesea hieroglyphica**
Vigne vierge japonais	Boston ivy / Japanese ivy	**Parthenocissus tricuspidata**
Vigne vierge vraie	Five leaved ivy / Virginia creeper	**Parthenocissus quinquefolia**
Vigne vierge vraie	Five leaved ivy	**Ampelopsis quinquefolia**
Vinaigrier	Smooth sumach	**Rhus glabra**
Vinettier de Darwin	Darwin's barberry	**Berberis darwinii**
Violette	Violet	**Viola**
Violette africaine	African violet	**Saintpaulia**
Violette à deux fleurs	Twin flowered violet	**Viola biflora**
Violette de la Chandeleur	Snowdrop	**Galanthus nivalis**
Violette des chiens	Heath dog violet	**Viola canina**
Violette cornuta	Horned violet	**Viola cornuta**
Violette hederacea	Australian violet / Ivy-leafed violet	**Viola hederacea**
Violette hérissée	Hairy violet	**Viola hirta**
Violette lactée	Pale heath violet	**Viola lactea**
Violette odorante	Sweet violet	**Viola odorata**
Violette des marais	Marsh violet	**Viola pedata**
Violette pied d'oiseau	Bird's foot violet	**Viola pedata**
Violette des bois	Wood dog violet	**Viola reichenbachiana**
Violette de rivin	Common dog violet	**Viola riviniana**
Violette d'Usambara	African violet	**Saintpaulia**
Violier	Wallflower	**Cheiranthus cheiri**
Violier d'hiver	Snowdrop	**Galanthus nivalis**
Viorne cotoneuse	Wayfaring tree	**Viburnum lantana**
Viorne à feuilles d'érable	Viburnum acerifolium	**Viburnum acerifolium**
Viorne lentago	Sheepberry	**Viburnum lentago**
Viorne manciennne	Wayfaring tree	**Viburnum lantana**
Viorne obier	Guelder rose	**Viburnum opulus**
Viorne odororante	Sweet viburnum	**Viburnum odoratissimum**
Vipérine commune	Viper's bugloss	**Echium vulgare**
Vipérine pourpre	Purple viper's bugloss	**Echium plantagineum**
Virginier à bois jaune	Yellow wood	**Cladrastis lutea**
Viscaire des Alpes	Alpine catchfly	**Lychnis alpina**
Vitis coignetiae	Crimson glory vine	**Vitis coignetiae**
Volubilis	Common morning glory	**Ipomoea purpurea**
Volubilis argenté	Silver morning glory	**Argyreia splendens**
Vriesea hieroglyphica	King of the bromeliads	**Vriesea hieroglyphica**
Vriesea splendens	Flaming sword	**Vriesea splendens**

W

Wahlenbergia albomarginata	New Zealand bluebell	
		Wahlenbergia albomarginata
Wahlenbergie à feuilles de lierre	Ivy-leafed bellfower	
		Wahlenbergia hederacea
Washingtonia filifera	Desert fan palm	**Washingtonia filifera**
Washingtonia robusta	Thread palm	**Washingtonia robusta**
Westringia fruticosa	Australian rosemary / Australian sassafras	
		Westringia fruticosa
Wigginsia orwerkiana	Colombian ball cactus	**Wigginsia vorwerkiana**
Wolfie sans racine	Least duckweed	**Wolffia arrhiza**
Woodsia des Alpes	Alpine woodsia	**Woodsia alpina**
Woodsia ilvensis	Rusty woodsia	**Woodsia ilvensis**
Woodwardie radicans	Chain fern	**Woodwardia radicans**
Woodwardie virginica	American chain fern / Virginia chain fern	**Woodwardia virginica**
Worsleya	Blue amaryllis	**Worsleya**

X

Xamthème	Immortelle	**Xeranthemum annuum**
Xanthorhiza simplicissima	Yellow-root	**Xanthorhiza simplicissima**
Xanthorrhoea	Grass tree	**Xanthorrhoée**

Y

Yeuse	Holm oak	**Quercus ilex**
Yucca aloifolia	Spanish bayonet	**Yucca aloifolia**
Yucca filamentosa	Adam's needle	**Yucca filamentosa**
Yucca gloriosa	Spanish dagger	**Yucca gloriosa**

Z

Zanichellie des marais	Horned pondweed	**Zannichellia palustris**
Zantedeschia elliotiana	Golden arum lily	**Zantedeschia elliotiana**
Zephyranthes atamasco	Atamasco lily	**Zephyranthes atamasco**
Zostère à feuilles étroites	Narrow-leaved eel-grass	**Zostera angustifolia**
Zostère marine	Common eel-grass	**Zostera marina**

Latin	*Français*	English

A

Latin	*Français*	English
Abies alba	*Sapin argenté / Sapin commun / Sapin des Vosges*	Silver fir
Abies amabilis	*Sapin amabilis*	Pacifc fir
Abies balsamea	*Sapin Baumier*	Balsam fir
Abies cephalonica	*Sapin de Céphalonie*	Greek fir
Abies concolor	*Sapin concolor*	White fir
Abies delavayi	*Sapin delaveyi*	Delavay fir
Abies grandis	*Sapin de Vancouver*	Giant fir / Grand fir
Abies homolepis	*Sapin homolepis*	Nikko fir
Abies koreana	*Sapin de Corée*	Korean fir
Abies lasiocarpa	*Sapin lasiocarpa*	Subalpine fir
Abies nordmanniana	*Sapin de Nordmann*	Caucasian fir
Abies procera	*Sapin noble*	Noble fir
Abies veitchii	*Sapin de Veitch*	Veitch fir
Acacia	*Mimosa*	Mimosa
Acacia baileyana	*Acacia baileyana*	Cootmandra wattle
Acacia cultriformis	*Mimosa couteau*	Knife-leaf wattle
Acacia dealbata	*Mimosa*	Silver wattle
Acacia longifolia	*Chenille*	Sydney golden wattle
Acacia pravissima	*Acacia pravissima*	Ovens wattle
Acacia pulchella	*Acacia pulchella*	Western prickly Moses
Acacia verticillata	*Acacia verticillata*	Prickly Moses
Acalypha hispida	*Acalypha hispida*	Red-hot cat's tail
Acalypha wilkesiana	*Ricinelle*	Jacob's coat / Copperleaf
Acanthus mollis	*Acanthe à feuilles molles / Branc-ursine*	Bear's breeches
Acer buergerianum	*Érable buergerianum*	Trident maple
Acer campestre	*Érable champêtre*	Maple
Acer capillipes	*Érable capillipes*	Snake-bark maple
Acer cappadocium	*Érable de Cappadocie*	Cappadocian Maple
Acer carpinifolium	*Erable à feuilles de charme*	Hornbeam maple
Acer circinatum	*Érable à feuilles rondes*	Vine maple
Acer crataegifolium	*Érable à feuilles d'aubépine*	Hawthorn maple
Acer davidii	*Érable davidii*	Père David's maple / Snake-bark maple
Acer ginnala	*Érable du fleuve Amour*	Amur maple
Acer griseum	*Érable gris*	Paper bark maple
Acer grosseri var. hersii	*Érable grosseri var. hersii*	Her's maple
Acer japonicum	*Érable du Japon*	Full moon maple / Japanese maple
Acer lobelii	*Érable de Lobel*	Lobel's maple
Acer macrophyllum	*Érable macrophyllum*	Oregon maple

Acer monspessulanum	Érable de Montpellier	Montpelier maple
Acer negundo	Érable negundo	Ash-leaved maple / Box elder
Acer nikoense	Érable nikoense	Nikko maple
Acer opalus	Érable d'Italie	Italian maple
Acer palmatum	Érable du Japon	Japanese maple
Acer palmatum 'Senkaki'	Érable palmatum 'Senkaki'	Cork bark maple
Acer pensylvanicum	Érable jaspé	Snake-bark maple
Acer plantanoides	Érable plane	Norway maple
Acer pseudoplatanus	Érable sycomore	Sycamore
Acer rubrum	Érable rouge / Plaine rouge	Red maple
Acer rufinerve	Érable rufinerve	Snake-bark maple
Acer saccharum	Érable à sucre	Sugar maple
Acer saccherinum	Érable argenté / Plaine blanche	Silver maple
Acer velutinumm vanvolxemii	Érable velutinum vanvolxemii	Van Volxem's maple
Aceras anthropophorum	Orchis Homme-pendu	Man orchid
Achillea	Achillée	Achillea
Achillea millefolium	Achillée millefeuille	Yarrow
Achillea ptarmica	Achillée sternutatoire / Bouton d'argent	Sneezewort
Aciphylla aurea	Aciphylla aurea	Golden Spaniard
Aciphylla scott-thomsonii	Aciphylla scott-thomsonii	Giant Spaniard
Aciphylla squarrosa	Aciphylla Squarrosa	Bayonet plant
Acokanthera oblongifolia	Acokanthera oblongifolia	Wintersweet
Aconitum	Aconit	Aconite
Aconitum anglicum	Aconit anglicum	Monkshood
Aconitum napellus	Aconit napel	Helmet flower
Aconitum vulparia	Aconit tu-loup	Wolf's bane
Acorus calamus variegatus	Acore vrai	Sweet flag / Myrtle flag
Actaea	Actée en épi / Herbe de St. Christophe	Baneberry
Actaea pachypoda	Actée pachypoda	Doll's eyes / White baneberry
Actaea rubra	Actée rouge	Red baneberry
Actinidia arguta	Actinidie denticulée	Bower vine
Actinidia chinensis	Kiwi / Souris végétale	Chinese gooseberry / Kiwi fruit
Actinidia polygama	Actinidie polygame	Silver vine
Adansonia	Adansonia	Boabab
Adenium	Rose du désert	Desert rose
Adenophora	Adenophora	Gland bellflower
Adiantum capillus veneris	Capillaire de Montpellier	Maidenhair fern
Adiantum capillus veneris	Cheveux de Vénus	Maidenhair fern
Adiantum cuneatum	Capillaire cunéiforme	Delta maidenhair
Adiantum pedantum	Capillaire pedantum	Northern maidenhair fern

Adiantum 'Grandiceps' *Capillaire raddianum 'Grandiceps'*
Tassel maidenhair
Adlumia fungosa *Adlumia fungosa* Alleghany vine / Climbing fumitory
Adonis annua *Adonis d'automne* Pheasant's eye
Adonis vernalis *Adonis printanière* Spring adonis
Adoxa moschatellina *Moschatelline* Moschatel
Adromischus festivus *Adromischus festivus* Plovers' eggs
Aechmea fasciata *Aechmea fasciata* Um plant / Silver vase plant
Aechmea "Foster's favourite" *Aechmea "Foster's favourite"*
Laquered wine cup
Aechmea fulgens *Aechmea fulgens* Coral berry
Aegopodium podagraria *Herbe aux goutteux*
Goat weed / Ground elder / Bishop's weed (In Scotland)
Aegopodium podagraria 'Variegatum'
Égopode panaché / Herbe aux goutteux panaché
Variegated Bishop's weed / Variegated gout weed
Aeonium haworthii *Aeonium haworthii* Pinwheel
Aeschyanthus pulcher *Aeschynanthus pulcher* Lipstick plant / Royal red bugler
Aesculus *Marronnier* Buckeye
Aesculus californica *Marronnier de Californie* California nutmeg
Aesculus x carnea *Marronnier à fleurs rouges* Red horsechestnut
Aesculus chinensis *Marronnier de Chine* Chinese horse chestnut
Aesculus flava *Marronnier jaune* Sweet buckeye / Yellow buckeye
Aesculus glabra *Marronnier glabra* Ohio buckeye
Aesculus hippocastanum *Marronnier / Pavier* Horse chestnut
Aesculus indica *Marronnier d'Inde* Indian horse chestnut
Aesculus x neglecta *Aesculus x neglecta* Sunrise horse-chestnut
Aesculus parviflora *Marronnier paviflora / Pavier blanc*
Bottlebrush buckeye
Aesculus pavia *Pavier rouge* Red buckeye
Aesculus turbinata *Marronnier à fruit turbiné* Japanese horse chestnut
Aethionema grandiflorum *Aethionema grandiflorum* Persian stone cress
Aethusa cynapium *Petite ciguë* Fool's parsley
Agapanthus africanus *Agapanthe* African lily / Agapanthus
Agastache *Agastache* Mexican giant hyssop
Agave americana *Agave d'Amérique* Century plant
Agave filifera *Agave filifera* Thread agave
Agave victoriae-reginae *Agave victoriae-reginae* Royal agave
Ageratum *Agérate bleue* Floss flower
Aglaonema *Aglaonema* Chinese evergreen
Agonis *Agonis* Willow myrtle
Agonis flexuosa *Agonis flexuosa* Agrimony

Agropyrum	*Agropyre*	Couch grass
Agrostemma githago	*Nielle des blés*	Corn cockle
Aichryson x domesticum varieg.	*Aichryson x domesticum varieg.*	Cloud grass
Ajuga chamaepitys	*Bugle jaune*	Ground-pine
Ajuga pyramidalis	*Bugle pyramidalis*	Limestone bugle / Pyramidial bugle
Ajuga reptans	*Bugle rampante*	Bugle
Akebia quinata	*Akebia quinata*	Chocolate vine
Albizia julibrissin	*Arbre de soie*	Silk tree
Alcea *Passe-rose / Rose à bâton / Rose trémière*		Hollyhock
Alchemilla alpina	*Alchémille des Alpes*	Alpine lady's mantle
Alchemilla vulgaris *Alchémille commune*		Common lady's mantle / Lady's mantle
Ailanthus altissima	*Ailante*	Tree of heaven
Ailanthus altissima	*Faux-Vernis du Japon*	Tree of heaven
Alisma gramineum	*Flûteau à feuilles de graminée*	Ribbon-leaved water plantain
Alisma lanceolatum	*Plantain d'eau lancéolé*	Narrow water plantain
Alisma plantago-aquatica	*Flûteau / Plantain d'eau*	Water plantain
Alisma plantago-aquatica	*Plantain d'eau commun*	Common water plantain
Allamanda cathartica	*Allamanda cathartica*	Golden trumpet
Alliaria petiolata	*Alliare officinale*	Garlic mustard
Allium	*Oignon*	Onion
Allium ampeloprasum	*Gros ail*	Wild leek
Allium carinatum	*Ail caréné*	Keeled garlic
Allium moly	*Ail doré*	Allium moly / Lly leaf
Allium neapolitanumi	*Ail blanc*	Allium neapolitanum
Allium oleraceum	*Ail des champs*	Field garlic
Allium paradoxum	*Allium paradoxum*	Few flowered leek
Allium roseum	*Ail rose*	Rosy garlic
Allium schoenoprasum	*Ciboulette sauvage*	Chives
Allium scorodoprasum	*Ail rocambole*	Sand leek
Allium sphaerocephalon	*Ail a tête ronde*	Round headed leek
Allium triquetrum	*Ail triquêtre*	Three-cornered leek
Allium ursinum	*Ail des ours*	Ramsons
Allium vineale	*Ail des vignes*	Crow garlic
Alloplectus nummularia	*Alloplectus nummularia*	Clog plant
Alpinia zerumbet	*Alpinia zerumbet*	Shell flower
Althaea hirsuta	*Guimauve hérisée*	Rough mallow
Alyssum alyssoides	*Alysson à calice persistant*	Small alison
Aloysia triphylla	*Citronella verveine*	Lemon verbena
Ambrosia	*Ambrosie*	Ragweed

Amorpha	*Faux indigo*	False indigo
Amorpha canescens	*Amorpha canescens*	Lead plants
Alkanna tinctoria	*Orcanette*	Dyer's alkanet
Alnus cordata	*Aulne à feuilles en cœur*	Italian alder
Alnus glutinosa	*Aulne glutineux / Verne*	Alder
Alnus incana	*Aulne blanc*	Grey alder
Alocasia macrorrhiza	*Grande tayove / Taro*	Giant elephant's ear / Taro
Aloe	*Aloè*	Aloe
Aloe arborescens	*Corne de bélier*	Aloe arborescens
Aloe arborescens	*Corne de cerf*	Aloe arborescens
Aloe aristata	*Aloès aristata*	Lace aloe / Torch plant
Aloe variegata	*Aloès variegata*	Partridge breasted aloe
Alonsoa warscewiczii	*Alonsoa warscewiczii*	Mask flower
Alopecurus pratensis aureomarginata	*Alopecurus pratensis aureomarginata*	Golden foxtail
Alpinia calcarata	*Alpinia calcarata*	Indian ginger
Alternanthera ficoidea	*Alternanthera ficoidea*	Parrot leaf
Althaea officinalis	*Guimauve officinale*	Marsh-mallow
Amaranthus albus	*Amarante blanche*	White pigweed
Amaranthus caudatus	*Queue de renard*	Love-lies-bleeding / Tassel flower
Amaranthus hybridus erythrostachys	*Amarante hybride*	Prince's feather
Amaranthus retroflexus	*Amarante réfléchie*	Pigweed
Amaryllis belladonna	*Amaryllis belladonna*	Belladonna Lily
Amelanchier canadensis	*Amélanchier du Canada*	Juneberry / Serviceberry / Shadbush
Ampelopsis quinquefolia	*Vigne vierge vraie*	Five leaved ivy
Amsonia	*Amsonia*	Blue star
Anacamptis pyramidalis	*Orchis pyramidial*	Pyramidial orchid
Anagallis arvensis	*Mouron rouge*	Scarlet pimpernel
Anagallis foemina	*Mouron bleu*	Blue pimpernal
Anagallis tenella	*Mouron délicat*	Bog pimpernel
Anagallis tenella	*Mouron des marécages*	Bog pimpernel
Ananas bracteatus	*Ananas bracteatus*	Red pineapple / Wild pineapple
Anigozanthos flavidus	*Anigozanthos flavidus*	Yellow kangaroo paw
Anchusa	*Buglosse*	Bugloss
Andredera	*Andredera*	Madiera vine / Mignonette vine
Andromeda polifolia	*Andromède à feuilles de polium*	Bog rosemary
Anemone	*Anémone*	Anemone / Windflower
Anemone apennina	*Anémone apennina*	Apennine anemone
Anemone coronaria	*Anémone des fleuristes*	Anemone coronaria
Anemone x hybrida	*Anémone du Japon*	Japanese anemone

Anemone nemorosa	*Anémone des bois*	Wood anemone
Anemone pavonia	*Anémone des jardins*	Anemone pavonia
Anemone ranunculoides	*Anémone fausse renoncule*	Anemone ranunculoides
Anemone sylvestris	*Anémone sylvestre*	Snowdrop windflower
Anemonopsis	*Anemonopsis*	False anemone
Angelica archangelica	*Angélique*	Angelica
Angelica sylvestris	*Angélique des bois*	Wild angelica
Angraecum sesquipedale	*Étoile de Bethléem*	Star-of-Bethleham orchid
Anguloa clowesii	*Anguloa clowesii*	Cradle orchid
Anigozanthus	*Anigozanthus*	Kangaroo paw
Anigozanthus manglesii	*Anigozanthus manglesii*	Red and green kangaroo paw
Annaphalis margaritacea	*Immortelle blanche*	Pearl everlasting
Annaphalis margaritacea	*Immortelle de Virginie*	Pearl everlasting
Annona	*Corossolier à fruit hérissé*	Cherimoya / Custard apple / Sweet sop
Annona reticulata	*Annona reticulata*	Bullock's heart
Antennaria	*Antennaria*	Cat's ears
Antennaria dioica	*Pied-de-chat dioïque*	Mountain everlasting
Anthemis	*Anthemis*	Chamomile / Dog fennel
Anthemis arvensis	*Anthémis des champs*	Corn chamomile
Anthemis arvensis	*Fausse camomile*	Corn chamomile
Anthemis cotula	*Camomille puante*	Stinking chamomile
Anthemis tinctoria	*Anthémis des teinturiers*	Yellow chamomile
Anthericum	*Anthericum*	Spider plant
Anthericum liliago	*Phalangère à fleur de lis*	St. Bernard's lily
Anthriscus caucalis	*Anthrisque commun*	Bur chervil
Anthriscus sylvestris	*Anthrisque sauvage*	Cow parsley
Anthurium andraeanum	*Anthurium andraeanum*	Tail flower
Anthurium crystallinum	*Anthurium crystallinum*	Crystal anthurium
Anthurium scherzerianum	*Anthurium scherzerianum*	Flaming flower
Anthyllis vulneraria	*Anthyllide vulnéraire*	Kidney vetch
Antigonon leptopus	*Antigonon*	Coral vine
Antirrhinum	*Guele-de-loup / Muflier*	Snapdragon
Antirrhinum majus	*Grand muflier / Guele-de-loup*	Common snapdragon
Aphanes arvensis	*Alchémille des champs*	Parsley piert
Aphelandra squarrosa	*Aphelandra squarrosa*	Zebra plant
Apium inundatum	*Ache aquatique*	Marshwort
Apium graveolens	*Céleri*	Wild celery
Apium nodiflorum	*Ache nodiflore*	Fool's watercress
Aponogeton distachyos	*Aponogéton*	Cape pondweed / Water hawthorn
Aporocactus flagelliformis	*Aporocactus flagelliformis*	Rat's tail cactus
Aquelegia	*Ancolie*	Aquelegia
Aquelegia alpina	*Ancolie des Alpes*	Alpine columbine

Aquilegia canadensis	*Ancolie du Canada*	Canadian columbine
Aquelegia vulgaris	*Ancolie commune*	Columbine
Aquelegia vulgaris	*Ancolie*	Granny's bonnets
Arabidopsis thaliana	*Arabette thaliana*	Thale cress
Arabis caucasica	*Arabette*	Arabis
Arabis caucasica	*Corbeille d'argent*	Arabis / Garden arabis
Arabis hirsuta	*Arabette poilu*	Hairy rock-cress
Aralia	*Angélique de Chine*	Japanese angelica tree
Araucaria araucana	*Déspoir des singes*	Chile pine / Monkey puzzle

Archontophoenix cunninghamia *Archontophoenix cunninghamia*
Norfolk Island pine / Northern bungalow palm

Araujia sericofera	*Araujia sericofera*	Cruel plant
Arbutus andrachne	*Arbousier andrachne*	Grecian strawberry tree
Arbutus menziesii	*Arbutus menziesii*	Madroña
Arbutus unedo	*Arbousier / Arbre aux fraises*	Strawberry tree

Archontophoenix alexandrae *Archontophoenix alexandrae*
Alexandra palm / King palm

Archontophoenix cunninghamiana *Archontophoenix cunninghamsiana*
Illawarra palm

Archontophoenix cunninghamiana *Archontophoenix cunninghamiana*
Piccabean palm

Arctium lappa	*Grande bardane*	Great burdock
Arctium minus	*Bardane à petites têtes*	Burdock
Arctostaphylos alpinus	*Raisin des Alpes*	Black bearberry
Arctostaphylos manzanita	*Busserole*	Manzanita
Arcotstaphylos nevadensis	*Arcotstaphylos nevadensis*	Pine-mat manzanita
Arctostaphylos stanfordiana	*Arctostaphylos stanfordiana*	Stanford manzanita
Arctostaphylos uva-ursi	*Busserole / Raisin d'ours*	Bearberry
Arctotheca calendula	*Arctotheca calendula*	Cape dandelion
Arctotis stoechadifolia	*Arctotis stoechadifolia*	African daisy
Arctous alpina	*Arbousier nain*	Arctous alpina
Arecastrum	*Cocos*	Queen palm
Arenaria	*Arénaire / Sabline*	Sandwort
Arenaria norvegica	*Sabline de Norvège*	Scottish sandwort
Arenaria serpyllifolia	*Sabline à feuilles de serpolet*	Thyme-leaved sandwort
Argemone mexicana	*Argémone mexicana*	Prickly poppy
Argyreia splendens	*Volubilis argenté*	Silver morning glory
Ariocarpus	*Anhalonie*	Living rock
Arisaema triphyllum	*Arisaema triphyllum*	Jack-in-the-pulpit
Arisarum proboscideum	*Arisarum proboscideum*	Mouse plant
Aristolochia clematitis	*Aristoloche clématite*	Birthwort
Aristolochia elegans	*Aristoloche*	Calico flower

Aristolocia grandiflora	*Aristoloche grandiflora*	Pelican flower / Swan flower
Armeria maritima	*Arméria maritime / Œillet marin*	Thrift / Sea pink
Armoracia rusticana	*Raifort*	Horse radish
Arnebia pulchra	*Arnebia pulchra*	Prophet flower
Arnoseris minima	*Chicorée de mouton*	Swine's succory
Aronia	*Aronia*	Chokeberry
Aronia arbutifolia	*Aronia arbutifolia*	Red chokeberry
Aronia melanocarpa	*Aronia melanocarpa*	Black chokeberry
Arrhenatherum elatius	*Avoine élevée / Fenasse / Fromental*	False oat grass
Artemisia	*Armoise*	Artemisia
Artemisia abrotanum	*Aurone / Fromental*	Old man / Southernwood
Artemisia absinthium	*Absinthe*	Absinthe
Artemisia absinthium	*Artemisia absinthium*	Wormwood
Artemisia arborescens	*Armoise arborescente*	Artemisia arborescens
Artemisia abrotanum	*Aurone / Citronelle*	Lad's love
Artemisia campestris	*Armoise champêtre*	Breckland mugwort
Artemisia dracunculus	*Dragone / Estragon*	Tarragon
Artemisia lactiflora	*Armoise lactiflora*	White mugwort
Artemisia maritima	*Armoise maritime*	Sea wormwood
Artemisia pontica	*Armoise pontica*	Roman wormwood
Artemisia vulgaris	*Armoise commune*	Mugwort
Arthropodium cirrhatum	*Arthropodium cirrhatum*	Rienga lily
Arthropodium cirrhatum	*Arthropodium cirrhatum*	Rock lily
Arthrotaxis selaginoides	*Arthrotaxis selaginoides*	King William pine
Arum italicum	*Arum d'Italie*	Large cuckoo pint
Arum maculatum	*Guet maculé*	Cuckoo pint / Lords and Ladies
Aruncus dioicus	*Barbe-de-bouc / Reine des bois*	Goat's beard
Arundinaria anceps	*Arundinaria anceps*	Anceps bamboo
Arundo donax	*Canne de Provence*	Giant reed
Asarum europaeum	*Asaret d'Europe*	Asrabacca / Wild ginger
Asclepias	*Asclépiade*	Silk weed
Asclepias curassavica	*Asclepias curassavica*	Blood flwer
Asclepias tuberosa	*Asclepias tuberosa*	Butterfly weed
Asimina triloba	*Asiminier triloba*	Pawpaw
Asparagus densiflorus 'Myersii'	*Asparagus densiflorus 'Myersii'*	Foxtail fern
Asparagus officinalis	*Asperge officinale*	Asparagus
Aspelenium bulbiferum	*Aspelenium bulbiferum*	Hen-and-chicken fern / Mother spleenwort
Aspelenium nidus	*Aspelenium nidus*	Bird's nest fern
Asperugo procumbens	*Rapette couchée*	Madwort

Asperula cynanchia	*Aspérule des sables / Herbe à l'esquinancie*	
		Squinancywort
Asphodelus aestivus	*Asphodèle*	Asphodel
Asphodelus albus	*Asphodèle albus*	White asphodel
Asphodeline lutea	*Bâton de Jacob*	Yellow asphodel
Aspidistra elatior	*Aspidistra elatior*	Cast-iron plant
Asplenium trichomanes	*Fausse capillaire*	Maidenhair spleenwort
Aster	*Aster du Jardin*	Michaelmas daisy
Aster amellus	*Œil de Christ*	Aster amellus
Aster tripolium	*Aster maritime*	Sea aster
Astragalus alpinus	*Astragale des Alpes*	Alpine milk-vetch
Astragalus danicus	*Astragale du Danemark*	Purple milk-vetch
Astragalus glycyphyllos	*Astragale a feuilles de réglisse*	Wild liquorice
Astragalus glycyphyllos	*Réglisse bâtarde*	Wild liquorice
Astrantia major	*Grande astrance / Radiaire*	Pink masterwort
Astrophytum asterias	*Astrophytum asterias*	Sea urchin / Silver dollar cactus
Astrophytum myriostigma	*Mitre d'évêque*	Bishop's cap / Bishop's mitre
Atherosperma moschatum	*Atherosperma moschatum*	Tasmanian sassafras
Athyrium filix-femina	*Fougère femelle*	Lady fern
Athyrium nipponicum	*Fougère femelle*	Painted fern
Atriplex halimus	*Arroche halime*	Tree purslane
Atriplex halimus	*Pourpier de mer*	Tree purslane
Atriplex hortensis rubra	*Belle-Dame rouge*	
		Red mountain spinach / Red orach
Atriplex laciniata	*Arroche lacinée*	Frosted orache
Atriplex littoralis	*Arroche du littoral*	Grass leaved orache
Atriplex patula	*Arroche étalée*	Common orache
Atropa belladonna	*Belladone*	Deadly nightshade
Aubrietia	*Aubriette*	Aubrietia
Aucuba japonica	*Aucuba de Japon*	Aucuba Japonica
Aurinia saxatilis	*Corbeille d'or*	Gold dust
Austrocedrus chilensis	*Austrocedrus chilensis*	Chilean incense cedar
Azolla caroliniana	*Azolla caroliniana*	Water fern
Azorina vidalii	*Campanule vidalii*	Campanula vidalii

B

Babiana rubro-cyanea	*Babiana rubro-cyanea*	Winecups
Baccharis halimifolia	*Séneçon en arbre*	Bush groundsel
Baldellia ranunculoides	*Fluteau fausse-renoncule*	Lesser water plantain
Ballota nigra	*Ballote noire*	Black horehound
Banksia ericifolia	*Banksia ericifolia*	Heath banksia

Barbarea vulgaris	*Barbarée commune / Herbe de Sainte-Barbe*	
		Common winter-cress
Barleria cristata	*Barleria cristata*	Philippine violet
Bartsia alpina	*Bartsie des Alpes*	Alpine bartsia
Bauhinia purpurea	*Bauhinia purpurea*	Butterfly tree / Orchid tree
Bauhinia variegata	*Bauhinia variegata*	Orchid tree
Beaucarnea recurvata	*Beaucarnea recurvata*	Elephant's foot / Pony tail
Beaumontia grandiflora	*Beaumontia grandiflora*	Herald's trumpet
Begonia	*Bégonia*	Begonia
Begonia bowerae	*Begonia bowerae*	Eyelash begonia
Begonia x cheimantha	*Begonia x cheimantha*	Christmas begonia
Begonia x cheimantha 'Gloire de Lorraine'	*Begonia x cheimant 'Gloire de Lorraine'*	Lorraine begonia
Begonia coccinea	*Begonia coccinea*	Angelwing begonia
Begonia dregei	*Begonia dregei*	Maple leaf begonia
Begonia fuchsiodes	*Begonia fuchsiodes*	Fuchsia begonia
Begonia masoniana	*Begonia masoniana*	Iron cross begonia
Begonia metallica	*Begonia metallica*	Metal leaf begonia
Begonia weltoniensis	*Begonia weltoniensis*	Maple leaf begonia
Belamcanda	*Fleur de léopard / Iris tigré*	Belamcanda
Blechnum spicant	*Blechne / Fougère pectinée*	Hard fern
Bellis	*Pâquerette*	Daisy
Bellis Perennis	*Pâquerette vivace*	Double daisy
Berberidopsis coralina	*Berberidopsis coralina*	Coral plant
Berberis	*Épine-vinette*	Barberry
Berberis darwinii	*Vinettier de Darwin*	Darwin's barberry
Berteroa incana	*Alysson blanchatre*	Hoary alison
Bessera elegans	*Bessera elegans*	Coral drops
Beta vulvaris	*Bette maritime*	Sea beet
Betula	*Bouleau*	Birch
Betula albo-sinensis	*Betula albo-sinensis*	White Chinese birch
Betula alleghaniensis	*Bouleau jaune*	Yellow birch
Betula maximowicziana	*Betula maximowicziana*	Monarch birch
Betula nana	*Bouleau nain*	Arctic birch / Dwarf birch
Betula papyrifera	*Bouleau à canots*	Canoe birch / Paper birch
Betula pendula	*Bouleau pleureur*	Weeping birch
Betula pendula 'Dalecarlica'	*Bouleau lacinié*	Swedish birch
Betula pendula 'Youngii'	*Bouleau pleureur 'Youngii'*	Young's weeping birch
Betula pubescens	*Bouleau pubescent*	Downy birch
Betula szechuanica	*Bouleau szechuanica*	Szechuan birch
Betula utilis	*Betula utilis*	Himalayan birch
Betula utilis jacquemontii	*Betula utilis jacquemontii*	West Himalayan birch

Bidens cernua	*Bident penché*	Nodding bur-marigold
Bidens tripartita	*Bident trifoliolé*	Trifid bur-marigold
Bignonia capreolata	*Bignonia capreolata*	Cross vine / Trumpet flower
Billbergia nutans	*Billbergia nutans*	Queen's tears
Billbergia x windii	*Billbergia x windii*	Angel's tears
Blackstonia perfiolata	*Centaurée jaune / Chlora perfiolé*	Yellow-wort
Borago officinalis	*Bourrache*	Borage
Borzicactus celsianus	*Borzicactus celsianus*	Old man of the Andes
Borzicactus trolii	*Borzicactus trolii*	Old man of the Andes
Boswellia	*Boswellie*	Frankincense
Bougainvillea	*Bougainvillée*	Bougainvillea
Bouteloua gracilis	*Bouteloua gracilis*	Blue grama / Mosquito grass
Bouvardia ternifolia	*Bouvardia ternifolia*	Scarlet trompetilla
Brachychiton acerifolius	*Brachychiton acerifolius*	Illawarra flame tree
Brachychiton populneus	*Brachychiton populneus*	Kurrajong
Brachycome iberidifolia	*Brachycome iberidifolia*	Swan river daisy
Brachyglottis repanda	*Brachyglottis repanda*	Pukapuka / Rangiora
Brassavola nodosa	*Brassavola nodosa*	Lady of the night
Brassica nigra	*Moutarde noire*	Black mustard
Brassica oleracea	*Chou d'ornement*	Ornamental cabbage
Breynia disticha	*Breynia disticha*	Snow bush
Brimeura amethystina	*Jacinthe d'Espagne*	Spanish bluebell
Brimeura amethystina	*Jacinthe des pyrénées*	Spanish bluebell
Briza	*Brize / Tremblotte*	Quaking grass
Briza maxima	*Amourette / Grande Brize*	Greater quaking grass
Briza media	*Brize commune*	Common quaking grass
Bromelia balansae	*Bromelia balansae*	Heart of flame
Bromus ramosus	*Brome rameux*	Hairy brome grass
Broussonetia papyrifera	*Mûrier à papier*	Paper mulberry
Browallia speciosa	*Browallia speciosa*	Bush violet
Bruckenthalia spiculifolia	*Bruckenthalia spiculifolia*	Spike heath
Brunfelsia pauciflora	*Brunfelsia pauciflora*	Yesterday-today-and-tomorrow
Brunnera macrophylla	*Brunnera macrophylla*	Siberian bugloss
Brunsvigia josephenae	*Amaryllis de Joséphine*	Josephine's lily
Bryonia cretica	*Bryone dioîque*	White bryony
Bulbocodium	*Bulbocode*	Meadow saffron
Buddleia davidii	*Arbuste à papillons / Buddleia*	Buddleia
Bulbocodium vernum	*Crocus rouge*	Bulbocodium vernum
Bunias orientalis	*Bunias d'orient*	Warty cabbage
Buphthalmum salicifolium	*Buphthalmum salicifolium*	Yellow ox-eye
Bupleurum falcatum	*Buplèvre des haies*	Sickle Hare's-ear
Bupleurum fruticosum	*Oreille-de-lièvre*	Shrubby hare's ear

Bupleurum rotundifolium	*Buplèvre à feuilles rondes*	Thorow-wax
Bupleurum tenuissimum	*Buplèvre grêle*	Slender hare's ear
Butia	*Butia*	Yatay palm
Butia capitata	*Butia capitata*	Jelly palm
Butomus umbellatus	*Butome / Jonc fleuri*	Flowering rush
Buxus	*Buis*	Box
Buxus balearicus	*Buis de Mahon*	Balearic box
Buxus microphylla	*Buis à petites feuilles*	Small leaved box
Buxus wallichiana	*Buxus wallichiana*	Himalayan box

C

Cabomba caroliana	*Cabombe de Caroliana*	
	Fanwort / Fish grass / Washington grass	
Caesalpinia	*Brésillet*	Caesalpinia
Caesalpinia gilliesii	*Oiseau de Paradis*	Caesalpinia gilliesii
Caesalpinia pulcherrima	*Flamboyant*	Barbados pride
Cakile maritima	*Coquillier maritime / Roquette de mer*	Sea rocket
Caladium x hortulanum	*Caladium x hortulanum*	Angels' wings
Calamentha	*Clinopode*	Calamint
Calathea makoyana	*Calathea makoyana*	Peacock plant
Calathea zebrina	*Calathea zebrina*	Zebra plant
Calceolaria	*Calcéolaire*	Calceolaria
Calendula	*Souci*	Marigold
Calendula officinalis	*Souci des jardins*	Pot marigold
Calocedrus decurrens	*Libocedrus decurrens*	Incense cedar
Calla palustris	*Calla palustris*	Bog arum
Calliandra eriophylla	*Calliandra eriophylla*	Fairy duster
Callistemon	*Callistemon*	Bottlebrush
Callistemon speciosus	*Callistemon speciosus*	Albany bottlebrush
Callistephus	*Aster de Chine /Reine-marguerit*	China aster
Callitriche palustris	*Callitriche des marais*	Common water starwort
Calluna vulgaris	*Brande / Callune fausse-bruyère*	Ling / Scotch heather
Calochortus	*Calochortus*	Cat's ears / Mariposa tulip
Calochortus albus	*Calochortus albus*	Globe lily
Calochortus amabilis	*Tulpe de Mormons*	
	Golden fairy lantern / Golden globe tulip	
Calochortus luteus	*Calochortus luteus*	Yellow mariposa
Calothamnus villosus	*Calothamnus villosus*	Woolly netbush
Caltha palustris	*Populage des marais*	Kingcup / Marsh marigold
Calycanthus	*Calycanthe*	Calycanthus

Calycanthus floridus *Arbre aux anémones / Arbre Pompadour*
Carolina allspice
Calycanthus occidentalis *Calycanthe occidentalis* California allspice

Calystegia sepium *Liseron des haies* Great bindweed
Calystegia silvatica *Liseron d'Amérique* American bindweed
Calystegia soldanella *Chou marin / Liseron de mer* Sea bindweed
Callitriche hermaphroditica *Callitriche hermaphrodite* Narrow water starwort
Camelina sativa *Caméline cultivée* Gold of pleasure
Camellia japonica *Camellia du Japon* Japanese camellia
Campanula *Campanule* Bellflower / Campanula
Campanula barbata *Campanule barbue* Bearded bellflower
Campanula cochlearifolia *Campanule menue* Fairy thimbles
Campanula glomerata *Campanule agglomérée* Clustered bellflower
Campanula isophylla *Étoile de Bethléem / Étoile de Marie*
Campanula isophylla
Campanula latifolia *Campanule à feuilles larges* Giant Bellflower
Campanula medium *Campanule à grosses fleurs / Campanule carillon*
Canterbury bell
Campanula patula *Campanule étalée* Spreading bellflower
Campanula pyramidalis *Campanule pyramidale* Chimney bellflower
Campanula rapunculoides *Campanule fausse-raiponce* Creeping bellflower
Campanula rapunculus *Campanule raiponce* Rampion bellfower
Campanula rotundifolia *Campanule à feuilles rondes*
Harebell / Bluebell (In Scotland)
Campanula trachelium *Gantelée* Nettle leaved bellflower
Camptosorus rhizophyllus *Camptosorue* Walking fernn
Canarina canariensis *Canarina canariensis* Canary Island bellflower
Canna *Balisier* Canna
Camassia *Quamash* Quamash
Campsis grandiflora *Bignone de Chine* Bignonia / Chinese trumpet creeper
Campsis radicans *Jasmin trompette* Trumpet vine / Trumpet creeper
Campsis radicans *Jasmin de Virginie* Trumpet creeper / Trumpet honeysuckle
Capsella bursa-pastoris *Bourse à pasteur* Shepherd's purse
Capsicum annuum *Piment commun* Ornamental pepper
Cardamine amara *Cardamine amère* Large bittercress
Cardamine bulbifera *Dentaire bulbifère* Coral root
Cardamine impatiens *Cardamine impatiente* Narrow leaved bittercress
Cardamine pratensis *Cardamine des prés / Cressonnette*
Bitter cress / Cuckoo flower / Lady's smock
Cardiocrinum giganteum *Cardiocrinum giganteum* Giant lily

Cardiospermum grandiflorum	*Pois de cœur*	
	Baloon vine / Heart pea / Winter cherry	
Carduus nutans	*Chardon penché*	Musk thistle
Carduus tenuilorus	*Chardon à capitues grêles*	Seaside thistle
Carex buchananii	*Laîche buchananii*	Leatherleaf sedge
Carex elata	*Lâiche en gazon*	Tufted sedge
Carex elata aurea	*Lâiche elata aurea*	Bowles's golden sedge
Carex grayi	*Laîche grayi*	Mace sedge
Carex pendula	*Laîche pendante*	Pendulous sedge
Carex riparia	*Lâiche riparia*	Greater pond sedge
Carica papaya	*Carica papaya*	Pawpaw
Carissa grandiflora	*Carissa grandiflora*	Natal plum
Carlina	*Carline*	Thistle
Carlina acaulis	*Carline des Alpes*	Alpine thistle
Carlina vulgaris	*Carline commune*	Carline thistle
Carnegiea gigantea	*Carnegiea gigantea*	Saguaro
Carpinus	*Charme*	Hornbeam
Carpinus betulus	*Charme commun*	Common hornbeam
Carpinus caroliniana	*Charme d'Amérique*	American hornbeam
Carpobrotus edulis	*Figue des Hottentots*	Hottentot fig / Kaffir fig
Carum carvi	*Cumin des prés*	Caraway
Carum verticillatum	*Carum verticillé*	Whorled caraway
Carya	*Hickory / Noyer d'Amérique*	Hickory
Carya cordiformis	*Noyer des marais*	Bitternut
Carya cordiformis	*Noyer d'Amérique*	Bitternut hickory
Carya glabra	*Noyer à balais*	Pignut / Pignut hickory
Carya glabra	*Noyer des pourceaux*	Pignut / Pignut hickory
Carya ovata	*Noyer blanc d'Amérique*	Shag-bark hickory
Caryopteris	*Barbe bleue*	Caryopteris
Cassia artemisioides	*Casse argentée*	Silver cassia / Wormwood cassia
Cassia didymobotrya	*Senné didymobotrya*	Golden wonder
Cassia fistula	*Averse dorée*	
	Golden shower / Indian laburnum /Pudding pipe-tree	
Castanea	*Châtaignier*	Chestnut
Castanea dentata	*Châtaigner d'Amérique*	American chestnut
Castanea sativa	*Châtaignier*	Spanish chestnut / Sweet chestnut
Castanospermum	*Castanospermum*	Black bean tree / Moreton Bay chestnut
Catalpa bignionoides	*Catalpa commun*	Indian bean tree
Catananche	*Cupidone*	Blue cupidone
Catharanthus roseus	*Catharanthus roseus*	Rose periwinkle
Ceanothus	*Céanotte*	Californian lilac / Ceanothus
Ceanothus rigidus	*Céanothe de Monterey*	Monterey ceanothus

Ceanothus thyrsiflorus repens *Céanothe thyrsiflorus repens*
Creeping blue blossom
Cedrus *Cèdre* Cedar
Cedrus atlantica *Cèdre de l'Atlas* Atlas cedar
Cedrus atlantica glauca *Cèdre de l'Altas bleu* Blue Atlas cedar
Cedrus deodara *Cèdre de l'Himalaya* Deodar
Cedrus libani *Cèdre du Liban* Cedar of Lebanon
Ceiba pentandra *Arbre à Kapok / Kapokier* Kapok / Silk cotton tree
Celastrus orbiculatus *Célastre orbicule* Oriental bittersweet / Staff vine
Celastrus scandens *Célastre grimpant* American bittersweet / Staff tree
Celastrus scandens *Bourreau des arbres* American bittersweet / Staff tree
Celosia cristata *Célosie crête de coq 'Fairy fountains'* Fairy fountain
Celosia cristata *Amarante crête-de-coq /Passe-velours* Fairy fountain
Celtis australis *Micocoulier de Provence* Nettle tree
Celtis occidentalis *Miscoulier de Virginie* Hackberry
Centaurea *Centaurée* Knapweeed
Centaurea aspera *Centaurée rude* Rough star thistle
Centaurea calcitrapa *Chardon Étoilé / Chausse-trappe* Star thistle
Centaurea cyanus *Barbeau bleu* Bluebottle
Centaurea cyanus *Bleuet* Bluebottle
Centaurea cyanus *Bleuet des champs* Cornflower
Centaurea jacea *Centaurée jacée* French hardhead
Centaurea montana *Bleuet vivace* Centaurea montana
Centaurea moschata *Centaurée barbeau* Sweet sultan
Centaurea nigra *Centaurée noire* Hardhead
Centaurea nemoralis *Petite centaurée délicat* Slender centaury
Centaurea scabiosa *Centaurée scabieuse* Greater knapweed
Centaurea solstitalis *Centaurée du solstice* St. Barnaby's thistle
Centaurium erythraea *Petite centaurée commune* Common centaury
Centaurium littorale *Petite centaurée du littoral* Seaside centaury
Centaurium tenuiflorum *Petite centauré à fleurs ténues* Channel centaury
Centaurium scilloides *Petite centaurée fauss-scille* Perennial centaury
Centranthus ruber *Valériane rouge* Red valerian
Cephalaria gigantea *Cephalaria gigantea* Giant scabious / Yellow scabious
Cephalocereus senilis *Cierge barba de vieillard* Old man cactus
Cephalophyllum alstonii *Cephalophyllum alstonii* Red spike
Cephalotaxus harringtonia *Cephalotaxus harringtonia*
Cow's tail pine / Plum yew
Cephalanthera damasonium *Céphalanthéra pale* Broad helleborine
Cephalanthera longifolia*Céphalanthéra à feuilles étroites* Narrow helleborine
Cephalanthera rubra *Céphalanthéra rose* Red helleborine
Cerastium alpinum *Céraiste des Alpea* Alpine mouse ear

Cerastium arvense	*Céraiste des champs*	Field mouse-ear
Cerastium brachypetalum	*Céraiste à courts pétales*	Grey mouse-ear
Cerastium cerastoides	*Céraiste faux-céraiste*	Starwort mouse ear
Cerastium glomeratum	*Céraiste à fleurs agglomérée*	Sticky mouse-ear
Cerastium pumilum	*Céraiste visqueux*	Curtis's mouse-ear
Cerastium semicandrum	*Céraiste à 5 étamines*	Little mouse-ear
Cerastium tomentosum	*Céraiste tomentosum*	Snow-in-summer
Ceratophyllum demersum	*Cornifle emergé*	Hornwort
Cercidiphyllum japonicum	*Cercidiphyllacé du Japon*	Katsura
Cercis	*Gainier*	Redbud
Cercis canadensis	*Gainier du Canada*	Eastern redbud
Cercis siliquastrum	*Arbre de Judée*	Judas tree
Ceropegia sandersonii	*Ceropegia sandersonii*	Fountain flower / Parachute plant
Ceropegia woodii	*Ceropegia woodii*	Heart vine / Rosary vine / String-of-hearts
Ceterach officinarum	*Ceterach officinarum*	Rusty-back fern
Chaenomeles japonica	*Cognassier du Japon*	Flowering quince / Japanese quince / Japonica
Chaenorhinum minus	*Petite linaire*	Small toadflax
Chaerophyllum aureum	*Cerfeuil doré*	Golden chervil
Chaerophyllum temulentum	*Cerfeuil penché*	Rough chervil
Chamaecereus silvestri	*Chamaecereus silvestri*	Peanut cactus
Chamaecyparis	*Faux cyprès*	False cypress
Chamaecyparis lawsoniana	*Cyprès de Lawson*	Lawson cypress
Chamaecyparis lawsoniana	*Faux-cyprès de Lawson*	Lawson cypress
Chamaecyparis nootkatensis	*Cyprès de Nootka*	Nootka cypress
Chamaecyparis obtusa	*Hinoki*	Hinoki cypress
Chamaecyparis pisifera	*Sawara*	Sawara cypress
Chamaecyparis thyoides	*Chamaecyparis thyoides*	White cypress
Chamaedaphne calyculata	*Chamédaphné calyculata*	Leatherleaf
Chamaedorea elegans	*Chamaedorea elegans*	Dwarf mountain palm / Parlour palm
Chamaelaucium uncinatum	*Chamaelaucium uncinatum*	Geraldton waxflower
Chamaemelum nobile	*Chamomille romaine*	Chamomile / Common chamomile
Chamaenerion angustifolium	*Épilobe en épi / Laurier St. Antoine*	Rose-bay willow-herb
Chamaerops humilis	*Chamaerops humilis*	Dwarf fan palm / European fan palm
Cheiranthus cheiri	*Giroflée / Giroflée jaune / Rameau d'or / Violier*	Wallflower
Chelidonium	*Chélidoine / Grande Éclaire / Herbe aux verrues*	Celandine
Chelidonium majus	*Éclaire / Grande chélidoine*	Celandine
Chelone	*Galane*	Turtle-head

Chenopodium album *Chénopode blanc*   Fat hen
Chenopodium bonus-henricus *Bon-Henri /Épinard sauvage*
                                                Good King Henry
Chenopodium ficifolium *Chénopode à feuilles de figuier*
                                                Fig leafed goosefoot
Chenopodium glaucum *Chénopode glauque*   Oak-leaved goosefoot
Chenopodium hybridum   *Chénopode hybride* Sowbane
Chenopodium murale *Chénopode des murs*   Nettle leaved goosefoot
Chenopodium polyspermum *Chénopode à graines nombreuses*
                                                Many-seed goosefoot
Chenopodium rubrum *Chénopode rouge*   Red goosefoot
Chenopodium urbicum *Chénopode des villages* Upright goosefoot
Chenopodium vulvaria *Arroche puante*   Stinking goosefoot
Chicorium intybus   *Chicorée sauvage*   Chicory
Chimonanthus praecox *Chimonanthe précoce*   Wintersweet
Chinochloa conspicua *Chinochloa conspicua* Hunangemoho grass
Chionodoxa   *Gloire de niege*   Glory-of-the-snow
Chionanthus retusus *Arbre à franges de Chine* Chinese fringe tree
Chionanthus virginicus *Arbre à franges / Arbre de neige* Fringe tree
Chlorophytum comosum *Chlorophytum comosum*   Spider plant
Chorisia speciosa   *Chorisia speciosa*   Floss silk tree
Chorizema illicifolium   *Chorizema illicifolium*   Holly flame pea
Choisya ternata   *Orangier du Mexique* Mexican orange blossom
Chrysalidocarpus lutescens *Chrysalidocarpus lutescens* Golden-feather palm
Chrysalidocarpus lutescens *Chrysalidocarpus lutescens*   Yellow palm
Chrysanthemum   *Chrysanthème*   Chrysanthemum
Chrysanthemum frutescens *Anthémis*   Marguerite
Chrysanthemum leucanthemum *Grande marguerite* Ox-eye-daisy
Chrysanthemum rubellum *Margueritte d'automne* Chrysanthemum rubellum
Chrysanthemum segetum '*Chrysanthème de blés / Marguerite dorée*
                                                Corn marigold
Chrysanthemum x superbum *Chrysanthemum x superbum* Shasta daisy
Chrysosplenium alternifolium   *Dorine à feuilles alternes*
                                                Alternate golden saxifrage
Chrysosplenium oppositifolium *Dorine à feuilles opposées*
                                                Golden saxifrage
Chrysosplenium oppositifolium *Cresson doré* Golden saxifrage
Chusquea culeou   *Chusquea culeou*   Chilean bamboo
Cicendia filiformis   *Cicendies filiforme*   Slender cicendia
Cicerbita alpina   *Laitue des Alpes*   Alpine sow-thistle / Mountain sow thistle
Cicerbita macrophylla   *Laitue à grandes feuilles*   Blue sow-thistle
Cicuta virosa *Ciguë aquatique /Cicutaire vireuse*   Cowbane

Cimicifuga	*Cimicifuge*	Bugbane
Cinnamomum camphora	*Camphorier / Camphora vrai*	
		Cinnamomum camphora
Circaea intermedia	*Circée des Alpes*	Alpine enchanter's nightshade
Circaea intermedia	*Circée intermédiare*	Upland enchanter's nightshade
Circaea lutetiana	*Circée de Paris*	Common enchanter's nightshade
Cirsium	*Chardon / Cirse*	Thistle
Cirsium acaulon	*Cirse acaule*	Dwarf thistle
Cirsium arvense	*Cirse des champs*	Creeping thistle
Cirsium dissectum	*Cirse des prairies*	Meadow thistle
Cirsium eriophorum	*Cirse laineux*	Woolly thistle
Cirsium palustre	*Cirse des marais*	Marsh thistle
Cirsium tuberosum	*Cirse tubéreux*	Tuberous thistle
Cirsium vulgare	*Cirse à feuilles lancéolées*	Spear thistle
Cissus antarctica	*Cissus antarctica*	Kangaroo vine
Cissus discolor	*Cissus discolor*	Rex begonia vine
Cissus rhombifolia	*Cissus rhombifolia*	Grape ivy
Cissus striata	*Cissus striata* Ivy of Uraguay / Miniature grape ivy	
Cistus	*Ciste*	Rock rose
Cistus ladanifer	*Ciste à gomme*	Cistus ladanifer
Citrofortunella mitis	*Citrofortunella mitis*	Calamondin
Cladanthus arabicus	*Anthémis d'Arabie*	Cladanthus arabicus
Cladrastis lutea	*Virginier à bois jaune*	Yellow wood
Claytonia sibirica	*Montie de Sibérie*	Pink purslane
Claytonia virginica / perfiolata	*Montie perfolée*	Spring beauty
Cleistocactus strausii	*Cleistocactus strausii*	Silver torch
Clematis	*Clématite*	Clematis
Clematis flammula	*Flammule*	Clematis flammula
Clematis vitalba	*Clématite des haies*	Old man's beard / Traveller's joy
Cleome	*Cléome*	Spider flower
Clethra alnifolia	*Clethra alnifolia*	Sweet pepper-bush
Clethra arborea	*Clethra arborea*	Lily of the valley tree
Clianthus puniceus	*Clianthus puniceus*	Parrot's bill
Clinopodium vulgare	*Sarriette commune*	Wild basil
Clintonia uniflora	*Clintonia uniflora*	Queencup
Clusia rosea	*Clusia rosea*	
		Autograph tree / Copey / Fat pork tree / Pitch apple
Cobaea scandens	*Cobée grimpante*	Cup and saucer vine
Cochlearia danica	*Cranson du Danemark*	Early scurvy-grass
Cochlearia officinalis	*Cranson officinal*	Common scurvey-grass
Codiaeum	*Croton*	Croton
Codiaeum variegatum	*Croton panaché*	Variegated croton

Coeloglossum viride	*Orchis grenouille*	Frog orchid
Coix lachryma-jobi	*Larmes de Job*	Job's tears
Colchicum autumnale	*Colchique d'automne / Tue-chien / Veillote*	
		Autumn crocus / Meadow saffron
Colchicun luteum	*Colchique jaune*	Yellow autumn crocus
Colocasia esculenta	*Madère / Taro*	Taro
Columnea gloriosa	*Columnea gloriosa*	Goldfish plant
Colutea arborescens	*Baguenaudier commun*	Bladder senna
Comarostaphylis diversifolia	*Comarostaphylis diversifolia*	Summer holly
Commelina coelistis	*Comméline*	Day flower
Conium maculatum	*Grande ciguë*	Hemlock
Conopodium majus	*Châtaigne de terre / Conopode dénudé*	Pignut
Consolida	*Pied d'alouette annuel*	Larkspur
Consolida ambigua	*Pied-d'alouette des jardins*	Giant larkspur
Convallaria majalis	*Muguet*	Lily of the valley
Convolvulus arvensis	*Liseron des champs*	Field bindweed
Convolvulus tricolor	*Belle-du-jour*	Morning glory
Conyza canadenis	*Vergerette du Canada*	Canadian fleabane
Corallorhiza trifida	*Racine-de-corail*	Coral-root orchid
Cordyline australis	*Cordyline australis*	New Zealand palm lily
Cordyline fruticosa	*Cordyline fruticosa*	Ti tree
Cordyline fruticosa	*Cordyline fruticosa*	Good-luck plant
Coreopsis	*Coreopsis*	Tickseed
Coriandrum sativum	*Coriandre cultivée*	Coriander
Cornus alba	*Cornouiller blanc*	Red-barked dogwood
Cornus canadensis	*Cornouiller canadensis*	Creeping dogwood
Cornus capitata	*Cornus capitata*	Bentham's cornel
Cornus controversa 'Variegata'	*Cornouiller controversa 'Variegata'*	
		Wedding-cake tree
Cornus florida	*Cornouiller à fleurs*	Flowering dogwood
Cornus mas	*Cornouiller mâle*	Cornelian cherry
Cornus nuttallii	*Cornouiller nuttallii*	Mountain dogwood / Pacific dogwood
Cornus sanguinea	*Vernouiller*	Dogwood
Cornus suecica	*Cornouiller de Suède*	Dwarf cornel
Corokia cotoneaster	*Corokia cotoneaster*	Wire netting bush
Coronilla	*Coronille*	Coronilla
Coronopus didymus	*Sénebière didyme*	Slender wart cress
Coronopus squamatus	*Sénebière corne-de-cerf*	Common wart cress
Corrigiola littoralis	*Corrigiola dsa grèves*	Strapwort
Cortaderia selloana	*Herbe de pampas*	Pampass grass
Corylus avellana	*Coudrier / Noisettier*	Cobnut / Hazel
Corylus avellana contorta	*Noisetier tortueux*	Corkscrew nut

Corylus colurna	*Coudrier de Byzance*	Turkish hazel
Corylus colurna	*Coudrier do Levant*	Turkish hazel
Corylus colurna	*Noisetier de Constantinople*	Turkish hazel
Corylus maxima	*Avelnier / Grand coudrier*	Filbert
Cosmos atrosanguineus	*Cosmos atrosanguineus*	Chocolate cosmos
Costus speciosus	*Costus speciosus*	Malay ginger
Cotinus coggygria	*Arbre à perruques*	Smoke tree / Venetian sumach
Cotinus coggygria	*Sumac fustet*	Smoke tree Venetian sumach
Cotoneaster frigidus	*Cotoneaster frigidus*	Tree cotoneaster
Cotoneaster horizontalis	*Cotoneaster horizontalis*	Wall-spray
Cotoneaster simonsii	*Cotoneaster de l'Himalaya*	Khasia berry
Cotula coronopifolia	*Cotule coronopifolia*	Brass buttons
Cotula coronopifolia	*Cotule à feuilles de senebière*	Buttonweed
Cotyledon umbilicus	*Ombilic*	Navelwort
Crambe cordifolia	*Crambé à feuille en cœur*	Crambe cordifolia
Crambe maritima	*Chou marin*	Sea kale
Crassula arborescens	*Crassula arborescens*	Silver jade plant
Crassula falcata	*Crassula falcata*	Aeroplane propellor
Crassula ovata	*Crassula ovata* Friendship tree / Jade tree / Money tree	
Crassula tillaea	*Tillée mousse*	Mossy stonecrop
+Crataegomespilus dardarii	*Crataegomespilus dardarii*	Bronvaux medlar
Crataegus	*Aubépine / Épine / Mai*	Thorn
Crataegus crus-galli	*Épine ergot de coq*	Cockspur thorn
Crataegus flava	*Épine à fruits jaunes*	Yellow haw
Crataegus laevigata	*Aubépine / Épine blanche*	May
Crataegus monogyna	*Aubépine*	Hawthorn
Crataegus mongyna biflora	*Aubépine*	Glastonberry thorn
Crataegus phaenopyrum	*Aubépine phaenopyrum*	Washington thorn
Crataegus tanacetifolia	*Épine à feuilles de tanasie*	Tansy-leaved thorn
Crepis biennis	*Crépide bisannuelle*	Rough hawksbeard
Crepis foetida	*Crépide fétide*	Southern hawksbeard
Crepis incana	*Crepide incana*	Pink dandelion
Crepis mollis	*Crépide tendre*	Northern hawksbeard
Crepis paludosa	*Crépide des marais*	Marsh hawksbeard
Crepis vesicaria	*Crépide à vésicules*	Beaked hawksbeard
Crinodendron hookeriana	*Arbre aux lanternes*	Lantern tree
Crithmum maritimum	*Criste marine / Perce-pierre*	Rock samphire
Crocosmia x crocosmiflora	*Montbretia*	Montbretia
Crocus angustifolius	*Crocus angustifolius*	Cloth of gold crocus
Crocus nudiflorus	*Crocus d'automne*	Autumn crocus
Crocus sativus	*Safran d'automne*	Saffron crocus
Crocus vernus	*Crocus vernus*	Dutch crocus

Crocus vernus	*Crocus printanier*	Spring crocus
Crotalaria agatiflora	*Crotalaria agatiflora*	Canary bird bush
Cryptanthus acaulis	*Cryptanthus acaulis*	Green earth star
Cryptanthus bromelioides	*Cryptanthus bromelioides*	Rainbow star
Cryptogramma crispa	*Cryptogramma crispa*	Parsley fern
Cryptomeria japonica	*Cryptomeria japonica / Sugi*	Japanese cedar
Cryptostegia grandiflora	*Cryptostegia grandiflora*	Rubber vine
Cucubalus	*Cucubale*	Bladder campion
Cunninghamia lanceolata	*Sapin chinois*	Chinese fir
Cunonia capensis	*Cunonia du Cap*	African red alder
Cuphea hyssopifolia	*Cuphea hyssopifolia*	False heather
Cuphea ignea	*Cuphea ignea*	Cigar flower
Cupressocyparis leylandii	*Cyprès de Leyland*	Leyland cypress
Cupressus	*Cyprès*	Cypress
Cupressus cashmeriana	*Cyprès de Kashmir*	Kashmir cypress
Cupressus arizonica	*Cyprès de l'Arizona*	Arizona cypress / Smooth cypress
Cupressus lusitanica	*Cyprès de Busaco / Cyprès de Goa /Cyprès pleureur*	

Cedar of Goa / Mexican cypress

Cupressus macrocarpa *Cyprès de Lambert / Cyprès de Monterey*

Monterey cypress

Cupressus sempervirens *Cyprès de Provence*

Italian cypress / Mediterranean cypress

Cuscuta epithymum	*Cuscute du thym*	Common dodder
Cuscuta europaea	*Cuscute d'Europe*	Greater dodder
Cyanotis kewensis	*Cyanotis kewensis*	Teddy-bear vine
Cyanotis somaliensis	*Cyanotis somaliensis*	Pussy ears
Cyathea arborea	*Cyathea arborea*	West Indian tree fern
Cyathea australis	*Cyathea australis*	Australian tree fern
Cyathea medullaris	*Cyathea medullaris*	Black tree fern
Cycas revoluta	*Cycas revoluta*	Japanese sago palm
Cyclamen	*Cyclamen*	Cyclamen
Cyclamen hederifolium	*Cyclamen de Naples*	Sowbread
Cydonia oblonga	*Cognassier commun*	Quince
Cymbalaria muralis	*Linaire cymbalaire / Ruine-de-Rome*	

Ivy-leafed toadflax / Kenilworth ivy

Cynara cardunculus	*Cardon*	Cardoon
Cynara scolymus	*Artichaut commun*	Globe artichoke
Cynoglossum germanicum	*Cynoglosse d'Allemagne / Langue de chien*	

Great hound's tongue

Cynoglossum nervosum	*Cynoglosse nervosum*	Himalayan hounds tongue
Cynoglossum officinale	*Cynoglosse officinale /Langue-de-chien*	

Hound's tongue

Cyperus longus	*Souchet*	Galingale
Cyperus papyrus	*Souchet à papier*	Papyrus
Cyphomandra betacea	*Tomate en arbre*	Tree tomato
Cypripedium acaule	*Cypripedium acaule*	Moccasin flower
Cypripedium calceolus	*Sabot de Vénus*	Lady's slipper orchid / Slipper orchid
Cypripedium calceolus	*Cauphinellpripedium calceolus*	Yellow lady's slipper orchid
Cypripedium reginae	*Cypripedium reginae*	Showy lady's slipper orchid
Cyrilla racemiflora	*Bois-cuir*	Leatherwood
Cyrtomium falcatum	*Cyrtomium falcatum*	Fishtail fern / Holly fern
Cystopteris bulbifera	*Cystopteris bulbifera*	Berry bladder fern
Cystopteris fragilis	*Cystopteris fragile*	Brittle bladder fern
Cythea medulalaris	*Cythea medulalaris*	Mamaku
Cytisus	*Genêt*	Broom
Cytisus albus	*Genêt blanc*	White broom
Cytisus battandieri	*Cytisus battandieri*	Moroccan broom / Pineapple broom
Cytisus x praecox	*Genêt*	Warminster broom
Cytisus purpureus	*Genêt pourpré*	Purple broom
Cytisus scoparius	*Genêt à balais*	Broom

D

Daboecia cantabrica	*Bruyère de Saint-Dabeoc*	St. Dabeoc's heath
Dactylis glomerata	*Dactyle aggloméré / Dactyle peltonné*	Cock's foot / Orchard grass
Dactylorhiza fuchsii	*Orchis de Fuchs*	Common spotted orchid
Dactylorhiza incarnata	*Orchis incarnat*	Early marsh orchid
Dactylorhiza maculata	*Orchis à tubercules digités*	Heath spotted orchid
Dactylorhiza majalis	*Orchis à feuilles larges*	Irish marsh orchid
Dactylorhiza praetermissa	*Orchis négligé*	Southern marsh orchid
Dactylorhiza purpurella	*Orchis d'Ecosse*	Northern marsh orchid
Damasonium alisima	*Damasonium étoilé*	Star-fruit
Danae racemosa	*Laurier d'Alexandrie*	Alexandrian laurel
Daphne	*Daphné*	Daphne
Daphne cneorum	*Thymélée des Alpes*	Daphne cneorum
Daphne laureola	*Daphné lauréole / Laurier des bois*	Spurge laurel
Daphne mezereum	*Bois-gentil / Bois joli / Graou*	Mezereon
Dasylirion	*Dasylirion*	Bear grass
Daucus carota	*Carotte commune*	Wild carrot
Datura	*Stramoine odorante*	Angels' trumpets
Datura stramonium	*Herbe à la taupe / Pomme épineause*	Thorn-apple
Davallia canariensis	*Davallia canariensis*	Hare's foot fern

Davallia maresii	*Davallia maresii*	Squirrel's foot fern
Davidia involucrata	*Arbre aux mouchoirs*	Dove tree / Ghost tree / Pocket handkerchief tree
Davidia involucrata	*Arbre aux pochettes*	Dove tree / Ghost tree / Pocket handkerchief tree
Delphinium	*Dauphinelle / Pied d'alouette*	Delphinium
Dendrochilum glumaceum	*Dendrochilum glumaceum*	Silver chain
Deschampsia caespitosa	*Canchie cespiteuse*	Tufted hair grass
Descurainia sophia	*Sisymbre sagesse*	Flixweed
Dianella	*Dianella*	Flax lily
Diapensia lapponica	*Diapensie*	Diapensia
Dianthus	*Œillet*	Carnation
Dianthus	*Œillet mignardise*	Pink
Dianthus alpinus	*Œillet des Alpes*	Alpine pink
Dianthus armeria	*Œillet des bois / Œillet velu*	Deptford pink
Dianthus barbatus	*Jalousie / Œillet de poète*	Sweet William
Dianthus chinensis	*Œillet de Chine*	Indian pink
Dianthus deltoides	*Œillet couché*	Maiden pink
Dianthus gratianopolitanus	*Œillet bleuatre*	Cheddar pink
Dicentra cuculiaria	*Cœur de Jeannette*	Dutchman's breeches
Dicentra spectabilis	*Cœur de Marie*	Bleeding heart
Dicksonia antarctica	*Dicksonia antarctica*	Australian tree fern
Dictamnus albus	*Fraxinelle*	Burning bush
Dieffenbachia	*Dieffenbachia*	Dumb cane / Leopard Lily
Dierama	*Diérame*	Angel's fishing rod / Wandflower
Digitalis grandiflora	*Digitale jaune à grandes fleurs*	Yellow foxglove
Digitalis purpurea	*Digitale / Digitale pourpre*	Foxglove
Digitalis purpurea	*Gant de Notre-Dame*	Foxglove
Dillenia indica	*Dillénie undica*	Elephant apple
Dimorphotheca	*Souci*	African daisy / Cape marigold
Dimorphotheca pluvialis	*Souci pluvial*	Rain daisy
Dionaea muscipula	*Dionée attrape mouches / Dionée gobe-mouches*	Venus flytrap
Dioon edule	*Dioon edule*	Virgin's palm
Dioscorea discolor	*Igname*	Ornamental yam
Dioscorea elephantipes	*Pied-d'éléphant*	Elephant's foot
Diosma ericoides	*Diosma ericoides*	Breath of heaven
Diospyros kaki	*Kaki / Plaqueminier kaki*	Kaki / Persimmon
Diospyros lotus	*Plaqueminier faux lotier*	Date plum
DiaspDiplotaxis muralis	*Diplotaxis des murailles*	Stink weed / Wall rocket
Diphylleia cymosa	*Diphyllée*	Umbrella leaf
Dipsacus fullonium	*Chardon à foulon / Cardère sauvage*	Teasel

Dipsacus pilosus	*Cardère poilue*	Shepherd's rod
Discaria toumatou	*Discaria toumatou*	Wild Irishman
Disporum	*Disporum*	Fairy bells
Distictis buccinatoria	*Distictis buccinatoria*	Mexican blood flower
Dizygotheca elegantissima	*Dizygotheca elegantissima*	False aralia
Dodecatheon	*Gyroselle*	Shooting stars
Dombeya x cayeuxii	*Dombeya x cayeuxii*	Pink snowball
Doronicum pardalianches	*Doronic tue-pantheres*	Leopard's bane
Dorotheanthus bellidiformis	*Dorotheanthus bellidiformis*	Ice plant
Dorotheanthus belliformis	*Ficoïde*	Livingstone daisy
Draba aizoides	*Drave faux-aizoon*	Yellow whitlow grass
Draba incana	*Drave grisâtre*	Twisted whitlow-grass
Draba muralis	*Drave des murs*	Common whitlow-grass
Dracaena fragrans	*Dragonnier odorant*	Corn plant
Dracaena marginata	*Dragonnier de Madagascar*	Madagascar dragon tree
Dracaena sanderiana	*Dragonnier de Sander*	Ribbon plant
Dracocephalum	*Dracocéphale*	Dragon's head
Dracunculus vulgaris	*Serpentaire*	Dragon tree
Drimys lanceolata	*Drimys lanceolata*	Mountain pepper
Drimys winteri	*Drimys winteri*	Winter's bark
Drosera	*Rossolis*	Sundew
Drosera anglica	*Rossolis d' Angleterre*	Great sundew
Drosera capensis	*Rossolis du Cap*	Cape sundew
Drosera intermedia	*Rossolis intermédiaire*	Long-leaved sundew
Drosera rotundifolia	*Rossolis à feuilles rondes*	Common sundew
Dryas octopetala	*Dryade à huit pétales*	Mountain avens
Dryopteris carthusiana	*Dryoptéris carthusiana*	Narrow buckler fern
Dryopteris dilatata	*Dryoptéris dilatata / Spinuleux*	Broad buckler fern
Dryopteris erythrosora	*Fougère erythrosora*	Japanese shield fern
Dryopteris filix-mas	*Fougère mâle*	Male fern
Dryopteris goldiana	*Fougère goldiana*	Giant wood fern
Duranta repens	*Durante*	Pigeon berry / Skyflower

E

Eccremocarpus scaber *Bignone de Chili*
Chilean glory flower / Eccremocarpus / Glory vine
Echevaria pulvinata *Echevaria pulvinata*   Plush plant
Echinacea   *Echinacea*   Coneflower
Echinocactus grusonii *Echinocactus grusonii*
Golden barrel cactus / Mother-in-law's-seat
Echinocereus schmollii *Echinocereus schmollii*   Lamb's tail cactus
Echinops spaerocepha   *Échinop à tête ronde* Globe thistle
Echium plantagineum   *Vipérine pourpre*   Purple viper's bugloss
Echium vulgare   *Vipérine commune*   Viper's bugloss
Eichornia crassipes   *Jacinthe d'eau*   Water hyacinth
Elaeagnus   *Chalef*   Elaeagnus
Elaeagnus angustifolia *Olivier de Bohême*   Oleaster
Elaeocarpus reticulatus*Elaeocarpus reticulatus*   Blueberry ash
Elatine hexandra   *Elatine à six étamines* Waterwort
Elatine hydropiper   *Elatine poivre d'eau*   Eight stamened waterwort
Eleocharis acicularis *Scirpe épingle*   Needle spike rush
Elodea   *Élodée*   Elodea
Elodea canadensis   *Élodée du Canada*   Canadian waterweed
Elodea nuttallii   *Élodée de Nuttall*   Esthwaite waterweed
Embothrium coccineum *Embothrium coccineum*   Chilean firebush
Emilia javanica   *Cacalie éclarte / Émile* Tassel flower
Empetrum nigrum   *Camarine noire*   Crowberry
Eomecon chionantha *Eomecon chionantha*   Snow poppy
Epicaris impressa   *Epicaris impressa*   Australian heath
Epigaea repens   *Epigée*   Mayflower / Trailing arbutus
Epilobium   *Épilobe*   Willow herb
Epilobium alsinifolium*Épilobe à feuilles d'alsine* Chickweed willow-herb
Epilobium anagallidifolium *Epilobe des Alpes*   Alpine willow-herb
Epilobium angustifolium album *Laurier de Saint-Antoine album*
White rosebay
Epilobium brunnescens *Épilobe de Nouvelle Zélande*
New Zealand willow-herb
Epilobium hirsutum   *Épilobe hirsute*   Great willow-herb
Epilobium lanceolatum *Épilobe à feuilles lancéolées*
Spear-leaved willow-herb
Epilobium montanum *Épilobe de montagne*   Broad-leaved willow-herb
Epilobium obscurum *Épilobe foncé*   Short-fruited willow-herb
Epilobium palustra   *Épilobe des marais*   Marsh willow-herb
Epilobium parviflorum *Épilobe à peties fleurs*   Hoary willow-herb

Epilobium roseum	*Épilobe rosé*	Pale willow-herb
Epimedium alpinum	*Epimedium alpinum*	Barrenwort
Epipactis atrorubens	*Épipactis sanguine*	Dark red helleborine
Epipactis helleborine	*Épipactis à feuilles larges*	Common helleborine
Epipactis leptochila	*Épipactis à labelle étroite*	Narrow-lipped helleborine
Epipactis palustris	*Épipactis des marais*	Marsh helleborine
Epipactis phyllanthes	*Épipactis à fleurs vertes*	Green-flowered helleborine
Epipactis purpurata	*Épipactis pourprée*	Violet helleborine
Epiphyllum	*Cactus orchidée*	Strap cactus / Orchid cactus
Epiphyllum anguliger	*Epiphyllum anguliger*	Fishbone cactus
Epipogium aphyllum	*Épipognon sans feuilles*	Ghost orchid
Epipremnum pictum	*Epipremnum pictum*	Silver vine
Episcia cupreata	*Episcia cupreata*	Flame violet
Episcia dianthiflora	*Episcia dianthiflora*	Lace flower
Eranthis hyemalis	*Ellebore d'hiver / Éranthe*	Winter aconite
Eremurus	*Eremurus*	Foxtail lily / King's spear
Erica arborea	*Bruyère en arbre*	Tree heath
Erica australis	*Bruyère d'Espagne*	Spanish tree heath
Erica canaliculata	*Erica canaliculata*	Channelled heath
Erica carnea	*Bruyère des neiges*	Alpine heath / Winter heath
Erica ciliaris	*Bruyère ciliée*	Dorset heath
Erica cinerea	*Bruyère cendrée*	Bell heather
Erica lusitanica	*Bruyère du Portugal*	Portuguese heath
Erica mackaiana	*Bruyère de Mackay*	Mackay's heath
Erica scoparia	*Brande*	Besom heath
Erica scoparia	*Bruyère à balai*	Besom heath
Erica terminalis	*Bruyère de Corse*	Corsican heath
Erica tetralix	*Bruyère tétragone / Caminet / Clarin*	
		Cross-leaved heath
Erica vagans	*Bruyère vagabonde* `	Cornish heath
Erigeron	*Vergerette*	Fleabane
Erigeron acer	*Vergerette acre*	Blue fleabane
Erigeron alpinus	*Vergerette dea Alpes*	Alpine fleabane
Erigeron borealis	*Vergerette dea Alpes*	Highland fleabane
Erinacea anthyllis	*Erinacea anthyllis*	Hedgehog broom
Erinus alpinus	*Érine des Alpes*	Fairy foxglove
Eriobotrya japonica	*Bibacier / Loquat / Néflier du Japon*	Loquat
Eriocaulon aquaticum	*Joncinelle*	Pipewort
Eriogonum	*Eriogonum*	Wild buckwheat
Eriogonum giganteum	*Eriogonum giganteum*	St. Catherine's lace
Eriophorum angustifolium	*Eriophorum angustifolium*	Common cotton-grass
Erodium cicutarium	*Bec-de-grue commun*	Common storksbill

Erodium maritimum	*Bec-de-grue maritime*	Sea storksbill
Erodium moschatum	*Bec musqué*	Musk storksbill
Erucastrum gallicum	*Fausse roquette de France*	Hairy rocket
Eryngium alpinum	*Chardon bleu des Alpes*	Eryngium alpinum
Eryngium campestre	*Chardon-Roland / Panicaut champêtre*	
		Watling street thistle
Eryngium maritimum	*Panicaut de mer*	Sea holly
Erysimum cheiranthoides	*Vélar fause-giroflée*	Treacle mustard
Erysimum hieraciifolium	*Vélar*	Siberian wallflower
Erythrin*Érythrine*		Erythrina
Erythrina coralloides	*Érythrine coralloides*	Flame coral tree / Naked coral tree
Erythrina crista-galli	*Érythrine crête de coq*	Cockspur coral-tree
Erythronium dens-canis	*Dent de chien*	Dog's-tooth violet
Eritrichium nanum	*Roi des Alpes*	Eritrichium nanum
Escholtzia stauntonii	*Escholtzia stauntonii*	Mint bush
Espostosa lanata	*Espostosa lanata*	Cotton ball
Eucalyptus	*Eucalyptus*	Gum tree
Eucalyptus camaldulensis	*Eucalyptus camaldulensis*	
		Murray river gum / River red gum
Eucalyptus coccifera	*Eucalyptus coccifera*	Tasmanian snow gum
Eucalyptus dalrympleana	*Eucalyptus dalrympleana*	Mountain gum
Eucalyptus ficifolia	*Eucalyptus ficifolia*	Flowering gum
Eucalyptus glaucescens	*Eucalyptus glaucescens*	Tigiringi gum
Eucalyptus globulus	*Gommier bleu*	Blue gum / Tasmanian blue gum
Eucalyptus gunnii	*Eucalyptus de Gunn*	Cider gum
Eucalyptus niphophila	*Eucalyptus niphophila*	Snow gum
Eucalyptus perriniana	*Eucalyptus perriniana*	Spinning gum / White Sally
Eucalyptus viminalis	*Eucalyptus à feuilles d'osier*	Manna gum / Ribbon gum
Eucomis	*Eucomis*	Pineapple flower
Eucomis pallidiflora	*Eucomis pallidiflora*	Giant pineapple flower
Eucomis pallidiflora	*Eucomis pallidiflora*	Giant pineapple lily
Eucommia ulnoides	*Eucommia ulnoides*	Gutta-percha tree
Eucryphia cordifolia	*Eucryphia cordifolia*	Ulmo
Eugenia myrtifolia	*Myrte d'Australie*	Australian brush cherry
Euonymus alatus	*Fusain ailé*	Winged spindle
Euonymus europaeus	*Bonnet-de-prêtre / Fusain d'Europe*	Spindle tree
Euonymus japonicus	*Fusain du Japon*	Japanese spindle
Eupatorium cannabinum	*Eupatoire à feuilles de chanvre*	Hemp agrimony
Eupatorium purpureum	*Eupatorium purpureum*	Joe Pye weed
Eupatorium rugosum	*Eupatoire rugeua*	
		Hardy age / Mist flower / White snakeroot
Euphorbia	*Euphorbe*	Milkweed / Spurge

Euphorbia amygdaloides *Euphorbe des bois*   Wood spurge
Euphorbia fulgens   *Euphorbe fulgens*   Scarlet plume
Euphorbia gorgonensis *Euphorbia gorgonensis* Gorgon's head
Euphorbia marginata *Euphorbe panaché*
                                          Snow-on-the-mountain / Snow-in-summer
Euphorbia milii   *Couronne d'épine*   Crown of thorns
Euphorbia pulcherrima *Poinsettia*   Poinsettia
Euphorbia obesa   *Euphorbia obesa*   Gingham golf ball
Euphrasia officinalis *Casse-lunettes / Euphraise officinal*   Eyebright
Exaculum pusillum   *Cicendia fluette*   Guernsey centaury
Exacum affine   *Exacum affine*   Persian violet
Expostoa lanata   *Expostoa lanata*   Peruvian old man cactus

F

Fagopyrum esculentum*Blé noir / Sarrasin*   Buckwheat
Fagus grandifolia   *Hêtre d'Amérique*   American beech
Fagus orientalis   *Hêtre d'Orient*   Oriental beech
Fagus sylvatica   *Hêtre*   Beech
Fagus sylvatica pendula *Hêtre pleureur*   Weeping beech
Fagus sylvatica purpurea *Hêtre pourpré*   Copper beech
Falcaria vulgaris   *Falcaria commun*   Longleaf
Fallugia paradoxa   *Fallugia paradoxa*   Apache plume
Fatshedera lizei   *Fatshedera lizei*   Tree ivy
Fatsia japonica   *Fatsia japonica*   Japanese aralia
Faucaria tigrina   *Guele de tigre*   Tiger-jaws
Feijoa sellowiana   *Feijoa sellowiana*   Pineapple guava
Felicia amelloides   *Margueritte du Cap / Pâquerette*   Blue margueritte
Felicia bergeriana   *Felicia bergeriana*   Kingfisher daisy
Fenestraria aurantiaca var. rhopalophylla
                    Fenestraria aurantiaca rhopalophylla   Baby's toes
Ferocactus   *Ferocactus*   Barrel cactus
Ferona elephantum   *Féronier*   Elephant apple
Ferula   *Férule*   Giant fennel
Festuca glauca   *Festuca glauca*   Blue fescue
Ficus   *Figuier*   Fig
Ficus benghalensis   *Figuier des Banyans*   Banyan
Ficus benjamina   *Ficus benjamina*   Weeping fig
Ficus deltoides   *Ficus deltoides*   Mistletoe fig
Ficus elastica   *Caoutchouc*   India rubber tree / Rubber plant
Ficus lyrata   *Ficus lyrata*   Fiddle-leaf fig
Ficus macrophylla   *Ficus macrophylla* Australian banyan / Moreton Bay fig

Ficus pumila	*Ficus pumila*	Creeping fig
Ficus religiosa	*Figuer des pagodes*	Bo / Peepul / Sacred fig tree
Ficus rubiginosa	*Ficus rubiginosa*	Port Jackson fig / Rusty-leaved fig
Filago gallica	*Cotonnière de France*	Narrow cudweed
Filago germanica	*Cotonnière d'Allemagne*	Common cudweed
Filago minima	*Cotonnière naine*	Small cudweed
Filipendula ulmaria	*Reine des prés / Spirée ulmaire*	Meadowsweet
Filipendula vulgaris	*Filipendule à 6 petales*	Dropwort
Fittonia verschaffeltii	*Fittonia verschaffeltii*	Painted net leaf / Silver net-leaf
Fitzroya cupressoides	*Alerce*	Patagonian cypress
Foeniculum vulgare	*Fenouil commun*	Fennel
Fothergilla gardenii	*Fothergilla gardenii*	Witch alder
Fontinalis antipyretica	*Fontinale*	Water moss / Willow moss
Fragaria vesca	*Fraisier commun*	Wild strawberry
Francoa appendiculata	*Francoa appendiculata*	Bridal wreath
Frangula alnus	*Bourdaine / Neprun*	Alder buckthorn
Frankenia laevis	*Bruyère marine / Frankenénie liss*	Sea heath
Fraxinus	*Frêne*	Ash
Fraxinus americana	*Frêne blanc*	White ash
Fraxinus angustifolia	*Frêne oxyphylle*	Narrow leafed ash
Fraxinus excelsior 'Pendula'	*Frêne pleureur*	Weeping ash
Fraxinus ornus	*Frêne à fleurs*	Manna ash
Fraxinus oxycarpa	*Frêne oxyphylle*	Claret ash
Fraxinus pennsylvanica	*Frêne vert*	Green ash / Red ash
Fraxinus velutina	*Frêne de l'Arizona*	Arizona ash
Fremontodendron	*Fremontodendron*	Flannel flower
Fritillaria imperialis	*Couronne impériale*	Crown imperial
Fritillaria meleagris	*Fritillaire pintade*	Fritillary
Fritillaria meleagris	*Méléagre / Œuf de pintade / Œuf de pintade*	Snake's head fritillery
Fritillaria pudica	*Fritillaire pudica*	Yellow fritillary
Fritillaria recurva	*Fritillaire recurva*	Scarlet Fritillary
Fuchsia arborescens	*Fuchsia arborescent*	Tree fuchsia
Fuchsia magellanica	*Fuchsia magellanica*	Lady's eardrops
Fumaria oficinalis	*Fumeterre officinale*	Fumitory
Fungus	*Champignon*	Mushroom

G

Gagea lutea	*Gagée jaune*	Yellow star of Bethlehem
Gaillardia	*Gaillardia*	Blanket flower
Galanthus nivalis 'Flore pleno'	*Perce-neige 'Flore pleno'*	Double Common snowdrop
Galanthus nivalis	*Perce-neige*	Snowdrop
Galanthus nivalis	*Clochette d'hiver*	Snowdrop
Galanthus nivalis	*Violier d'hiver*	Snowdrop
Galanthus nivalis	*Violette de la Chandeleur*	Snowdrop
Galanthus nivalis	*Nivéole*	Snowdrop
Galanthus nivalis	*Galantine*	Snowdrop
Galanthus plicatus byzantinus	*Byzantine*	Snowdrop plicatus byzantinus
Galega officinalis	*Galéga officinal / Lilas d'Espagne / Rue de chèvre*	Goat's rue
Galeopsis angustifolia	*Galópsis à feuilles étroites*	Red hemp-nettle
Galeopsis speciosa	*Galópsis orné*	Large hemp-nettle
Galinsoga parviflora	*Galinsoga à petites fleurs*	Gallant soldier
Galium	*Gaillet*	Bedstraw
Galium aparine	*Gaillet gratteron*	Goosegrass
Galium boreale	*Gaillet du nord*	Northern bedstraw
Galium mollugo	*Gaillet commun*	Hedge bedstraw
Galium odoratum	*Caille-lait / Gaillet*	Woodruff
Galium odoratum	*Aspérule odorante / Belle-étoile /Petit muguet*	Woodruff
Galium palustre	*Gaillet des marais*	Marsh bedstraw
Galium Parisiense	*Gaillet de Paris*	Wall bedstraw
Galium saxatile	*Gaillet des rochers*	Heath bedstraw
Galium tricornutum	*Gaillet à trois cornes*	Small goosegrass
Galium uliginosum	*Gaillet fangeux*	Fen bedstraw
Galium verum	*Gaillet jaune*	Lady's bedstraw
Galtonia candicans	*Jacinthe du Cap*	Summer hyacinth
Gardenia jasminoides	*Jasmin du Cap*	Cape jasmine
Garrya elliptica	*Garrya elliptica*	Silk-tassel bush
Gaultheria shallon	*Gaultheria shallon*	Shallon
Gaylussacia	*Gaylussacie*	Huckleberry
Gaylussacia baccata	*Gaylussacia baccata*	Black huckleberry
Gelsemium sempervirens	*Gelsemium sempervirens*	Carolina jasmine / False jasmine
Genista	*Genêt*	Broom
Genista aetnensis	*Genêt del'Etna*	Mount Etna broom
Genista anglica	*Genêt d'Angleterre*	Petty whin

Genista hispanica	*Genêt d'Espagne*	Spanish gorse
Genista pilosa	*Arnigo / Genêt poilu*	Hairy greenweed
Genista tinctoria	*Genestrolle / Genêt des teinturiers*	Dyers' greenweed
Gentiana	*Gentiane*	Gentian
Gentiana acaulis	*Gentiana acaulis*	Stemless gentian
Gentiana amarella	*Gentiane amère*	Felwort gentian
Gentiana anglica	*Gentiane d'Angleterre*	Early gentian
Gentiana asclepiadea	*Gentiane asclepiadea*	Willow gentian
Gentiana campestris	*Gentiane champêtre*	Field gentian
Gentiana clusii	*Gentiane clusii*	Trumpet gentian
Gentiana germanica	*Gentiane d'Allemagne*	Chiltern gentian
Gentiana lutea	*Grande gentiane*	Great yellow gentian
Gentiana lutea	*Gentiana jaune*	Great yellow gentian
Gentiana pneumonanthe	*Gentiane pneumonanthe*	Marsh gentian
Gentiana uliginosa	*Gentiane des marais*	Welsh gentian
Gentiana verna	*Gentiane printanière*	Spring gentian
Geranium columbinum	*Géranium des colombes*	Long stalked cranesbill
Geranium columbinum	*Pied-de-pigeon*	Long stalked cranesbill
Geranium dissectum	*Géranium découpé*	Cut-leaved cranesbill
Geranium endressii	*Géranium d'endresse*	French cranesbill
Geranium lucidum	*Géranium luisant*	Shining cranesbill
Geranium lucidum	*Rouget*	Shining cranesbill
Geranium nodosum	*Géranium noueux*	Knotted cranesbill
Geranium phaeum	*Géranium brun*	Dusky cranesbill
Geranium pratense	*Géranium des prés*	Meadow cranesbill
Geranium purpureum	*Géranium pourpré*	Little robin
Geranium pusillum	*Géranium fluet*	Small flowered cranesbill
Geranium pyrenaicum	*Géranium des Pyrénées*	Pyrenean cranesbill
Geranium robertianum	*Herbe à Robert*	Herb Robert
Geranium rotundifolium	*Geranium à feuilles rondes*	Round-leaved cranesbill
Geranium sanguineum	*Géranium sanguin*	Bloody cranesbill
Geranium sylvaticum	*Géranium des bois*	Wood cranesbill
Geranium versicolor	*Géranium changeant*	Pencilled cranesbill
Gerbera jamesonii	*Gerbera jamesonii*	Barberton daisy
Geum	*Benoîte*	Avens
Geum chiloense	*Benoîte à fleurs jaunes*	Geum "Lady Stratheden"
Geum montanum	*Benoîte des montagnes*	Alpine avens
Geum rivale	*Benoîte de rivage*	Water avens
Geum urbanum	*Benoîte commune*	Herb Bennet
Gevuina avellana	*Noisetier du Chili*	Chilean hazel
Ginkgo biloba	*Arbe aux 40 écus*	Maidenhair tree

Gladiolus	*Glaïeul*	Gladiolus
Gladiolus illyricus	*Glaïeul d'Illurie*	Gladiolus illyricus
Glaucium flavum	*Glaucière jaune / Pavot cornu*	
		Horned poppy / Yellow horned poppy
Glaux maritima	*Glauce*	Sea milkwort
Glechoma hederacea	*Lierre terrestre*	Ground ivy
Glechoma hederacea 'Variegata'	*Lierre terrestre panachée*	
		Variegated ground ivy
Gleditsia caspica	*Févier caspica*	Caspian locust
Gleditsia japonica	*Févier du Japon*	Japanese locust
Gleditsia triacanthas	*Févier d'Amérique*	Honey locust
Glyceria maxima	*Glycérie aquatique*	Glyceria
Glycyrrhiza glabra	*Réglisse*	Liquorice
Globularia	*Globulaire*	Globularia
Gnaphalium luteoalbum	*Gnaphale blanc-jaunâtre*	Jersey cudweed
Gnaphalium norvegicum	*Gnaphale de Norvège*	Highland cudweed
Gnaphalium supinum	*Gnaphale nain*	Dwarf cudweed
Gnaphalium sylvaticum	*Gnaphale des forêts*	Heath cudweed
Gnaphalium undulatum	*Gnaphale ondulé*	Cape cudweed
Goodyera repens	*Goodyère rampante*	Creeping lady's tresses
Gomphrena globosa	*Amarantoïde*	Globe amaranth
Gordonia lasianthus	*Gordonia à feuilles glabrées*	Loblolly bay
Graptopetalum paraguayense	*Graptopetalum paraguayense*	
		Mother of pearl plant
Graptophyllum pictum	*Graptophyllum pictum*	Caricature plant
Grevillea robusta	*Grevillea robusta*	Silky oak
Griselinia littoralis	*Griselinia littoralis*	Broadleaf
Groenlandia densa	*Potamot dense*	Opposite pondweed
Guzmania monostachia	*Guzmania monostachia*	Striped torch
Gymnadenia canopsea	*Gymnadénia a long éperon*	Scented orchid
Gymnocladus dioica	*Chicot du Canada*	Kentucky coffee tree
Gynura aurantiaca	*Gynure*	Velvet plant
Gypsophila	*Gypsophile*	Gypsophila

H

Haemanthus albiflos	*Haemanthus albiflos*	Paintbrush
Haemanthus coccineus	*Haemanthus coccineus*	Blood lily
Halesia	*Arbre aux cloches d'argent*	Snowdrop tree
Halesia carolina	*Arbre aux cloches*	Silver bell
Halimione portulacoides	*Arroche pourpière*	Sea purslane
Hamamelis	*Noisetie de sorcière*	Witch hazel
Hamamelis japonica	*Hamamélide du Japon*	Japanese witch hazel
Hamamelis mollis	*Hamamélis velouté*	Chinese witch hazel
Hamamelis virginiana	*Hamamélis virginiana*	Virginia witch hazel
Hammarbya paludosa	*Malaxis des marais*	Bog orchid
Hardenbergia violacea	*Hardenbergia violacea*	
		Australian sarsparilla / Coral pea / Vine lilac
Hatiora salicornoides	*Hatiora salicornoides*	Bottle plant / Drunkard's dream
Hebe pinguifolia	*Hebe pinguifolia*	Disk-leaved hebe
Hedera	*Lierre*	Ivy
Hedera canariensis	*Lierre des Canaries*	Canary Island Ivy
Hedera colchica	*Lierre de Perse*	Persian ivy
Hedera colchica 'Dentata'	*Lierre de Perse*	Elephant's ears
Hedera colchica 'Sulphur Heart'	*Hedera colchica 'Sulphur Heart'*	
		Paddy's pride
Hedera helix 'Deltoides'	*Lierre helix deltoides*	Shield ivy / Sweetheart ivy
Hedera helix digitata	*Lierre helix digitata*	Finger-leafed ivy
Hedera helix var.hibernica	*Lierre d'Irlande*	Irish ivy
Hedera helix pedata	*Lierre helix pedata*	Bird's foot ivy
Hedera nepalensis	*Lierre nepalensis*	Nepalese ivy
Hedera rhombea	*Lierre de Japon*	Japanese ivy
Hedychium	*Gandasuk / Hédychie*	Ginger lily
Hedychium coronarium	*Hédychie coronarium*	White ginger lily
Hedyotis michauxii	*Rubiacées*	Creeping bluets
Hedysarum coronarium	*Sainfoin à bouquets / Sainfoin d'Espagns*	
		French honeysuckle
Helenium	*Hélénie*	Sneezewort
Helianthemum	*Hélianthème*	Rock rose
Helianthemum apenninum	*Hélianthème des Appennines*	White rock-rose
Helianthemum canum	*Hélianthème blanchâtre*	Hoary rock-rose
Helianthemum nummularium	*Hélianthème commun*	Common rock-rose
Helianthus	*Soleil*	Sunflower
Helianthus annuus	*Soleil annuel / Tournesol*	Annual sunflower
Helianthus salicifolius	*Helianthus salicifolius*	Willow-leaved sunflower
Helianthus tuberosus	*Artichaut d'hiver / Topinambour*	Jerusalem artichoke

Helichrysum	*Immortelle*	Garland flower
Helichrysum bracteatum	*Immortelle à bractées*	Everlasting flower / Strawflower
Helichrysum italicum	*Helichrysum italicum*	Curry plant
Heliconia	*Heliconia*	Lobster claws
Heliconia psittacorum	*Heliconia psittacorum*	Parrot's flower
Helictotrichon sempervirens	*Helictotrichon sempervirens*	Blue oat grass
Heliotrope arborescens	*Fleur des dames / Héliotrope de Pérou / Herbe de Saint-Fiacre*	Heliotrope arborescens
Helleborus foetidus	*Ellébore fétide /Pied-de-griffon*	Stinking hellebore
Helleborus niger	*Rose de Noël*	Christmas rose
Helleborus viridis	*Ellébore vert / Herbe à la bosse*	Green Hellebore
Helonias bullata	*Helonias bullata*	Swamp pink
Hemerocallis	*Hémérocalle*	Day lily
Hemerocallis fulva	*Hémérocalle fulva / Lis jaune*	Tawny day lily
Hemerocallis lilio-asphodelus	*Hémérocalle jaune / Lis jaune*	Yellow day lily
Hemerocallis minor	*Hemerocallis minor*	Grass leaved daylily
Hepatica nobilis	*Anémone hépatique*	Hepatica
Hesperis matronalis	*Julienne des dames / Julienne des jardins*	Dame's violet / Sweet rocket
Heracleum mantegazzianum	*Berce du Cauccase*	Giant hogweed
Heracleum sphondylium	*Berce commune / Patte d'ours*	Hogweed
Herminium monarchis	*Herminium a un bulbe*	Musk orchid
Hermodactylus tuberosus	*Hermodactylus tuberosus*	Widow iris
Herniaria ciliata	*Herniaire ciliée*	Rupture-wort
Herniaria glabra	*Herniaire glabre*	Smooth rupture-wort
Heteromeles arbutifolia	*Heteromeles arbutifolia*	Christmas berry / Toyon
Heuchera	*Heuchera*	Alum root
Hibiscus mutabilis	*Hibiscus mutabilis*	Confederate rose / Cotton rose
Hibiscus trionum	*Hibiscus trionum*	Flower of the hour
Hidalgoa	*Hidalgoa*	Climbing dahlia
Hieracium	*Épervière*	Hawkweed
Himantoglossum hircinum	*Orchis bouc*	Lizard orchid
Hippeastrum	*Amaryllis*	Amaryllis
Hippeastrum vittatum	*Amaryllis de Rouen*	Hippeastrum vittatum
Hippocrepis	*Hippocrepis*	Vetch
Hippocrepis comosa	*Fer-à-cheval / Hippocrépis à toupet*	Horseshoe vetch
Hippophäe rhamnoides	*Argousier*	Sea buckthorn
Hippuris vulgaris	*Pesse d'eau*	Marestail
Hirschfeldia incana	*Herschfeldie grisâtre*	Hoary mustard
Hoheria populnea	*Hoheria populnea*	Lace-bark
Hoheria sexstylosa	*Hoheria sexstylosa*	Ribbon wood

Holcus mollis	*Holcus mollis*	Creeping soft grass
Holcus mollis Variegatus	*Holcus mollis Variegatus*	
		Variegated creeping soft grass
Holmskioldia sanguinea	*Holmskioldia sanguinea*	
		Chinese hat plant / Mandarin's hat plant
Homogyne alpina	*Homogyne des Alpes*	Alpine coltsfoot / Purple coltsfoot
Honkenya peploides	*Pourpier de mer*	Sea sandwort
Hordeum jubatum	*Orge barbue*	Foxtail barley / Squirrel tail grass
Horminum pyrenaicum	*Horminum pyrenaicum*	Dragon's mouth
Hornungia peteraea	*Hutchinsie des pierres*	Hutchinsia
Hosta	*Funkia / Hosta*	Funkia / Plantain lily
Hosta hypoleuca	*Hosta hypoleuca*	White-backed hosta
Hosta plantaginea	*Hosta plantaginea*	August lily
Hottonia palustris	*Hottonie des marais*	Water violet
Howea forsteriana	*Howée*	Sentry palm / Thatch-leaf plant / Paradise palm
Hoya carnosa	*Hoya carnosa*	Wax plant
Huernia zebrina	*Huernia zebrina*	Owl eyes
Humea elegans	*Humea elegans*	Incense plant
Humulus lupulus	*Houblon*	Hop
Hunnemannia fumariifolia	*Hunnemannia fumariifolia*	Mexican tulip poppy
Hyacinthoides hispanica	*Jacinthe d'Espagne*	Spanish bluebell
Hyacinthoides non-scripta	*Jacinthe des bois*	Bluebell / English bluebell
Hyacinthus	*Jacinthe*	Hyacinth
Hydrangea	*Hortensia*	Hydrangea
Hydrangea anomala petiolaris	*Hortensia grimpant*	Climbing hydrangea
Hydrangea quercifolia	*Hortensia à feuilles de chêne*	Oak leafed hydrangea
Hydrocharis morsus-ranae	*Hydrocharis des Grenouilles*	Frog-bit
Hydrocleys nymphoides	*Hydroclís nymphoides*	Water poppy
Hydrocotyle vulgaris	*Écuelle d'eau*	Marsh pennywort
Hylocereus undatus	*Hylocereus undatus*	Queen-of-the-night
Hymenocallis narcissiflora	*Hymenocallis narcissiflora*	Peruvian daffodil
Hymenosporum flavum	*Hymenosporum flavum*	
		Native Australian frangipani
Hyoscyamus niger	*Jusquiame noire*	Henbane
Hypericum	*Millepertuis*	St. John's-wort
Hypericum androsaemum	*Androsème officinal / Toute-bonnne*	Tutsan
Hypericum calycinum	*Millepertuis à grandes fleurs*	
		Aaron's beard / Rose of Sharon
Hypericum elodes	*Élodés des marais*	Marsh St. John's wort
Hypericum hirsutum	*Millepertuis velu*	Hairy St. John's wort
Hypericum humifusum	*Millepertuis couché*	Trailing St. John's wort
Hypericum montanum	*Millepertuis de montagne*	Pale St. John's wort

Hypericum perforatum	*Herbe à mille trous*	Common St. John's wort
Hypericum perforatum	*Millepertuis perforé*	Common St. John's wort
Hypericum pulchrum	*Millepertuis élégant*	Elegant St. John's wort
Hypericum tetrapterum	*Millepertuis à quatre ailes*	Square St. John's wort
Hypochoeris glabra	*Porcelle glabre*	Smooth catsear
Hypochoeris maculata	*Porcelle maculée*	Spotted catsear
Hypochoeris radicata	*Porcelle enracinée*	Common catsear
Hypoestes phyllostachya	*Hypoestes phyllostachya*	
		Freckle face / Polka-dot plant
Hyssopus officinalis	*Hysope officinale*	Hyssop

I

Iberis	*Corbeille d'argent*	Candytuft
Iberis amara	*Iberis amer*	Wild candytuft
Ilex aquifolium	*Houx*	Holly
Ilex aquifolium 'Argentea Marginata'	*Houx 'Argentea Marginata'*	
		Silver margin holly
Ilex aquifolium 'Ferox'	*Houx des hérissons*	Hedgehog holly
Ilex aquifolium ferox argentea	*Houx des hérissons argenté*	
		Silver hedgehog holly
Ilex aquiflium flavescens	*Houx aquiflium flavescens*	Moonlight holly
Ilex aquifolium 'Watereriana'	*Houx aquifolium 'Watereriana'*	
		Waterer's gold holly
Ilex cornuta	*Houx cornu*	Horned holly
Ilex crenata	*Houx crenata*	Box-leafed holly / Japanese holly
Ilex dipyrena	*Houx dipyrena*	Himalayan holly
Ilex glabra	*Houx glabra*	Inkberry
Ilex laevigata	*Houx laevigata*	Smooth winterberry
Ilex latifolia	*Houx latifolia*	Tarajo holly
Ilex x meserveae	*Houx x meserveae*	Blue holly
Ilex opaca	*Houx d'Amérique*	American holly
Ilex verticillata	*Houx verticillata*	Winterberry
Illecebrum verticillatum	*Illécèbre verticillé*	Coral necklace
Illicium anisatum	*Badianier*	Chinese anise
Illicium floridanum	*Illicium floridanum*	Purple anise
Impatiens balsamina	*Balsamine / Impatiente*	Balsam
Impatiens glandulifera	*Balsamind de l'Himalaya*	Himalayan Balsam
Impatiens noli-tangere	*Impatiente / Ne-me-touchez-pas*	Touch -me-not
Impatiens parviflora	*Balsamine a petites fleurs*	Small balsam
Indigofera	*Indigotier*	Indigo

Inula conyza	*Herbe aux mouches / Inule squarreuse*	Ploughman's spikenard
Inula crithmoides	*Inule faux-crithmum*	Golden samphire
Inula helenium	*Grande aunée*	Elecampane
Inula helenium	*Inule aunée*	Elecampane
Inula salicina	*Inule à feuilles de saule*	Irish fleabane
Ionopsidium acaule	*Ionopsidium acaule*	Violet cress
Ipomoaea	*Ipomée*	Ipomoaea
Ipomoea alba	*Ipomoea alba*	Moon flower
Ipomoea coccinea	*Ipomoea coccinea*	Red morning glory / Star ipomoea
Ipomoea hederacea	*Belle-du-jour*	Morning glory
Ipomoea x multifida	*Ipomoea x mulitfida*	Cardinal climber / Hearts-and-honey vine
Ipomoaea purpurea	*Volubilis*	Common morning glory
Ipomoea quamoclit	*Ipomoea quamoclit*	Cupid flower / Cypress vine
Iresine herbistii	*Iresine herbistii*	Beefsteak plant
Iresine lindenii	*Iresine lindenii*	Blood leaf
Iris	*Iris*	Iris
Iris ensata	*Iris ensata*	Japanese flag
Iris discolor	*Iris discolor*	Willd iris
Iris foetidissima	*Iris fétide / Iris gigot*	Gladwin / Stinking iris / Roast-beef plant
Iris latifolia	*Iris d'Angleterre*	English iris
Iris missouriensis	*Iris missouriensis*	Missouri flag
Iris pallida	*Iris de Florence / Iris à parfum*	Dalmatian iris
Iris pseudacorus	*Iris faux-acore / Iris des marais*	Yellow flag
Iris pumila	*Iris pumila*	Dwarf bearded iris
Iris setosa	*Iris setosa*	Bristle pointed iris
Iris sibirica	*Iris de Sibérie*	Siberian flag
Iris spuria	*Iris bâtard*	Butterfly iris
Iris susiana	*Iris de Suse*	Mourning widow
Iris unguicularis	*Iris unguicularis*	Algerian iris / Algerian winter iris / Winter iris
Iris tectorum	*Iris evansia*	Japanese roof iris
Iris variegata	*Iris variegata*	Variegated iris
Iris versicolor	*Iris versicolore*	Blue flag / Purple water flag
Isatis tinctoria	*Pastel des teinturiers*	Woad

J

Jasione montana	*Jasione des montagnes*	Sheep's bit
Jasminium	*Jasmin*	Jasmine
Jasminium grandiflorum	*Jasmin d'Espagne*	Royal jasmine / Spanish jasmine
Jasminium humile	*Jasmin d'Italie*	Yellow jasmine
Jasminium mesneyi	*Jasminium mesneyi*	Primrose jasmine
Jasminium nudiflorum	*Jasmin d'hiver*	Winter jasmine
Jasminium officinale	*Jasmin commun*	Jessamine
Jubaea chilensis	*Cocotier du Chili*	Chilean wine palm / Coquito
Juglans	*Noyer*	Walnut
Juglans ailantifolia	*Juglans ailantifolia*	Japanese walnut
Juglans cathayensis	*Noyer de Chine*	Chinese walnut
Juglans cinera	*Noyer cendré*	Butternut
Juglans microcarpa	*Noyer des rochers*	Little walnut / Texan walnut
Juglans nigra	*Noyer noir*	Black walnut
Juncus effusus spiralis	*Jonc épars*	Corkscrew rush
Juniperus	*Genévrier*	Juniper
Juniperus chinensis	*Genévrier de Chine*	Chinese juniper
Juniperus conferta	*Genévrier des rivages*	Shore juniper
Juniperus davurica	*Genévrier davurica*	Dahurian juniper
Juniperus drupacea	*Genévrier de Syrie*	Syrian juniper
Juniperus horizontalis	*Genévrier rampante*	Creeping juniper
Juniperus procumbens	*Genévrier procumbens*	Bonin Isles juniper
Juniperus recurva	*Genévrier recurva*	Drooping juniper
Juniperus recurva	*Genévrier recurva*	Himalayan weeping juniper
Juniperus rigida	*Genévrier rigida*	Temple juniper
Juniperus sabina	*Genévrier Sabine*	Savin
Juniperus scopulorum	*Genévrier scopulorum*	Rocky mountain juniper
Juniperus virginiana	*Genévrier de Virginie*	Pencil cedar
Justicia adhatoda	*Carmantine en arbre*	Snake bush
Justicia brandegeana	*Carmantine brandegeana*	Shrimp plant
Justicia carnea	*Carmantine carnea*	King's crown

K

Kalanchoe blossfeldiana	*Kalanchoe blossfeldiana*	Flaming Katy
Kalanchoe diagremontiana	*Kalanchoe diagremontiana*	Mexican hat plant
Kalanchoe fedtschenko	*Kalanchoe fedtschenkoi*	South American air plant
Kalanchoe tomentosa	*Plante panda*	Panda plant / Pussy ears
Kalmia angustifolia	*Laurier des moutons*	Sheep laurel

Kalmia latifolia	*Laurier américain / Laurier des montagnes*	
		Calico bush
Kennedia nigricans	*Kennedia nigricans*	Black bean
Kerria japonica	*Corète du Japon*	Kerria japonica
Kickxis	*Kickxie*	Fluelln
Kickxia elatine	*Linaire élatine*	Sharp-leaved fluellen
Kickxia spuria	*Linaire bâtarde velvote*	Round-leaved fluellen
Kigelia pinnata	*Kigélie / Saucissonier*	Sausage tree
Knautia arvensis	*Scabieuse*	Scabious
Knautia arvensis	*Knautie des champs / Oreille d'àne* Field scabious	
Knightia excelsa	*Knightia excelsa* New Zealand honeysuckle / Rewarewa	
Kniphofia	*Kniphofie / Tritome* Red-hot poker / Torch lily	
Kochia scoparia trichophylla *Kochie* Burning bush / Summer cypress		
Koelreuteria paniculata *Savonnier* Golden-rain tree / Pride of India		
Koenigia islandica	*Koenigia d'Islande*	Iceland purslane
Kolkwitzia amabilis *Kolkwitzia amabilis*		Beauty bush

L

Lablab purpureus *Dolique d'Égypte* Australian pea / Hyacinth bean / Lablab		
Laburnum alpinum *Cytise des Alpes*		Scotch laburnum
Laburnum anagyroides *Aubour / Cytise /Faux-ébénier*		
	Common laburnum / Golden chain	
Laburnum x warterei 'Vossii' *Laburnum x warterei 'Vossii'*		
	Voss's laburnum	
Lactuca saligna	*Laitue à feuilles de saulle*	Least lettuce
Lactuca serriola	*Laitue scariole*	Prickly lettuce
Lactuca virosa	*Laitue vireuse*	Greater prickly lettuce
Lagerstroemia indica *Lilas d'été*		Crape myrtle
Lagerstroemia speciosa *Lilas des indes*		Pride of India
Lagerstroemia speciosa *Lagerstoemia speciosa*		Queen's crape myrtle
Lagunaria patersonii *Lagunaria patersonii*		
	Norfolk Island hibiscus / Queensland pyramidial tree	
Lagurus ovatus	*Gros minet*	Hare's tail grass
Lagurus ovatus	*Queue de lièvre*	Hare's tail grass
Lamarckia aurea	*Lamarckie aurea*	Golden top
Lamium	*Lamier*	Dead nettle
Lamium album *Lamier blanc / Ortie blanche*		White dead-nettle
Lamium amplexicaule *Lamier amplexicaule*		Henbit
Lamium hybridum	*Lamier hybride*	Cut-leaved dead-nettle

Lamium maculatum	*Lamier maculé*	Spotted dead-nettle
Lamium purpureum	*Lamier pourpre / Ortie rouge*	Red deadnettle
Lapageria rosea	*Lapageria rosea*	Chilean bellflower / Copihue
Lapsana communis	*Graceline / Lapsane commune*	Nipplewort
Lapidium sativum	*Cresson alénois*	Cress
Larix decidua	*Mélèze de Europe*	European larch
Larix kaempferi	*Mélèze du Japon*	Japanese larch
Larrea	*Larrée*	Creosote bush
Lathraea clandestina	*Dentaire*	Toothwort
Lathyruus aphaca	*Gesse aphylle*	Yellow vetchling
Lathyrus grandiflorus	*Gesse à grandes fleurs*	Everlasting pea
Lathyrus hirsutus	*Gesse hérissée*	Hairy pea
Lathyrus japonicus	*Gesse maritime*	Sea pea
Lathyrus latifolius	*Pois vivace*	Everlasting pea
Lathyrus latifolius	*Gesse à larges feuilles*	Everlasting pea
Lathyrus latifolius	*Pois vivace*	Perennial pea
Lathyrus montanus	*Gesse de montagne*	Bitter vetch
Lathyrus nervosus	*Lathyrus nervosus*	Lord Anson's blue pea
Lathyrus nissolia	*Gesse sans vrille*	Grass vetchling
Lathyrus palustris	*Gesse des marais*	Marsh pea
Lathyrus pratensis	*Gesse des prés*	Meadow pea
Lathyrus odoratus	*Pois de senteur*	Sweet pea
Lathyrus rotundifolia	*Lathyrus rotundifolia*	Persian everlasting pea
Lathyrus sylvestris	*Pois vivace*	Everlasting pea
Lathyrus tuberosus	*Macusson*	Fyfield pea
Laurelia serrata	*Laurelia serrata*	Chilean laurel
Laurus	*Laurier*	Bay tree / Laurel
Laurus nobilis	*Laurier noble*	Bay laurel
Laurus nobilis	*Lauie-sauce*	Sweet bay
Lavandula	*Lavande*	Lavender
Lavatera arborea	*Lavatère arborescente / Mauve du jardin*	Tree mallow
Lavatera cretica	*Lavatère de crète*	Cornish mallow
Lavatera olbia	*Lavatère d'Hyères*	Lavatera olbia
Lavatera trimestris	*Lavatère à grandes fleurs*	Lavatera trimestris
Lavendula dentata	*Lavande dentata*	French lavender
Lavendula stoechas	*Lavande stoechas*	French lavender
Layia platyglossa	*Layie*	Tidy tips
Ledum groenlandicus	*Thé du Labrador*	Labrador tea
Ledum palustre	*Thé du Labrador*	Labrador tea
Legousia hybrida	*Miroir de Venus*	Venus's looking -glass
Lemaireocereus marginatus	*Lemaireocereus marginatus*	Organ pipe cactus
Lemna	*Lenticule*	Duck weed

Lemna gibba	*Lentille d'eau bossue*	Fat duckweed
Lemna minor	*Petite lentille d'eau*	Common duckweed
Lemna trisulca	*Lentille d'eau trilobée*	Ivy duckweed
Leonotis leonorus	*Queue de lion*	Lion's ear
Leontodon autumnalis	*Liondent d'automne*	Autumn hawkbit
Leontodon hispidus	*Liondent hispide*	Greater hawkbit
Leontopodium	*Edelweiss*	Edelweiss
Leonurus cardiaca	*Agripaume cardiaque*	Motherwort
Lepidium campestre	*Passerage champêtre*	Common pepperwort
Lepidium latifolium	*Passerage à feuilles large*	Dittander
Lepidium ruderale	*Passerage des décombres*	Narrow leafed pepperwort

Leptospermum scoparium *Leptospermum scoparium*
Manuka / New Zealand tea tree

Leucadendron argenteum	*Arbre d'argent*	Silver tree
Leucocoryne ixiodes	*Leucocoryne ixiodes*	Glory-of-the-sun

Leucogenes leontopodium *Edelweiss de Nouvelle-Zélande*
North Island edelweiss

Leucojum	*Nivéole du printemps*	Snowflake

Leucojum aestivum *Nivéole aestivum / Nivéole d'été*
Summer snowflake / Loddon lily

Leucojum autumnale	*Nivéole automnale*	Autumn snowflake
Leucojum vernum	*Nivéole perce-neige*	Spring snowflake
Lewisia rediviva	*Lewisia rediviva*	Bitter root
Leycesteria formosa	*Leycesteria formosa*	Himalayan honeysuckle
Leymus arenarius	*Élyme des sables*	Lyme grass
Liatris	*Liatride*	Gay feathers
Liatris pycnostachya	*Liatris pycnostachya*	Kansas gay feather
Libertia grandiflora	*Libertia grandiflora*	New Zealand satin flower
Ligusticum scoticum	*Livèche d'Écosse*	Lovage
Ligustrum japonicum	*Troène du Japon*	Japanese privet
Ligustrum lucidum	*Troène de Chine*	Chinese privet
Ligustrum vulgare	*Troène*	Privet
Lilium	*Lis*	Lily
Lilium auratum	*Lis doré du Japon*	Golden-rayed lily of Japan
Lilium bulbiferum	*Lilium bulbiferum*	Fire lily / Orange lily

Lilium canadense *Lis canadense* Canada lily / Meadow lily / Wild yellow lily
Lilium candidum *Lis blanc / Lis de la Madone / Lis de la Saint-Jean*
Madonna lily

Lilium chalcedonicum	*Lis chalcedonicum*	Scarlet turk's cap lily
Lilium lancifolium	*Lis tigré*	Tiger lily
Lilium longiflorum	*Lilium à longues fleurs*	

Bermuda lily / Easter lily / White trumpet lily

Lilium mackliniae	Lis mackliniae	Manipur lily
Lilium martagon	Lis martagon	Martagon lily / Turkscap lily
Lilium pardalinum	Lis pardalinum	Leopard Lily / Panther lily
Lilium pyrenaicum	Lis des Pyrénées	Pyrenean lily / Yellow turkscap lily
Lilium regale	Lis royal	Regal lily
Lilium superbum	Lis superbum	Swamp lily
Lilium x testaceum	Lis couleur Isabelle	Nankeen lily
Limnanthes douglasii	Limnanthe douglasii	Poached egg plant / Meadow foam
Limonium	Lavande de mer / Statice	Statice
Limonium bellidifolium	Statice a feuilles de paquerette	Matted sea-lavender
Limonium binervosum	Statice a deux nervures	Rock sea-lavender
Limonium humile	Statice nain	Lax sea-lavender
Limonium vulgare	Immortelle bleue / Lavande de mer / Saladelle	Sea lavender
Limosella aquatatica	Limoselle aquatique	Common mudwort
Linaria	Linaire	Toadflax
Linaria alpina	Linaire des Alpes	Alpine toadflax
Linaria arenaria	Linaire des sables	French toadflax
Linaria genistifolia dalmatica	Linaire dalmatica	Dalmatian toadflax
Linaria pelisseriana	Linaire de Pellisier	Jersey toadflax
Linaria purpurea	Linaire pourprée	Purple toadflax
Linaria repens	Linaire rampante	Pale toadflax
Linaria supina	Linaire couchée	Prostrate toadflax
Linaria vulgaris	Linaire commune	Common toadflax
Lindera benzoin	Laurier benzoin	Benjamin / Spiceberry
Lindheimera texana	Lindheimera texana	Star daisy
Linnaea borealis	Linée boréale	Twin flower
Linum	Lin	Flax
Linum bienne	Lin à feuilles étroites	Pale flax
Linum catharticum	Lin purgatif	Fairy flax
Linum flavum	Lin jaune	Golden flax / Yellow flax
Linum perenne	Lin vivace	Perennial flax
Linum usitatissimum	Lin cultivé	Cultivated flax
Liparis loeselii	Liparis de Loesel	Fen orchid
Liquidambar orientalis	Liquidambar orientalis	Oriental sweet gum
Liquidambar styraciflua	Copalme d'Amérique	Sweet gum
Liriodendron chinense	Tulipier de Chine	Chinese tulip tree
Liriodendron tulipifera	Tulipier	Tulip tree
Liriope	Liriope	Lilyturf
Listera	Listère	Twablades
Listera cordata	Listère à feuilles cordées	Lesser twayblades
Listera ovata	Listère à feuilles ovales	Common twayblades

Lithocarpus densiflorus *Lithocarpus densiflorus*   Tanbark oak
Lithodora   *Grémil*   Lithospermum
Lithops   *Pierre vivante / Plante-caillou*   Living stones / Stone plant
Lithospermum officinale   *Grémil officinal / Herbe aux perles*
                                Common gromwell
Lithospermum purpuro-caerulea *Grémil pourpre-violet*
                                Purple gromwell
Littorella uniflora   *Littorelle uniflore*   Shore-weed
Livistona australis   *Livistona australis*
               Australian cabbage palm / Gippsland fountain palm
Livistona chinensis   *Palmier évental de Chine*
                  Chinese fan palm / Chinese fountain palm
Lloydia serotina   *Lloydie tardive*   Snowdon lily
Lobelia cardinalis   *Lobélie cardinalis*   Cardinal flower
Lobelia dortmanna   *Lobélie de Dortmann*   Water lobelia
Lobelia urens   *Lobélie brûlante*   Heath lobelia
Lobularia maritima *Alysson maritime / Corbeille d'argent*   Sweet alyssum
Loiseleuria procumbens *Azalée des Alpes*   Alpine azalea / Wild azalea
Loiseleuria procumbens *Azalée couchée / Azalée naine*
                         Alpine azalea / Wild azalea
Loiseleuria procumbens *Loiseleuria procumbens*   Trailing azalea
Lomatium nudicaule *Lomatium nudicaule*   Pestle parsnip
Lonicera x brownii   *Lonicera x brownii*   Scarlet trumpet honeysuckle
Lonicera caprifolium *Chèvrefeuille des jardins*   Perfoliate honeysuckle
Lonicera etrusca   *Chèvrefeuille d'Italie*   Etruscan honeysuckle
Lonicera japonica   *Chèvrefeuille du Japon*   Japanese honeysuckle
Lonicera periclymenum *Chèvrefeuille des bois*   Honeysuckle / Woodbine
Lonicera periclymenum 'Serotina'   *Lonicera periclymenum 'Serotina'*
                         Late Dutch honeysuckle
Lonicera sempervirens *Chèvrefeuille toujours vert*   Trumpet honeysuckle
Lonicera sempervirens *Chèvrefeuille de Virginie*   Coral honeysuckle
Lonicera xylasteum   *Chèvrefeuille des bois*   Fly honeysuckle
Lophophora williamsii *Peyote / Plante qui fait les yeux émerveillés*
                         Dumpling cactus
Lotus berthelotii   *Lotier berthelotii*   Coral gem
Lotus corniculatus   *Lotier corniculé / Pied-de-poule*
                     Common birdsfoot trefoil
Ludwigia palustris   *Ludwigia des marais*   Hampshire purslane
Lunaria annua   *Herbe aux écus / Monnai du Pape / Monnayère*
                     Honesty
Lupinus   *Lupin*   Lupin
Lupinus arboreus   *Lupin arborescent*   Tree lupin

Luzula	*Luzule*	Woodrush
Luzula nivea	*Luzule nivea*	Snowy woodrush
Luzula sylvatica	*Luzule sylvatica*	Greater woodrush
Lychnis alpina	*Viscaire des Alpes*	Alpine catchfly
Lychnis chalcedonica	*Croix de Malte*	Jerusalem cross / Maltese cross
Lychnis coronaria	*Coquelourde des jardins*	Lychnis coronaria
Lychnis flos-cuculi	*Fleur de coucou / Fleur de Jupiter*	Ragged Robin
Lychnis viscaria	*Viscaire*	Red catchfly
Lycium barbarum	*Lyciet jasminoïdes*	Chinese box thorn /Duke of Argyll's tea tree
Lycopus europaeus	*Chanvre d'eau / Lycope d'Europe*	Gipsywort
Lycoris aurea	*Lycoris aurea*	Golden spider lily
Lycoris radiata	*Lycoris radiata*	Red spider lily
Lygodium japonicum	*Lygodium japonicum*	Japanese climbing fern
Lyonothamnus floribundus	*Lyonothamnus floribundus*	Catalina ironwood
Lysichiton americanus	*Lysichiton americanus*	Yellow skunk cabbage
Lysimachia nemorum	*Lysimaque des bois*	Yellow pimpernel
Lysimachia nummularia	*Lysimaque nummulaire*	Creeping Jenny
Lysimachia nummularia aurea	*Herbe aux écus*	Moneywort
Lysimachia punctata	*Lysimaque punctata*	Dotted loosestrife / Garden loosestrife
Lysimachia thyrsiflora	*Corneille en bouquets*	Tufted loosestrife
Lysimachia vulgaris	*Lysimaque commune*	Yellow loosestrife
Lythrum hyssopifolia	*Salicaire à feuilles d'hysoppe*	Hyssop-leaved loostrife
Lythrum salicaria	*Lysimaque rouge / Salicaire commune*	Purple loosestrife

M

Macadamia integrifolia	*Macadamia integrifolia*	Macadamia nut / Queensland nut
Macfadyena unguis-cati	*Macfadyena unguis-cati*	Cat's claw
Maclura pomifera	*Bois d'arc / Orangier des osages*	Osage orange
Magnolia acuminata	*Magnolia à feuilles acuminées*	Cucumber tree
Magnolia denudata	*Magnolia de Yulan*	Lily tree / Yulan
Magnolia grandiflora	*Magnolia à grandea fleurs*	Bull bay
Magnolia hypoleuca	*Magnolia hypoleuca*	Japanese big leaf magnolia
Magnolia salicilfolia	*Magnolia salicilfolia*	Willow-leaved magnolia
Magnolia stellata	*Magnolia étoilé*	Star magnolia
Magnolia tripetala	*Magnolia parasol*	Magnolia tripetala
Magnolia virginiana	*Magnolia de Virginie*	Sweet bay
Mahonia aquifolium	*Mahonia à feuilles de houx*	Oregon grape
Maianthemum bifolium	*Maianthème à deux feuilles*	May lily
Maianthemum bifolium	*Fleur de mai / Petit muguet*	May lily

Malcolmia maritima	*Giroflée de Mahon*	Virginia stock
Malcolmia maritima	*Julienne de Mahon / Mahonille*	Virginia stock
Malus	*Pommier*	Apple
Malus baccata	*Pommier à baies*	Siberian crab
Malus hupehensis	*Malus hupehensis*	Hupeh crab
Malus x purpurea	*Malus x purpurea*	Purple crab
Malus sylvestris	*Pommier sauvage*	Crab apple
Malva	*Mauve*	Mallow
Malva moschata	*Mauve musquée*	Musk mallow
Malva neglecta	*Petite mauve*	Dwarf mallow
Malva sylvestris	*Grande mauve / Mauve sylvestre*	Common mallow
Malvaviscus arboreus	*Malvaviscus arboreus*	Sleepy mallow
Mammillaria	*Mammillaria*	Pincushion cactus
Mammillaria boscasana	*Mammillaria boscasana*	Powder-puff cactus
Mammillaria candida	*Mammillaria candida*	Snowball pincushion
Mammillaria elongata	*Mammillaria elongata*	Lace cactus
Mammillaria hahniana	*Mammillaria hahniana*	Old lady cactus
Mammillaria prolifera	*Mammillaria prolifera*	Strawberry cactus
Mammillaria zeilmanniana	*Mammillaria zeilmanniana*	Rose pincushion
Mandevilla laxa	*Mandevilla laxa*	Chilean jasmine
Mandragora	*Mandragore*	Mandrake
Manettia cordifolia	*Manettia cordifolia*	Firecracker vine
Manettia inflata	*Manettia inflata*	Brazilian firecracker
Maranta leuconeura "Erythroneura"	*Maranta leuconeura "Erythroneura"*	Herringbone plant
Maranta leuconeura kerchoviana	*Maranta leuconeura kerchoviana*	Rabbit tracks
Maranta leuconeura	*Maranta leuconeura*	Prayer plant
Margyricarpus pinnatus	*Margyricarpus pinnatus*	Pearl berry
Marrubium vulgare	*Marrube commun*	White horehound
Martynia annua	*Martynia annua*	Unicorn plant
Matricaria indora	*Matricaire maritime*	Scentless mayweed
Matteuccia struthiopteris	*Matteuccia struthiopteris*	Ostrich feather fern / Ostrich fern
Matthiola	*Giroflée quarantaine*	Stock
Matthiola incana	*Quarantaine*	Brompton stock / Sea stock
Matthiola sinuata	*Giroflée des dunes*	Great sea stock
Maytenus boaria	*Maytenus boaria*	Maiten
Meconopsis betonicifolia	*Pavot bleu de l'Himalaya*	Meconopsis betonicifolia
Meconopsis cambrica	*Méconopsis du pays de Galles*	Welsh poppy

Meconopsis grandis *Pavot bleu*		Blue poppy
Meconopsis integrifolia *Pavot jaune*		Lampshade poppy
Meconopsis napaulensis *Meconopsis napaulensis*		Satin poppy
Meconopsis quintuplinervia *Pavot grande*		Harebell poppy
Medicago arabica *Luzerne d'Arabie*		Spotted medick
Medicago arborea *Luzerne arborescente*		Moon trefoil / Tree medick
Medicago lupulina *Luzerne lupuline / Minette*		Black medick
Medicago sativa *Luzerne cultivée*		Lucerne
Melampyrum arvense *Blé de vache / Mélampyre des champs*		
		Field cow-wheat
Melampyrum cristatum *Mélampyre des prés*		Crested cow-wheat
Melampyrum sylvaticum *Mélampyre des bois*		Small cow-wheat
Melaneuca amarillaris *Melaneuca amarillaris*		Bracelet honey myrtle
Melaleuca elliptica *Melaleuca elliptica*		Granite bottlebrush
Melaleuca nesophylla *Melaleuca nesophylla*		Western tea-myrtle
Melaleuca quinquenervia *Melaleuca quinquenervia*		Paper bark tree
Melaleuca squarrosa *Melaleuca squarrosa*		Scented paper-bark
Melica altissima *Mélique*		Siberian melic
Melia azedarach *Margousier azedarach*		Bead tree / Persian lilac
Melianthus major *Mélianthe*		Honeybush
Melica altissima *Melica altissima*		Tall melic
Melicytus ramiflorus *Melicytus ramiflorus*		Mahoe / Whiteywood
Melilotus alba *Mélilot blanc*		White melilot
Melilotus indica *Mélilot des Indes*		Small-flowered melilot
Melilotus altissima *Mélilot élevé*		Golden melilot
Melilotus officinalis *Mélilot officinal*		Balm / Common melilot
Melittis *Mélitte*		Bastard balm
Melocactus communis *Cactus melon*		Melon cactus / Turk's cap
Menispermum *Ménisperme*		Moonseed
Menispermum canadense *Menispermum canadense*		
		Canada moonseed / Yellow parilla
Mentha *Menthe*		Mint
Mentha aquatica *Menthe aquatique*		Water mint
Mentha x piperita *Menthe poivrée*		Peppermint
Mentha piperita "Citrata" *Menthe poivrée*		Eau-de-Cologne mint
Mentha pulegium *Menthe pouliot*		Pennyroyal
Mentha requienii *Menthe de Corse*		Corsican mint
Mentha spicata *Menthe en épi*		Spear-mint
Mentha suavolens *Menthe à feuilles rondes*		Apple mint
Mentha suavolens variegata *Mentha suavolens variegata*		
		Variegated apple mint
Mentzelia lindleyi *Bartonia dorée*		Golden bartonia

Menyanthes trifoliata	*Trèfle d'eau*	Bog bean / Buckbean
Mercurialis annua	*Mercuriale annuelle*	Annual mercury
Mercurialis perennis	*Mercuriale des bois*	Dog's mercury
Meryta sinclairii	*Meryta sinclairii*	Puka
Merremia tuberosa	*Merremia tuberosa*	Wood rose / Yellow morning glory
Mesembryanthemum crystallinum	*Ficoïde glaciale*	Ice plant
Mespilus germanica	*Néflier*	Medlar
Metassequoia glyptostroboides	*Metassequoia glyptostroboides*	Dawn redwood
Metrosiderus excelsa	*Arbre de rata*	New Zealand Christmas tree / Pohutukawa
Metrosideros robusta	*Arbre de rata*	New Zealand Christmas tree / Rata
Meum athamanticum	*Méon*	Baldmoney
Meum athamanticum	*Fenouil des Alpes*	Spignel-meu
Milium effusum	*Milium effusum*	Wood millet
Miltonopsis	*Miltonia*	Pansy orchid
Mimosa pudica	*Sensitive pudique*	Humble plant / Sensitive plant
Mimulus	*Mimulus*	Monkey musk
Mimulus guttatus	*Mimule tacheté*	Monkey flower
Mimulus luteus	*Mimulus luteus*	Yellow musk
Mimulus moschatus	*Mimulus musqué*	Musk
Minuartia rubella	*Minuartia rougeâtre*	Red sandwort
Minuartia stricta	*Minuartia raide*	Teesdale sandwort
Minuartia verna	*Minuartia du printemps*	Spring sandwort
Mirabilis	*Belle-de-nuit*	Four o'clock flower / Marvel of Peru
Miscanthus saccharifolia	*Miscanthus saccharifolia*	Amur silver grass
Misopates orontium	*Muflier des champs*	Lesser snapdragon
Mitchella repens	*Mitchella repens*	Partridge berry
Moehringia triniveria	*Moehringie à troisnervures*	Three-veined sandwort
Moenchia erecta	*Moenchia dresé*	Dwarf chickweed
Moleccella laevis	*Clochette d'Irlande*	Bells of Ireland / Shell flower / Shell ginger
Molinia caerulea 'Variegata'	*Molinia caerulea 'Variegata'*	Variegated purple moor grass
Monarda	*Monarde*	Bergamot
Monarda didyma	*Monarde pourprea*	Bee Balm
Moneses uniflora	*Pyrole uniflore*	St. Olaf's candlestick
Monotropa hypopitys	*Monotrope sucepin*	Yellow birdsnest
Monstera acuminata	*Monstera acuminata*	Shingle plant
Monstera deliciosa	*Monstera deliciosa*	Swiss cheese plant
Montia fontana	*Montie des fontaines*	Blinks
Morina	*Morina*	Whorl flower
Morus	*Mûrier*	Mulberry
Morus alba	*Mûrier blanc*	White mulberry

Morus nigra	*Mûrier noir*	Black mulberry
Murraya paniculata	*Murraya paniculata*	Orange jasmine
Musa	*Bananier*	Banana
Musa arnoldiana	*Bananier d'Abyssinie*	Abyssinian banana
Musa basjoo	*Bananier basjoo*	Japanese banana
Musa coccinea	*Bananier rouge*	Scarlet banana
Musa ornata	*Bananier à fleurs décoratives*	Flowering banana
Muscari comosum	*Muscari à toupet / Poireau roux*	Tassel grape hyacinth
Muscari neglectum	*Muscari à grappes*	Grape hyacinth
Mycelis muralis	*Laitue des murs*	Wall lettuce
Myosotidium hortensia	*Myosotidium hortensia*	Chatham Island forget-me-not
Myosotis	*Myosotis*	Forget-me-not
Myosotis alpestris	*Myosotis des Alpes*	Alpine forget-me-not
Myosoton aquaticum	*Stellaire aquatique*	Water chickweed
Myosotis discolor	*Myosotis bicolore*	Changing forget-me-not
Myosotis scorpioides	*Myosotis des marais*	Water forget-me-not
Myosotis sicula	*Myosotis de Sicile*	Jersey forget-me-not
Myosotis sylvatica	*Myosotis dea bois*	Wood forget-me-not
Myosurus minimus	*Queue de souris*	Mousetail
Myrica gale	*Galé odorante*	Bog myrtle
Myriophyllum alternifolium	*Myriophylle à feuilles alternes*	Alternate water-milfoil
Myriophyllum aquaticum	*Myriophyllue aquaticum*	Parrot's feather
Myriophyllum spicatum	*Myriophylle à épis*	Spiked water-milfoil
Myriophyllum verticillatum	*Myriophylle verticille*	Whorled water-milfoil
Myrrhis odorata	*Cerfeuil musqué*	Sweet Cicely
Myrsine africana	*Myrsine africana*	Cape Myrtle
Myrtillocactus geometrizans	*Myrtillocactus geometrizans*	Blue candle
Myrtus	*Myrte*	Myrtle

N

Najas flexilis	*Naiade flexible*	Slender naid
Nandina domestica	*Nandine fruitière*	Heavenly bamboo / Sacred bamboo
Narcissus	*Narcisse*	Daffodil
Narcissus bulbocodium	*Narcissus bulbocodium*	Hoop pettcoat daffodil
Narcissus eystenensis	*Narcissus eystenensis*	Queen Anne's double daffodil
Narcissus jonquilla	*Petite jonquille*	Jonquil
Narcissus jonquilla florepleno	*Narcissus jonquilla florepleno*	Queen Anne's jonquil
Narcissus obvallaris	*Narcissus obvallaris*	Tenby daffodil

Narcissus x odorus	*Narcisse campernellii*	Campernelle jonquil
Narcissus poeticus	*Jeannette / Narcisse des poètes / Porillon*	
		Poet's daffodil / Poet's narcissus
Narcissus poeticus recurva	*Narcisse des poètes*	Pheasant's eye
Narcissus pseudonarcissus	*Aiault /Faux narcisse*	Lent Lily /Wild daffodil
Narcissus pseudonarcissus	*Jonquille /Narcisse jaune*	Lent Lily /Wild daffodil
Narcissus tazetta	*Narcisse de Constantinople*	Bunch flowered daffodil
Narcissus triandrus	*Narcissus triandrus*	Angel's tears
Narthecium ossifragum	*Ossifrage / Narthèce*	Bog asphodel
Nelumbo	*Lotus / Nélumbium*	Lotus
Nelumbo lutea	*Lotus jaune d'Amérique*	American lotus
Nelumbo nucifera	*Lotus des Indes*	Sacred lotus
Nemesia	*Némésie*	Nemesia
Nemophila maculata	*Némophile maculata*	Five-spot baby
Nemophila menziesii	*Némophile*	Baby blue-eyes
Neoregalia carolinae	*Neoregalia carolinae*	Blushing bromeliad
Neotinea intacta	*Habenaria à fleurs denses*	Dense-flowered orchid
Neottia nidus-avis	*Néottie nid-d'oiseau*	Bird's nest orchid
Nepenthes	*Népenthés*	Pitcher plant
Nepeta cataria	*Herbe aux chats / Nepeta aux chats*	
		Catmint / Wild catmint
Nephrolepis cordifolia	*Néphrolépis cordifolia*	Ladder fern
Nephrolepis exaltata	*Néphrolépis exaltata*	Sword fern
Nerine sarniensis	*Amaryllis de Guernsey / Lis de Guernsey*	Guernsey lily
Nerium oleander	*Laurier rose*	Oleander
Nertera grandensis	*Nertera grandensis*	Bead plant
Nicandra physalodes	*Nicandra physalodes*	Apple of Peru / Shoofly
Nicotiana alata	*Tabac blanc odorant*	Nicotiana alata
Nicotiana sylvestris	*Tabac sylvestris*	Flowering tobacco
Nidularium fulgens	*Nidularium fulgens*	Blushing bromeliad
Nidularium innocentii	*Nidularium innocentii*	Bird's nest bromeliad
Nigella damascena	*Cheveux de Vénus / Nigelle de Damas*	Love-in-a-mist
Nopalxochia ackermannii	*Nopalxochia ackermannii*	Red orchid cactus
Nothogagus	*Faux Hêtre*	False beech
Nothogagus antarctica	*Hêtre antarctica*	Antarctic beech / Nirre
Nothofagus menziesii	*Nothofagus menziesii*	Silver beech
Nothofagus obliqua	*Nothofagus obliqua*	Roble
Nothofagus procera	*Nothofagus procera*	Rauli
Notocactus haselbergii	*Notocactus haselbergii*	Scarlet ball cactus
Notocactus scopa	*Notocactus scopa*	Silver ball cactus
Notospartium carmichaeliae	*Notospartium carmichaeliae*	Pink broom
Nuphar advena	*Nuphar advena*	American spatterdock

Nuphar advena	*Nénuphar advena*	Yellow pond lily
Nuphar lutea	*Nénuphar jaune*	Brandy Bottle / Yellow water lily
Nymphaea	*Lis d'eau / Nénuphar / Nymphéa*	Water lily
Nymphaea alba	*Nénuphar blanc*	White water lily
Nymphaea capensis	*Nénuphar bleu du Cap*	Cape blue water lily
Nymphoides peltata	*Limnanthème faux-nénuphar*	
		Fringed water lily / Water fringe
Nyssa	*Toupélo*	Tupelo
Nyssa sylvatica	*Nyssa sylvatica*	Black gum

O

Ochna serrulata	*Ochna serrulata*	Mickey mouse plant
Odontites verna	*Euphraise rouge*	Red bartsia
Oemleria cerasiformis	*Œmleria cerasiformis*	Indian plum / Oso berry
Oenanthe aquatica	*Œnanthe aquatique*	Fine-leafed water dropwort
Oenanthe fistulosa	*Œnanthe fistuleuse*	Tubular water dropwort
Oenanthe lachenalii	*Œnanthe de lachenal*	Parsley water dropwort
Oenanthe pimpinelloidesa	*Jeannette*	Callous-fruited water dropwort
Oenothera	*Œnothère / Onagre*	Evening primrose
Oenothera biennis	*Onagre bisannuelle*	Lesser evening primrose
Oenothera lamarkiana	*Onagre de Lamarck*	Large evening primrose
Oenothera stricta	*Onagre odorante*	Fragrant evening primrose
Olea europaea	*Olivier*	Olive
Olearia	*Oléaire*	Daisy bush
Omphalodes linifolia	*Gazon blanc / Nombril-de-Venus*	Venus's navelwort
Omphalodes verna	*Nombril-de-Vénus / Petite bourache*	Blue-eyed Mary
Oncidium flexuosum	*Oncidium flexuosum*	Dancing doll orchid
Oncidium papilio	*Oncidium papilion*	Butterfly orchid
Onobrychis viciifolia	*Esparcette / Sainfoin*	Sanfoin
Onoclea sensibilis	*Onocléa délicat*	Sensitive fern
Ononis fruticosa	*Bugrane fruticosa*	Shrubby restharrow
Ononis natrix	*Bugrane gluante*	Large yellow restharrow
Ononis reclinata	*Bugrane renversée*	Small rest-harrow
Ononis repens	*Arrête-bœuf / Bugrane rampante*	Rest-harrow
Ononis spinosa	*Bugrane épineuse*	Spiny rest-harrow
Onopordum acanthium	*Chardon aux ânes / Chardon d'Écosse*	
		Cotton thistle / Scotch thistle
Onopordum acanthium	*Onopordon faux-acanthe / Pet-d'âne*	
		Cotton thistle / Scotch thistle
Ophiopogon japonicus	*Herbe aux turquoises*	Japanese hyacinth
Ophrys apifera	*Ophrys abeille*	Bee orchid

Ophrys fuciflora	*Ophrys bourdon*	Late spider orchid
Ophrys insectifera	*Ophrys mouche*	Fly orchid
Ophrys sphegodes	*Ophrys araignée*	Spider orchid
Ophrys tenthredinifera	*Ophrys tenthredinifera*	Sawfly orchid
Opilismenus hirtellus	*Opilismenus hirtellus*	Basket grass
Oplopanax horridus	*Échinopanax*	Devil's club
Opuntia	*Raquette*	Opuntia / Prickly pear
Opuntia	*Nopal*	Opuntia / Prickly pear
Opuntia ficus-indica	*Figuier de Barbarie*	Edible prickly pear / Indian fig
Opuntia microdasys	*Oreille-de-lapin*	Bunny ears
Orchis laxiflora	*Orchis à fleurs laches / Orchis des pentecôtes*	

Jersey orchid / Loose-flowered orchid

Orchis militaris	*Orchis militaire*	Soldier orchid
Orchis mascula	*Orchis male*	Early purple orchid
Orchis morio	*Orchis bouffon*	

Gandergoose / Green veined orchid / Green-winged orchid

Orchis purpurea	*Orchis pourpre*	Lady orchid
Orchis simia	*Orchis singe*	Monkey orchid
Orchis ustulata	*Orchis brulé*	Burnt-tip orchid
Dictamnus	*Dictame*	Dittany
Origanum dictamnus	*Origan dictamnus*	Cretan dittany
Origanum vulgare	*Marjolaine / Marjolaine bâtarde / Marjolaine origan*	

Marjoram

Origanum vulgare	*Origan commun*	Wild marjoram
Ornithogalum nutans	*Étoile de Bethléhem*	Nodding star of Bethlehem
Ornithogalum pyrenaicum	*Aspergette*	Spiked star of Bethlehem
Ornithogalum thyrsoides	*Ornithogale*	Chincherinchee
Ornithogalum umbelletum	*Dame d'onze heures / Étoile de Bethléem*	

Star-of-Bethleham

Ornithogalum umbellatum	*Dame-d'onze heures / Étoile de Bethléem*	

Common star of Bethlehem

Ornithopus pinnatus	*Ornithope penné*	Orange birdsfoot
Ornithopus perpusillus	*Ornithope délicat*	Common birdsfoot
Ornithopus perpusillus	*Pied-d'oiseau*	Common birdsfoot
Orobanche alba	*Orobanche blanche / Orobanche du thym*	

Thyme broomrape

Orobanche caryophyllacea	*Orobanche giroflée*	Clove-scented broomrape
Orobanche elatior	*Orobanche élevée*	Knapweed broomrape
Orobanche purpurea	*Orobanche pourprée*	Yarrow broomrape
Orobanche rapum-genistae	*Orobanche des genêts*	Great broomrape
Orontium aquaticum	*Oronce*	Golden club
Orthilia secunda	*Pyrole unilatérale*	Yavering bells

Osmanthus fragrans	*Olivier odorant*	Fragrant olive
Osmunda cinnamonea	*Osmunda cinnamonea*	Cinnamon fern
Osmunda claytoniana	*Osmunda claytoniana*	Interrupted fern
Osmunda regalis	*Fougère royale / Osmonde royale*	Royal fern
Ostrya carpinifolia	*Charme houblon*	Hop hornbeam
Ostrya virginiana	*Ostryer de Virginie*	American hop hornbeam / Ironwood
Otanthus maritimus	*Otanthe maritime*	Cottonweed
Oxalis acetosella	*Pain de coucou*	Wood sorrel
Oxalis corniculata	*Oxalis corniculé*	Sleeping beauty
Oxalis pes-caprae	*Oxalis des Bermudes*	Bermuda buttercup
Oxydendron arboreum	*Oxydendron en arbre*	Sorrel tree
Oxyria digyna	*Oxyria à deux styles*	Mountain sorrel
Oxytropis campestris	*Oxytropis champêtre*	Yellow milk-vetch
Oxytropis halleri	*Oxytropis de Haller*	Purple mountain milk-vetch

P

Pachyphytum oviferum	*Pachyphytum oviferum*	Moonstones / Sugar-almond plum
Pachystachys coccinea	*Pachystachys coccinea*	Cardinal's guard
Pachysatchys lutea	*Pachysatchys lutea*	Lollipop plant
Paeonia	*Pivoine*	Peony
Paeonia cambessedesii	*Pivoine de Majorca*	Majorcan poppy
Paeonia suffruticosa	*Pivoine en arbre*	Moutan
Paliurus spina-christi	*Argalon / Épine du Christ*	Christ's thorn /Jerusalem thorn
Pancratium maratimum	*Lis narcisse / Lis matthiola Pancrais maritime*	Sea daffodil / Sea lily
Pandanus	*Baquois / Vacoua*	Screw pine
Pandanus veitchii	*Pandanus veitchii*	Veitch's screw pine
Pandorea pandorana	*Pandorea pandorana*	Wonga-wonga vine
Panicum capillare	*Herbe de Guinée*	Old witch grass
Papaver	*Pavot*	Poppy
Papaver argemone	*Pavot argémone*	Pale poppy
Papaver burseri	*Pavot des Alpes*	Alpine poppy
Papaver dubium	*Pavot douteux*	Long-headed poppy
Papaver hybridum	*Pavot hybride*	Bristly poppy
Papaver nudicaule	*Pavot d'Islande*	Iceland poppy
Papaver orientale	*Pavot d'Orient / Pavot de Tournefort*	Oriental poppy
Papaver rhoeas	*Coquelicot*	Corn poppy / Field poppy
Papaver somniferum	*Pavot somnifère*	Opium poppy
Paradisea liliastrum	*Lis de Saint-Bruno*	St. Bruno's lily
Parentucellia viscosa	*Bartsie visqueuse*	Yellow bartsia

Paris quadrifolia	*Parisette à quatre feuilles*	Herb Paris
Parkinsonia aculeata	*Parkinsonia aculeata*	Jerusalem thorn / Mexican palo verde
Parnassia palustris	*Herbe de Parnasse / Parnassie des marais*	
		Grass of Parnassus
Parochetus communis	*Fleur des dieux*	Shamrock pea
Parrotia persica	*Parrotia persica*	Persian ironwood
Parthenocissus quinquefolia	*Vigne vierge vraie*	
		Five leaved ivy / Virginia creeper
Parthenocissus tricuspidata	*Lierre japonais / Vigne vierge japonais*	
		Boston ivy
Parthenocissus tricuspidata	*Lierre de Japon / Vigne vierge japonaise*	
		Japanese ivy
Passiflora	*Passiflore*	Passion flower
Passiflora	*Fleur de passion*	Passion flower
Passiflora antioquensis	*Passiflora antioquensis*	Banana passion fruit
Passiflora caerulea	*Fleur de la Passion*	Blue passion flower
Passiflora coccinea	*Passiflore coccinea*	Red passion flower
Passiflora quadrangularis	*Barbadine*	Giant granadilla
Pastinaca sativa	*Panais cultivé*	Wild parsnip
Paulownia tomentosa	*Paulownia impérial*	Foxglove tree / Princess tree
Pedicularis palustris	*Pédiculaire des marais*	Red rattle
Pedicularis sylvatica	*Pédiculaire des bois*	Lousewort
Pedilanthus tithymaloides	*Pedilanthus tithymaloides*	Redbird flower
Pelargonium	*Geranium*	Geranium
Pelargonium tomentosum	*Pelargonium tomentosum*	Peppermint geranium
Pellaea atropurpurea	*Pellaea atropurpurea*	
		Purple rock brake / Purple stemmed cliff brake
Pellaea rotundifolia	*Pellaea rotundifolia*	Button fern
Pellionia daveauana	*Pellionia daveauana*	Watermelon begonia
Peltiphyllum peltatum	*Peltiphyllum peltatum*	Umbrella plant
Pennisetum alopecuroides	*Pennisetum alopecuroides*	Chinese fountain grass
Pennisetum setaccum	*Pennisetum setaccum*	African fountain grass
Pennisetum villosum	*Pennisetum villosum*	Feather-top
Penstemon newberryi	*Penstemon newberryi*	Mountain pride
Pentaglottis sempervirens	*Buglosse vivace*	Green alkanet
Pentas lanceolata	*Pentas lanceolata*	Egyptian star / Star-cluster
Peperomia argyreia	*Peperomia argyreia*	Watermelon plant
Peperomia caperata	*Peperomia caperata*	Emerald ripple
Peperomia clusiifolia	*Peperomia clusiifolia*	Baby rubber plant
Peperomia glabella	*Peperomia glabella*	Wax privet
Peperomia griseoargentea	*Peperomia griseoargenta*	
		Ivy peperomia / Silver-leaf peperomia

Peperomia magnoliifolia *Peperomia magnoliifolia*   Desert privet
Peperomia marmorata *Peperomia marmorata*   Silver heart
Peperomia scandens   *Peperomia scandens*   Cupid peperomia
Pereskia aculeata *Grosseillier de Barbades*   Barbados gooseberry / Lemon vine
Pereskia grandiflora *Pereskia grandiflora*   Rose cactus
Periploca graeca   *Périploque*   Silk vine
Persicaria amphibium *Renouée amphibe*   Amphibious bistort
Persicaria bistorta   *Bistorte*   Bistort
Petasites albus   *Pétasite blanc*   White butterbur
Petasites fragrans   *Héliotrope d'hiver*   Winter heliotrope
Petasites hybridus   *Chapeau-du-diable / Pètasite hybride*   Butterbur
Petasites japonicus   *Pétasite du Japon*   Creamy butterbur
Petrorhagia saxifraga *Tunique*   Tunic flower
Petroselinum crispum *Persil*   Parsley
Petroselinum segetum   *Persil des moissons*   Corn parsley
Petteria ramantacea   *Petteria ramantacea*   Dalmatian laburnum
Petunia   *Pétunia*   Petunia
Peucedanum officinale *Peucédan officinal / Queue-de-porc*   Hog's fennel
Peucedanum ostruthium *Peucédan impératoire*   Masterwort
Peucedanum palustre *Peucédan des marais*   Milk parsley
Phacelia campanularia *Phacelia campanularia*   California bluebell
Phalaris arundinacea picta *Phalaris arundinacea picta*   Gardener's garters
Phegopteris connectilis *Phegopteris connectilis*   Beech fern
Phellodendron amurense *Phellodendron amurense*   Amur cork tree
Philadelphus coronarius *Seringat*   Mock orange
Philodendron cordatum *Philodendron cordatum*   Heart leaf
Philodendron domesticum *Philodendron domesticum*
   Elephant's ears / Spade leaf
Philodendron erubescens*Philodendron erubescens*   Blushing philodendron
Phlomis fruticosa   *Sauge de Jérusalem*   Jerusalem sage
Phlox bifida   *Phlox bifida*   Sand phlox
Phlox drummondii   *Phlox annuel*   Annual phlox
Phlox stolonifera   *Phlox stolonifera*   Creeping phlox
Phoenix   *Dattier*   Date palm
Phoenix canariensis   *Dattier des Canaries*   Canary Island
Phoenix roebelenii *Phoenix roebelenii*   Miniature date palm / Pygmy date palm
Phormium cookianum *Phormium cookianum*   Mountain flax
Phormium tenax   *Lin de Nouvelle-Zélande*   New Zealand flax
Phygelius capensis   *Fuchsia du Cap / Scrofulaire du Cap*   Cape figwort
Phyllitis scolopendrium *Langue de bœuf / Langue de cerf*   Hart's tongue fern
Phyllocladus aspleniifolius *Phyllocladus aspleniifolius*   Tasman celery pine
Phyllodoce caerulea   *Phyllodoce bleuatre*   Menziesia

Phyllostachys aurea	*Bambou doré*	Fishpole bamboo / Golden bamboo
Phyllostachys aureosulcata	*Bambou aureosulcata*	Golden-groove bamboo
Phyllostachys bambusoides	*Bambou bambusoides*	Timber bamboo
Phyllostachys flexuosa	*Bambou flexuosa*	Zigzag bamboo
Phyllostachys nigra	*Bambou noir*	Black bamboo
Physalis	*Coqueret*	Chinese lantern
Physalis alkekengi	*Coqueret du Pérou*	Bladder cherry
Physalis alkekengi	*Alkéenege du Pérou*	Bladder cherry
Physalis alkekengi	*Alkékenge /Amour-en-cage / Lanterne japonais*	Winter cherry
Physalis peruviana	*Alkékenge de Pérou / Coqueret du Perou*	Cape gooseberry
Physalis peruviana	*Alkékenge de Pérou / Coqueret de Pérou*	Strawberry tomato
Physalis peruviana	*Lanterne japonaise*	Strawberry tomato
Physocarpus opulifolius	*Physocarpe opulifolius*	Ninebark
Physospermum cornubiense	*Physosperme de cornouailles*	Bladder seed
Physostegia	*Physostegia*	Obedient plant
Phyteuma orbiculare	*Raiponce orbiculaire*	Round-headed rampion
Phyteuma spicatum	*Raiponce en épi*	Spiked rampion
Phytolacca americana	*Phytolacca americana*	Red-ink plant / Virginia pokeweed
Picea	*Épicéa*	Spruce
Picea abies	*Épicéa commun*	Norway spruce
Picea abies	*Sapin de Norvège / Sapin rouge*	Norway spruce
Picea breweriana	*Épicéa de Brewer*	Brewer's spruce
Picea englemannii	*Épicéa d'Englemann*	Englemann spruce / Mountain spruce
Picea glauca	*Épinette blanche / Sapinette blanche*	White spruce
Picea likeangensis	*Picea likeangensis*	Lijiang spruce
Picea mariana	*Sapinette noir*	Black spruce
Picea morrisonicola	*Épicéa morrisonicola*	Taiwan spruce
Picea omorica	*Épicéa de Serbie*	Serbian spruce
Picea orientalis	*Sapinette d'Orient*	Caucasian spruce
Picea pungens	*Épicéa du Colorado*	Colorado spruce
Picea omorica	*Épicéa de Serbie*	Caucasian spruce
Picea sitchensis	*Épicéa de Sitka*	Sitka spruce
Picea smithiana	*Picea smithiana*	Morinda spruce / West Himalayan spruce
Picris echioides	*Picride vipérine*	Bristly ox-tongue
Picris hieracioides	*Picride épervière*	Hawkweed ox-tongue
Pieris floribunda	*Pieris floribunda*	Fetterbush / Mountain fetterbush
Pilea cadierei	*Plante aluminium*	Aluminium plant
Pilea involucrata	*Pilea involucrata*	Friendship plant
Pilea numulariifolia	*Pilea numulariifolia*	Creeping Charlie

Pimpinella major	*Grand boucage*	Greater burnet-saxifrage
Pimpinella saxifraga	*Petit boucage*	Burnet-saxifrage
Pinguicula grandiflora	*Grassette à grandes fleurs*	Giant butterwort
Pinguicula lusitanica	*Grassette du Portugal*	Pale butterwort
Pinguicula vulgaris	*Grassette commune*	Common butterwort
Pinus	*Pin*	Pine
Pinus aristata	*Pin aristata*	Bristle cone pine
Pinus armandii	*Pin armandii du père Armand David*	
		Armand pine / David's pine
Pinus banksiana	*Pin de Banks*	Jack pine
Pinus cembra	*Arolle / Pin cembro*	Arolla pine
Pinus cembroides	*Arolle / Pin cembro*	Mexican stone pine / Pinyon
Pinus contorta	*Pin vrillé*	Beach pine / Big-cone pine / Coulter pine
Pinus contorta latifolia	*Pin contorta latifolia*	Lodgepole pine
Pinus densiflora	*Pin rouge du Japon*	Japanese red pine
Pinus halpensis	*Pin d'Alep / Pin de Jerusalem*	Aleppo pine
Pinus x holfordiana	*Pin x holfordiana*	Holford's pine
Pinus jeffreyi	*Pin de Jeffrey*	Black pine / Jeffrey pine
Pinus larico nigra	*Pin noir d'Autriche*	Austrian pine
Pinus leucodermis	*Pin de Bosnie*	Bosnian pine
Pinus montezumae	*Pin de Montezuma*	
		Montezuma pine / Rough-barked Mexican pine
Pinus mugo	*Pin de montagne*	
		Dwarf pine / Mountain pine / Swiss mountain pine
Pinus muricata	*Pin d'Anthony*	Bishop pine
Pinus nigra	*Pin noir d'Autriche*	Black pine
Pinus nigra laricio	*Pin noir de Corse*	Corsican pine
Pinus parviflora	*Pin parviflora*	Japanese white pine
Pinus peuce	*Pin de Maceedoine*	Macedonian pine
Pinus pinaster	*Pin des landes / Pin maritime*	Cluster pine / Maritime Pine
Pinus pinea	*Pin parasol*	Stone pine / Umbrella pine
Pinus ponderosa	*Pin jaune*	Western yellow pine
Pinus pumila	*Pin pumila*	Dwarf Siberian pine
Pinus radiata	*Pin de Monterey*	Monterey pine
Pinus montzumae	*Pin de Montezuma*	Montezuma pine
Pinus rigida	*Pin rigida*	Northern pitch pine
Pinus strobus	*Pin Weymouth*	Eastern white pine / Weymouth pine
Pinus sylvestris	*Pin sylvestre*	Scots pine
Pinus thunbergii	*Pin noir du Japon*	Japanese black pine
Pinus virginiana	*Pin de Jersey / Pin de Virginie*	Virginia pine
Pinus wallichiana	*Pin pleuereur de l'Himalaya*	
		Bhutan pine / Himalayan pine

Pisonia umbellifera	*Pisonia umbellifera*	Bird-catcher tree / Para para
Pistacia lentiscus	*Arbre au mastic / Lentisque*	Mastic tree
Pistacia terebinthus	*Térébinthe*	Cyprus turpentine / Terebinth tree
Pistia stratiotes	*Laitue d'eau*	Water lettuce
Pittosporum crassifolium	*Pittosporum crassifolium*	Karo
Pittosporum tobira	*Pittosporum tobira*	Japanese pittosporum / Mock orange
Pittosporum undulatum	*Pittosporum undulatum*	Victorian box
Plantago coronopus	*Pied-de-corbeau / Plantain corne-de bœuf*	Buckshorn plantain
Plantago lanceolata	*Plantain lancéolé*	Ribwort plantain
Plantago major	*Grand plantain / Plantain majeur*	Rat's tail plantain
Plantago maritima	*Plantain maritime*	Sea plantain
Plantago media	*Plantain moyen*	Hoary plantain
Platanthera bifolia	*Orchis à deux feuilles*	Lesser butterfly orchid
Planthera chlorantha	*Orchis verdate*	Butterfly orchid
Platanus	*Platane*	Plane
Platanus acerifolia	*Platane de Londres*	London plane
Platanus orientalis	*Platane d'Orient*	Oriental plane
Platycerium	*Platycérium*	Stag's horn fern
Platycodon	*Platycodon*	Baloon flower
Platystemon californicus	*Platystemon californicus*	Cream cups
Plectranthus australis	*Plectranthus australis*	Swedish ivy
Plectranthus oertendahlii	*Plectranthus oertendahlii*	Prostrate coleus / Swedish ivy
Pleioblastus variegatus	*Pleioblastus variegatus*	Dwarf white stripe bamboo
Pleiospilos bolusii	*Pleomele bolusii*	Living rock / Mimicry plant
Plumbago auriculata	*Dentelaire du Cap*	Cape leadwort
Plumeria alba	*Plumeria alba*	West Indian jasmine
Plumeria rubra	*Frangipanier*	Frangipani
Podocarpus alpinus	*Podocarpe montagnard*	Plum yew / Tasmanian podocarp
Podocarpus macrophyllus	*Podocarpus macrophyllus*	Kusamaki
Podocarpus nivalis	*Podocarpus nivalis*	Alpine totara
Podophyllum emodi	*Podophyllue Indien*	Himalayan May apple
Podophyllum peltatum	*Podophyllum peltatum*	May apple
Polemonium caeruleum	*Polémoine blue / Valériane Grecque*	Jacob's ladder
Polianthes tuberosa	*Tubéreuse*	Tuberose
Polycarpon tetraphyllum	*Polycarpon à quatre feuilles*	Four-leaved allseed
Polygala calcaria	*Polygala des sols calcaires*	Chalk milkwort
Polygala chamaebuxus	*Polygale faux-buis*	Polygala chamaebuxus
Polygala serpyllifolia	*Polygala à feuilles de serpolet*	Heath milkwort
Polygala vulgaris	*Polygala commun*	Common milkwort
Polygonatum	*Sceau-de-Salomon*	Solomon's seal

Polygonatum commutatum	*Sceau-de-Salomon*	Great Solomon's seal
Polygonatum multiflorum	*Scaeu de Salomon multiflore*	
		Common Solomon's seal
Polygonatum odoratum	*Sceau de Salomon odorant*	Angled Solomon's seal
Polygonatum verticillatum	*Sceau de Salomon verticillé*	
		Whorled Solomon's seal
Polygonum	*Renouée*	Knotweed
Polygonum aubertii	*Renouée aubertii*	Mile a minute plant / Russian vine
Polygonum baldschuanicum	*Renouée*	Mile a minute plant / Russian vine
Polygonum aviculare	*Renouée des oiseaux*	Knotgrass
Polygonum bistorta	*Bistorte*	Bistort
Polygonum maritimum	*Renouée maritime*	Sea knotgrass
Polypodium glycyrrhiza	*Polypodium glycyrrhiza*	Liquorice fern
Polypodium virginianum	*Polypodium virginianum*	American wall fern
Polypodium vulgare	*Polypode commun*	Polypody
Polyscias filicifolia	*Polyscias filicifolia*	Fern-leaf aralia
Polyscias guilfoylei	*Polyscias guilfoylei*	Wild coffee
Polystichum acrostchoides	*Polystic*	Christmas fern
Polystichum aculeatum	*Polystic aculeatum*	
		Hard shield fern / Prickly shield fern
Polystichum lonchitis	*Polystic lonchitis*	Holly fern
Polystichum munitum	*Polystic munitum*	Giant holly fern
Polystichum setiferum	*Polystic setiferum*	Soft shield fern
Poncirus trifoliatta	*Poncirus trifoliatta*	Japanese bitter orange
Populus	*Peuplier*	Poplar
Pontederis cordata	*Pontédérie à feuilles en cœur*	Pickerel weed
Populus alba	*Peuplier blanc*	Abele / White poplar
Populus balsamifera	*Peuplier baumier*	Balsam Poplar / Tacamahac
Populus x berolinensis	*Peuplier de Berlin*	Berlin poplar
Populus x canadensis	*Peuplier euroaméricains*	Canadian poplar
Populus x candicans	*Peuplier x candicans*	Balm of Gilead / Black Italian poplar
Populus candicans	*Peuplier d'Ontario*	Ontario poplar
Populus canescens	*Grisard / Peuplier grisard*	Grey poplar
Populus deltoides	*Peuplier noir d'Amérique*	
		Cottonwood / Eastern cottonwood /Necklace poplar
Populus lasiocarpa	*Peuplier lasiocarpa*	Chinese necklace poplar
Populus nigra	*Liardier / Peuplier noir*	Black poplar
Populus nigra "Italica"	*Peuplier d'Italie*	Lombardy poplar
Populus tremula	*Tremble*	Aspen
Populus tremula 'Pendula'	*Tremble pleureur*	Weeping aspen
Populus tremuloides	*Peuplier tremble d'Amérique*	American aspen
Populus tremuloides	*Faux-tremble*	Quaking aspen

Populus trichocarpa *Baumier de l'Ouest*

Black cottonwood / Western balsam poplar

Porana panicultata	*Porana panicultata*	Bridal bouquet
Porana paniculata	*Porana paniculata*	Snow creeper
Portulacaria afra	*Pourpier en arbre*	Elephant bush
Potamogeton acutifolius	*Potamot à feuilles aiguës*	Sharp-leafed pondweed
Potamogeton alpinus	*Potamot alpin*	Reddish pondweed
Potamogeton berchtoldii	*Potamot de Berchtold⁻*	Slender pondweed
Potamogeton coloratus	*Potamot coloratus*	Plantain-leaved pondweed
Potamogeton compressus	*Potamot comprimé*	Wrack-like pondweed
Potamogeton crispus	*Potamot crépu*	American pondweed
Potamogeton filiformis	*Potamot filiforme*	Slender leafed pondweed

Potamogeton gramineus *Potamot à feuilles de graminée*

Various leaved pondweed

Potamogeton lucens	*luisant*	Shining pondweed
Potamogeton natans	*Potamot nageant*	Broad-leaved pondweed
Potamogeton nodosus	*Potamot noueux*	Loddon pondweed
Potamogeton obtusifolius	*Potamot à feuilles obtuses*	Blunt-leaved pondweed
Potamogeton pectinatus	*Potamot pectiné*	Fennel pondweed
Potamogeton perfiolatus	*Potamot perfolié*	Perfiolate pondweed
Potamogeton polygonifolius	*Potamot à feuilles de renouée*	Bog pondweed
Potamogeton praelongus	*Potamot allongé*	Long stalked pondweed
Potamogeton pusillus	*Potamot fluet*	Lesser pondweed
Potamogeton trichoides	*Potamot capillaire*	Hairlike pondweed
Potentilla anserina	*Ansérine*	Silverweed
Potentilla argentea	*Potentille argentée*	Hoary cinquefoil
Potentilla crantzii	*Potentille des Alpes*	Alpine cinquefoil
Potentilla erecta	*Potentille dressée*	Tormentil
Potentilla fruticosa	*Potentille ligneuse*	Shrubby cinquefoil
Potentilla palustris	*Comaret*	Marsh cinquefoil
Potentilla recta	*Potentille dressée*	Sulpher cinquefoil
Potentilla reptans	*Potentille rampante*	Creeping cinquefoil
Potentilla rupestris	*Potentille des rochers*	White cinquefoil
Potentilla sterilis	*Potentille faux-fraisier*	Barren strawberry
Primula polyanthus	*Primevère polyanthe*	Polyanthus
Primula auricula	*Auricule / Oreille d'ours*	Auricula
Primula denticulata	*Primula denticulata*	Drumstick primula
Primula elatior	*Primevère élevée*	Oxlip
Primula farinosa	*Primevère farineuse*	Bird's eye primrose
Primula florindae	*Primevère florindae*	Giant cowslip
Primula scotica	*Primevère d'Ecosse*	Scots primrose
Primula veris	*Coucou / Primevère officinale*	Cowslip

Primula vulgaris	*Primevère acaule*	Primrose
Prostanthera	*Prostanthera*	Mint bush
Prostanthera rotundifolia	*Prostanthera rotundifolia*	Round-leaved mint-bush
Protea cynaroides	*Protea cynaroides*	King protea
Protea repens	*Protea repens*	Sugar bush
Prunella grandiflora	*Brunelle grandiflora*	Large self heal
Prunella laciniata	*Brunelle laciniée*	Cut-leaved self-heal
Prunella vulgaris	*Brunelle commune*	Self heal
Prunus	*Cerisier*	Cherry
Prunus armeniaca	*Abricotier*	Apricot
Prunus avium	*Merisier des oiseaux*	Gean / Wild cherry
Prunus campanulata	*Prunus campanulata*	Bellflowered cherry / Taiwan cherry
Prunus cerasifera	*Prunier myrobolan*	Cherry plum / Myrobalan
Prunus davidiana	*Pécher de David*	David's peach
Prunus dulcis	*Amandier*	Almond
Prunus incisa	*Prunus incisa*	Fuji cherry
Prunus laureocerasus	*Laurier cerise*	Cherry laurel
Prunus lusitanica	*Laurier du Portugal*	Portugal laurel
Prunus malaheb	*Cerisier de Sainte-Lucie*	Prunus malaheb
Prunus mume	*Abricot japonais*	Japanese apricot
Prunus padus	*Cerisier à grappes*	Bird cherry
Prunus pennsylvanica	*Prunier de Pennsylvanie*	Pin cherry
Prunus persica	*Pêcher*	Peach
Prunus sargentii	*Prunus sargentii*	Sargent cherry
Prunus serotina	*Cerisier noir*	Black cherry / Wild rum cherry
Prunus serrulata var. spontanea	*Prunus serrula*	Hill cherry
Prunus spinosa	*Epine noire /Prunellier*	Blackthorn / Sloe
Prunus subhirtella	*Cerisier à fleurs japonais*	Higan cherry
Prunus subhirtella	*Prunus subhirtella*	Rosebud cherry
Prunus "Tai Haku"	*Prunus "Tai Haku"*	Great white cherry
Prunus virginiana	*Prunus virginiana*	Virginia bird cherry
Prunus x yedoensis	*Prunus x yedoensis*	Yoshino cherry
Pseudolarix amabilis	*Mélèze doré*	Golden larch
Pseudopanax arboreus	*Pseudopanax arboreus*	Five fingers
Pseudopanax crassifolius	*Pseudopanax crassifolius*	Lancewood
Pseudosasa japonica	*Pseudosasa japonica*	Arrow bamboo / Metake
Pseudotsuga menziesii	*Douglas vert / Sapin de Douglas*	Douglas fir
Pseudotsuga menziesii	*Sapin de l'Oregon*	Douglas fir
Pseudotsuga menzieii 'Glauca'	*Douglas bleu / Sapin de Douglas bleu*	Blue Douglas fir
Pseudowintera axillaris	*Pseudowintera axillaris*	Heropito / Pepper tree

Ptelea trifoliata	*Orme de Samarie / Ptélée*	Hop tree
Pteris cretica	*Pteris cretica*	Cretan brake
Pteris ensiformis	*Pteris ensiformis*	Snow brake
Pteris multifida	*Pteris multifida*	Spider fern
Pterocarya	*Pterocarya*	Wing nut
Pterocarya frazinifolia	*Pterocarya frazinifolia*	Caucasian wing nut
Pterocarya stenoptera	*Pterocarya stenoptera*	Chinese wing nut
Pterostyrax hispida	*Pterostyrax hispida*	Epaulette tree
Pueraria lobata	*Pueraria lobata*	Kadzu vine
Pulcaria dysenterica	*Pulicaire dysentérique*	Common fleabane
Pulcaria vulgaris	*Pulicaire commune*	Small fleabane
Pulmonaria longifolia	*Pulmonaire à feuilles longues*	Joseph & Mary
Pulmonaria officinalis	*Pulmonaire officinale*	Lungwort
Pulsatilla alpina	*Anémone des Alpes*	Alpine anémone
Pulsatilla vulgaris	*Anémone pulsatille*	Pasque flower
Punica granatum	*Grenadier*	Pomegranite
Punica granatum nana	*Grenadier nain*	Dwarf pomegranate
Puschkinia scilloides	*Puschkinia scilloides*	Striped squill
Pyracantha coccinea	*Buisson ardent*	Firethorn
Pyrola	*Pyrole*	Wintergreen
Pyrola media	*Pyrole moyenne*	Greater wintergreen
Pyrola minor	*Petite pyrole*	Common wintergreen
Pyrola rotundifolia	*Pyrole à feuilles rondes*	Wild lily of the valley / Round-leaved wintergreen
Pyrostegia venusta	*Pyrostegia venusta*	Flame flower / Flame vine / Golden shower
Pyrus	*Poirier*	Pear
Pyrus calleryana	*Poirier calleryana*	Callery pear
Pyrus torminalis	*Alisier torminal*	Wild service tree
Pyrus salicifolia pendula	*Poirier pleureur à feuilles de saule*	Weeping willow pear

Q

Quercus	*Chêne*	Oak
Quercus acutissima	*Chêne acutissima*	Sawtooth oak
Quercus agrifolia	*Chêne agrifolia*	Californian live oak
Quercus alba	*Chêne blanc d'Amérique*	American white oak
Quercus aliena	*Chêne aliena*	Oriental white oak
Quercus alnifolia	*Chêne alnifolia*	Golden oak of Cyprus
Quercus canariensi	*Chêne Zeen*	Algerian oak / Mirbeck's oak
Quercus casteifolia	*Chêne à feuilles de châtaigner*	Quercus casteifolia
Quercus cerris	*Chêne de Bourgogne / Chêne chevelu*	Turkey oak

Quercus coccifera	*Chêne kermès*	Kermes oak
Quercus coccinea	*Chêne écarlate*	Scarlet oak
Quercus dentata	*Chêne denté*	Daimio oak
Quercus frainetto	*Chêne de Hongrie*	Hungarian oak
Quercus garryana	*Chêne garryana*	Oregon oak
Quercus x heterophylla	*Chêne x heterophylla*	Bartram's oak
Quercus x hispanica 'Lucombeana'	*Chêne hispanica 'Lucombeana'*	
		Lucombe oak
Quercus ilex	*Chêne vert / Yeuse*	Holm oak
Quercus imbricaria	*Chêne à lattes*	Shingle oak
Quercus macranthera	*Chêne macranthera*	Caucasian oak
Quercus macrocarpa	*Chêne à gros fruits*	Bur oak
Quercus macrolepis	*Chêne Vélani*	Valonia oak
Quercus marilandica	*Jaquier noir*	Black Jack oak
Quercus mongolica	*Chêne de Mongolie*	Mongolian oak
Quercus nigra	*Chêne noir*	Water oak
Quercus palustris	*Chêne des marais*	Pin oak
Quercus phellos	*Chêne saule*	Willow oak
Quercus pontica	*Chêne d'Arménie*	Armenian oak / Pontine oak
Quercus petraea	*Chêne sessile*	Durmast oak
Quercus petraea	*Chêne rouvre / Chêne sessile*	Sessile oak
Quercus pontica	*Chêne pontin*	Pontine oak
Quercus robur	*Chêne pédonculé*	Pedunculate oak
Quercus robur fastigiata	*Chêne pédonculé pyramidial*	
		Fastigiate pedunculate oak
Quercus rubra	*Chêne rouge*	Red oak
Quercus suber	*Chêne-liège*	Cork oak
Quercus velutina	*Chêne noir / Quercitron / Chêne des teinturiers*	
		Black oak
Quercus virginiana	*Chêne de Carrolina*	Live oak
Quisqualis indica	*Quisqualis indica*	Rangoon creeper

R

Radiola linoides	*Radiole faux-lin*	Flax-seed
Ranunculus	*Renoncule*	Buttercup
Ranunculus acris	*Bouton d'or*	Meadow buttercup
Ranunculus acris flore pleno	*Renoncle âcre flore pleno / Bouton d'or*	
		Double meadow buttercup
Ranunculus alpestris	*Renoncule des Alpes*	Alpine buttercup
Ranunculus asiaticus	*Renoncule des fleuristes / Renoncule des jardins*	
		Persian buttercup

Ranunculus arvensis	*Renoncule des champs*	Corn buttercup
Ranunculus auricomus	*Renonclue à tête d'or*	Goldilocks / Wood goldilocks
Ranunculus bulbosa	*Renoncule bulbeuse*	Bulbous buttercup
Ranunculus ficaria	*Ficaire*	Lesser celandine
Ranunculus flammula	*Petite douve / Renoncule flamette*	Lesser spearwort
Ranunculus lingua	*Grande douve*	Greater spearwort
Ranunculus lyallii	*Renoncule lyallii*	Giant buttercup
Ranunculus parviflorus	*Renonculeàa peites fleurs*	Small flowered buttercup
Ranunculus repens	*Renoncule rampante*	Creeping buttercup
Ranunculus reptans	*Renoncule à tige rampante*	Creeping spearwort
Ranunculus sardous	*Renoncule sarde*	Hairy buttercup
Ranunculus sceleratus	*Renoncule scélérate*	Celery leafed buttercup
Raoulia australis	*Carpette argentée*	Raoulia australis
Raphanus raphanistrum	*Ravenelle*	Wild radish
Raphanus sativus	*Radis cultivé*	Radish
Ravenala madegascariensis	*Ravenala madegascariensis*	Traveller's tree
Reinwardtia indica	*Reinwardtia indica*	Yellow flax
Reseda	*Mignonette*	Mignonette
Reseda alba	*Réséda blanc*	White mignonette
Reseda lutea	*Réséda jaune*	Wild mignonette
Reseda luteola	*Gaude / Réséda dea teinturiers*	Weld
Reseda phyteuma	*Réséda raiponce*	Corn mignonette
Rhamnus	*Nerprun*	Buckthorn
Rhamnus cathartica	*Nerprun purgatif*	Common buckthorn
Rhamnus alaternus	*Neprun alaterne*	Italian buckthorn
Rhaphiolepis indica	*Rhaphiolepis indica*	Indian hawthorn
Rhapis excelsa	*Rhapis excelsa*	Bamboo Palm
Rhapis excelsa	*Rhapis excelsa*	Slender lady palm
Rheum	*Rhubarbe*	Rhubarb
Rhinanthus crista-galli	*Cocriste*	Greater yellow rattle
Rhinanthus crista-galli	*Petit cocriste*	Yellow rattle
Rhipsalidopsis gaertneri	*Cactus de Pâques*	Easter cactus
Rhipsalis	*Rhipsalis*	Mistletoe cactus
Rhipsalis cereuscula	*Rhipsalis cereuscula*	Coral cactus
Rhipsalis paradoxa	*Rhipsalis paradoxa*	Chain cactus
Rhododendron	*Azalée*	Azalea
Rhododendron calendulaceum	*Rhododendron calendulaceum*	Flame azalea
Rhododendron luteum	*Azalée pontique*	Azalea ponticum
Rhoicissus capensis	*Rhoicissus capensis*	Cape grape
Rhus	*Sumac*	Sumach
Rhus copallina	*Rhus copallina*	Dwarf sumach
Rhus glabra	*Sumac à bois glabre / Vinaigrier*	Smooth sumach

Rhus succedanea	*Sumac faux-vernis*	Wax tree
Rhus typhina	*Sumac amarante / Sumac de Virginie*	Stag's horn sumach
Rhus verniciflua	*Sumac verniciflua*	Varnish tree
Rhynchelytrum repens	*Rhynchelytrum repens*	Natal grass / Ruby grass
Rhynchosinapis monensis	*Moutarde giroflée*	Dune cabbage
Ribes	*Groseillier*	Currant
Ribes nigrum	*Cassis*	Black currant
Ribes odoratum	*Groseille doré*	Buffalo currant
Ribes rubrum	*Groseillier rouge*	Red currant
Ribes sanguineum	*Faux-Cassis*	Flowering currant
Ribes sanguineum	*Groseillier à fleurs / Groseillier sanguin*	Flowering currant
Ribes speciosum	*Ribes speciosum*	Fuchsia flowered currant
Ribes rubrum	*Groseillier des Alpes*	Mountain currant
Ribes uva-crispa	*Groseillier à maquereau*	Gooseberry currant
Ricinus communis	*Palma Christi / Ricin commun*	Castor oil plant
Robinia hispida	*Acacia rose*	Rose acacia
Robinia pseudoacacia	*Acacia blanc / Robinier faux-acacia*	`False acacia / Locust
Romneya coulteri	*Romneya coulteri*	Californian poppy
Romulea columnae	*Romulée à petites fleurs*	Sand crocus
Rorippa amphibia	*Rorippa amphibie*	Greater yellow cress
Rorippa islandica	*Rorippa d'Islande*	Marsh yellow cress
Rorippa nasturtium-aquaticum	*Cresson de fontaine*	Water-cress
Rorippa sylvestris	*Rorippa des forêts*	Creeping yellow cress
Rosa	*Rose*	Rose
Rosa banksiae	*Rosier de Banks*	Banksia rose
Rosa banksiae lutea	*Rosier jaune de Banks*	Yellow banksia
Rosa 'Dupontii'	*Rosier Dupontii*	Snowbush tree
Rosa eglanteria	*Églantier odorant*	Eglantine / Sweet briar
Rosa eglanteria	*Églantine*	Eglantine / Sweet briar
Rosa gallica versicolor	*Rosier gallica versicolor*	Rosa mundi
Rosa pimpinellifolia	*Rosier pimpernelle*	Burnet rose / Scotch rose
Rosa primula	*Rose primula*	Incense rose
Rosa rugosa	*Rosier multiflore*	Hedgehog rose / Japanese rose
Rosa 'Zéphirine Drouhin'	*Rosier 'Zéphirine Drouhin'*	Thornless rose
Rosmarinus officinalis	*Romarin*	Rosemary
Roystonea regia	*Roi des palmiers*	Cuban royal palm / Royal palm
Rubia peregrina	*Garance voyageuse*	Wild madder
Rubus	*Ronce*	Blackberry / Bramble (in Scotland)
Rubus caesius	*Ronce bleuâtre*	Dewberry
Rubus chamaemorus	*Ronce des tourbières*	Cloudberry

Rubus fruticosus	*Ronce commune*	Bramble
Rubus idaeus	*Framboisir*	Raspberry
Rubus odoratus	*Ronce odorante*	Flowering raspberry / Thimbleberry
Rubus saxatilis	*Ronce des rochers*	Stone bramble
Rudbeckia	*Rudbeckia*	Coneflower
Rudbeckia fulgida	*Rudbeckia fulgida*	Black-eyed Susan
Rudbeckia hirta	*Rudbeckie hérisée*	Black-eyed Susan
Rumex acetosa	*Oseille des prés*	Common sorrel
Rumex acetosella	*Petite oseille*	Sheep's sorrel
Rumex alpinus	*Patience des Alpes*	Monk's Rhubarb
Rumex conglomeratus	*Patience agglomérée*	Clustered dock
Rumex crispus	*Patience crépue*	Curled dock
Rumex hydrolapathum	*Patience d'eau*	Great water dock
Rumex longifolius	*Patience à feuilles longues*	Butter dock
Rumex maritimus	*Patience maritime*	Golden dock
Rumex patientia	*Epinard-oseille*	Patience dock
Rumex rupestris	*Patience des rochers*	Shore dock
Rumex obtusifolius	*Patience à feuilles obtuses*	Broad dock
Rumex palustris	*Patience des marais*	Marsh dock
Rumex pulcher	*Patience élégante*	Fiddle dock
Rumex sanguineus	*Patience sanguine*	Wood or Red-veined dock
Ruppia maritima	*Ruppia maritime*	Tassel pondweed
Ruppia spiralis	*Ruppia spiralée*	Coiled pondweed
Ruscus aculeatus	*Petit houx*	Butcher's broom
Ruscus aculeatus	*Fragon piquant*	Butcher's broom
Ruscus aculeatus	*Houx frelon*	Butcher's broom
Russelia equisetiformis	*Plante corail*	Coral plant
Ruta	*Rue*	Rue
Ruta graveolens	*Herbe de grace / Rue fétide*	Herb of grace

S

Sabal minor	*Palmier nain*	Dwarf palmeto
Sagina	*Sagine*	Pearlwort / Sagina
Sagina apetala	*Sagine apétale*	Annual pearlwort
Sagina maritima	*Sagine maritime*	Sea pearlwort
Sagina nodosa	*Sagine noueuse*	Knotted pearlwort
Sagina procumbens	*Sagine couchée*	Mossy pearlwort
Sagina saginoides	*Sagine des Alpes*	Alpine pearlwort
Sagina subulata	*Sagine subulée*	Heath pearlwort
Sagittaria latifolia	*Flèche d'eau américaine*	
		American arrowhead / Duck potato

Sagittaria sagittifolia	*Sagittaire à feuilles en flèche*	Arrow-head
Sagittaria sagittifolia 'Flore pleno'	*Flèche d'eau américaine*	Japanese arrowhead
Saintpaulia	*Violette d'Usambara*	African violet
Saintpaulia	*Violette africaine*	African violet
Salicornia europaea	*Salicorne d'Europe*	Glasswort
Salix	*Saule*	Willow
Salix aegyptiaca	*Saule aegyptiaca*	Musk willow
Salix alba	*Saule argenté / Saule blanc / Saule vivier*	Silver willow / White willow
Salix alba caerulea	*Saule blanc var coerulea*	Cricket bat willow
Salix alba vitellina	*Saule alba vitellina*	Golden willow
Salix arbuscula	*Saule arbuscula*	Mountain willow
Salix babylonica	*Saule pleureur*	Weeping willow
Salix caprea	*Saule marsault*	Goat willow
Salix caprea	*Marsault*	Pussy willow
Salix caprea Kilmarnock	*Marsault*	Kilmarnock willow
Salix chrysocoma	*Salix chrysocoma*	Golden weeping willow
Salix daphnoides	*Salix daphné / Saule noir*	Violet willow
Salix elaeagnos	*Salix elaeagnos*	Hoary willow
Salix herbacea	*Salix herbacea*	Dwarf willow
Salix herbacea	*Salix herbacea*	Least willow
Salix fragilis	*Salix fragilis*	Crack willow
Salix lanata	*Salix lanata*	Woolly willow
Salix matsudana 'Tortuosa'	*Salix matsudana tortuosa*	Dragon's claw willow
Salix 'Melanostachys'	*Saule d'Amérique / Saule noir*	Black willow
Salix pentandra	*Saule laurier*	Bay willow
Salix purpurea	*Osier rouge*	Purple osier
Salix repens	*Saule rampant*	Creeping willow
Salix reticulata	*Saule reticulé*	Net veined willow
Salsola kali	*Soude salsovie*	Saltwort
Salvia	*Sauge / Toute bonne*	Sage
Salvia argentea	*Sauge argentée*	Salvia argentea
Salvia horminoides	*Sauge faux-horminum*	Clary
Salvia leucantha	*Salvia leucantha*	Mexican bush sage
Salvia pratensis	*Sauge des prés*	Meadow sage
Salvia sclarea	*Orvale / Sauge sclarée / Toute-bonne*	Clary sage
Salvia splendens	*Sauge éclatante*	Salvia splendens
Salvia uliginosa	*Salvia uliginosa*	Bog sage
Sambucus	*Sureau*	Elder
Sambucus canadensis	*Sureau du Canada*	American elder
Sambucus ebulus	*Hièble*	Dwarf elder

Sambucus nigra aurea	*Sureau noir aurea*	Golden elder
Sambucus racemosa	*Sureau à grappes / Sureau rouge*	Red-berried elder
Samolus valerandi	*Samole de valérand*	Brookweed
Sandersonia aurantiaca	*Sandersonia aurantiaca*	Chinese lantern lily
Sanguinaria canadensis	*Sanguinaria canadensis*	Bloodroot
Sanguisorba	*Petite pimpernelle / Sanguisorbe*	Burnet
Sanguisorba canadensis	*Sanguisorba canadensis*	Canadian burnet
Sanguisorba officinalis	*Grande Pimpernelle / Sanguisorbe officinale*	Grass burnet
Sanicula europaea	*Sanicle d'Europe*	Sanicle
Sansiviera trifasciata	*Sansiviera trifasciata*	Mother-in-law's-tongue
Santolina	*Santoline*	Lavender cotton
Santolina chamaecyparissus	*Fausse Sanguenitte*	Cotton lavender
Santolina chamaecyparissus	*Santoline / Santoline blanche*	Cotton lavender
Santolina rosmarinifolia	*Santolina rosmarinifolia*	Holy flax
Sanvitalia procumbens	*Sanvitalia procumbens*	Creeping zinnia
Sapium sebiferum	*Sapium sebiferum*	Chinese tallow tree
Saponaria ocymoides	*Saponaire ocymoides*	Tumbing Ted
Saponaria officinalis	*Saponaire officinale / Savonnière*	Soapwort
Sarcococca	*Sarcococca*	Christmas box / Sweet box
Sarracenia flava	*Sarracène à fleurs jaunes*	Trumpets / Yellow pitcher plant
Sarracenia purpurea	*Sarracène pourpre*	Huntsman's cap / Pitcher plant
Satureja	*Sarriette*	Savory
Satureja montana	*Sarriette vivace*	Winter savory
Sauromatum venosum	*Sauromatum venosum*	Monarch of the East / Voodoo lily
Saururus cernuus	*Queue de lézard*	Lizard's tail / Swamp lily / Water dragon
Saussurea alpina	*Saussurée des Alpes*	Purple hawkweed
Saxegothaea conspicua	*Saxegothaea conspicua*	Prince Albert's yew
Saxifraga	*Saxifrage*	Saxifrage
Saxifraga aizoides	*Saxifrage jaune des montagnes*	Yellow mountain saxifrage
Saxifraga cernua	*Saxifrage penchée*	Drooping saxifrage
Saxifraga caespitosa	*Saxifrage gazonnante*	Tufted saxifrage
Saxifraga x geum	*Saxifrage benoîte*	Saxifraga x geum
Saxifraga granulata	*Saxifrage granulée*	Fair maids of France / Meadow saxifrage
Saxifraga hirculus	*Saxifrage œil de bouc*	Yellow marsh saxifrage
Saxifraga hirsuta	*Saxifrage herissée*	Kidney saxifrage
Saxifraga hypnoides	*Saxifrage faux hypne*	Mossy saxifrage
Saxifraga nivalis	*Saxifrage arctique*	Arctic saxifrage

Saxifraga oppositifolia	*Saxifrage à feuilles opposées*	Purple saxifrage
Saxifraga rivularis	*Saxifrage des ruisseaux*	Highland saxifrage
Saxifraga spathularis	*Saxifrage spathulée*	St. Patrick's cabbage
Saxifraga stellaris	*Saxifrage etoile*	Starry saxifrage
Saxifraga stolonifera	*Saxifraga stolonifera*	Mother of thousands
Saxifraga stolonifera 'Tricolor'	*Saxifraga stolonifera 'Tricolor'*	
		Strawberry geranium
Saxifraga tridactylites	*Saxifrage a trois doigis*	Fingered saxifrage
Saxifraga umbrosa	*Saxifrage des Pyrénées*	Pyrenean saxifrage
Saxifraga urbium	*Saxifraga urbium*	London pride
Scabiosa	*Scabieuse*	Scabious
Scabiosa atropurpurea	*Scabieuse des jardins*	Sweet scabious
Scabiosa columbaria	*Scabieuse colombaire*	Small scabious
Scadoxus multiflorus katherinae	*Scadoxus multiflorus katherinae*	
		Blood flower
Scadoxus puniceus	*Scadoxus puniceus*	Royal paintbrush
Scandix pecten-veneris	*Scandix peigne-de-Vénus*	Shepherd's needle
Schefflera actinophylla	*Arbre ombrelle*	Queensland umbrella tree
Scheuchzeria palustris	*Scheuchzérie des marais*	Rannoch rush
Schizanthus	*Schizanthus*	Butterfly flower / Poor man's orchid
Schizophragma hydrangeoides	*Schizophragma hydrangeoides*	
		Japanese hydrangea vine
Schlumbergera bridgesii	*Schlumbergera bridgesii*	Christmas cactus
Schlumbergera truncata	*Cactus crabe*	Crab cactus / Lobster cactus
Schinus molle	*Faux poivrier*	
	Californian pepper tree / Peruvian mastic tree / Peruvian pepper tree	
Schizostylis	*Schizostylis*	Kaffir Lily
Sciadopitys verticulata	*Pin parasol du Japon*	
	Japanese umbrella pine / Umbrella pine	
Scilla autumnalis	*Scille d'automne*	Autumn squill
Scilla peruviana	*Scilla du Pérou*	Peruvian scilla
Scilla sibirica	*Scille de Sibérie*	Siberian squill
Scilla verna	*Scille printanière*	Spring squill
Scirpus	*Jonquine / Scirpe*	Bulrush / Club rush
Scirpus holoschoenus	*Scirpe à tête ronde*	Round headed club-root
Scleranthus annuus	*Gnavelle annuelle*	Knawel
Scleranthus perennis	*Gnavelle vivace*	Perennial knawel
Scorpiurus	*Chenille*	Scorpion's tail
Scorzonera humilis	*Scorzonère basse*	Viper's grass
Scrophularia	*Scrofulaire*	Figwort
Scrophularia auriculata	*Scrofulaire aquatique*	Water figwort
Scrophularia nodosa	*Scrofulaire noueuse*	Common figwort

Scrophularia scorddonia	*Scrofulaire a feuilles de germandrée*	
		Balm-leaved figwort
Scrophularia vernalis	*Scrofulaire du printemps*	Yellow figwort
Scutellaria	*Scutellaire / Toque*	Skullcap
Scutellaria galericulata	*Scutellaire casquée / Toque en casque*	
		Common skullcap
Scutellaria minor	*Toque mineur*	Lesser skullcap
Sedum	*Orpin*	Stonecrop
Sedum acre	*Poivre de muraille*	Biting stonecrop / Wall-pepper
Sedum album	*Orpin blanc*	White stonecrop
Sedum anglicum	*Orpin d'Angleterre*	Engish stonecrop
Sedum dasyphyllum	*Orpin à feuilles épaisses*	Thick-leaved stonecrop
Sedum forsteranum	*Orpin de Forster*	Rock stonecrop
Sedum morganianum	*Sedum morganianum*	Burro's tail / Donkey-tail
Sedum reflexum	*Orpin réfléchi*	
		Large yellow stonecrop / Reflexed stonecrop
Sedum rosea	*Orpin rose / Rhodiole rose*	Roseroot
Sedum spectabile	*Sedum spectabile*	Ice plant
Sedum telephium	*Orpin reprise*	Orpine
Sedum villosum	*Orpin velu*	Pink stonecrop
Selaginella kraussiana	*Lycopode du jardinier*	Selaginella kraussiana
Selaganella lepidophylla	*Selaginella lepidophylla*	
		Resurrection plant / Rose of Jericho
Selenicereus grandiflorus	*Cierge à grandes fleurs*	Queen-of-the-night
Selinum carvifolia	*Sélinum à feuilles de carvi*	Cambridge parsley
Semele andrgyna	*Semele andrgyna*	Climbing butcher's broom
Semiarundinaria fastuosa	*Semiarundinaria fastuosa*	Narihira bamboo
Sempervivum	*Joubarbe*	Houseleek
Sempervivum arachnoideum	*Joubarbe toile d'araignée*	Cobweb houseleek
	Sempervivum tectorum *Joubarbe des toits*	
		Common houseleek / Roof houseleek
Senecio aquaticus	*Séneçon aquatique*	Marsh ragwort
Senecio articulans	*Plante chandelle*	Candle plant
Senecio confusus	*Senecio confusus*	Mexican flame vine
Senecio erucifolius	*Séneçon à feuilles de roquette*	Hoary ragwort
Senecio fluviatilis	*Séneçon des rivières*	Saracen's woundwort
Senecio x hybridus	*Cinéraire hybrides*	Cineraria
Senecio integrifolius	*Séneçon à feuilles entières*	Field fleawort
Senecio jacobaea	*Séneçon jacobée*	Common ragwort
Senecio macroglossus	*Senecio macroglossus*	Natal ivy / Wax vine
Senecio rowleyanus	*Senecio rowleyanus*	String-of-beads
Senecio smithii	*Séneçon smithii*	Magellan ragwort

Senecio squalidus	*Séneçon négligé*	Oxford ragwort
Senecio sylvaticus	*Séneçon des bois*	Heath groundsel
Senecio viscosus	*Séneçon visqueux*	Sticky groundsel
Sequoia sempervirens	*Sequoia sempervirens*	Coast redwood / Redwood

Sequoiadendron giganteum *Sequoiadendron giganteum*
Big tree / Giant redwood / Wellintonia

Serenoa repens	*Serenoa repens*	Saw palmetto / Scrub palmetto
Serratula tinctoria	*Sarrette / Serratule des teinturiers*	Sawwort
Seseli libanotis	*Persil de montagne / Séséli libanotis*	Moon carrot
Sesleria heufleriana	*Sesleria heufleriana*	Balkan blue grass

Setaria italica *Sétaire d'Italie / Millet à grappes / Millet d'Italie*
Foxtail millet / Italian millet

Shepherdia argentea	*Shepherdia argentea*	Buffalo Berry
Sherardia arvensis	*Rubéole des champs*	Field madder
Shortia galacifolia	*Shortia galacifolia*	Oconee bells
Sibthorpia europaea	*Sibthorpie d'Europe*	Cornish moneywort
Sibbaldia procumbens	*Sibbaldie couchée*	Least cinquefoil
Silaum silaus	*Fenouil des chevaux*	Pepper saxifrage
Silene	*Silène*	Campion / Catchfly
Silene acaulis	*Silène acaule*	Moss campion
Silene coeli-rosa	*Coquelourde rose de ciel*	Silene coeli-rosa
Silene conica	*Silène conique*	Sand catchfly
Silene noctiflora	*Silène du nuit*	Night-scented catchfly
Silene nutans	*Silène penché*	Nottingham catchfly
Silene otites	*Silène à petites fleurs*	Breckland catchfly
Silene pendula	*Silène de Crète*	Nodding catchfly
Silene vulgaris maritima	*Silène maritime*	Sea campion

Silene vulgaris maritima flore pleno *Silène maritime double*
Double sea campion

Silphium laciniatum	*Plante boussole*	Compass plant
Silybum marianum	*Chardon Marie*	Blessed Mary's thistle / Milk thistle
Simethis planifolia	*Simathis à feuilles plates*	Kerry lily
Sinapis alba	*Moutarde blanche*	White mustard
Sinapis arvensis	*Moutarde des champs / Sénevé*	Charlock
Sinningia speciosa	*Gloxinia*	Gloxinia
Sison amomum	*Sison amome*	Stone parsley
Sisymbrium altissimum	*Sisymbre fausse-moutarde*	Tumbling mustard
Sisymbrium officinale	*Herbe aux chantres*	Hedge mustard
Sisyrinchium bermudianum	*Bermudienne*	Blue-eyed grass
Sisyrinchium californicum	*Sisyrinchium californicum*	Golden-eyed grass
Sisyrinchium douglasii	*Sisyrinchium douglasii*	Grass widow / Spring bell
Sium latifolium	*Berle à larges feuilles*	Greater water parsnip

Smilacina racemosa	*Smilacina racemosa*	False spikenard
Smithiantha cinnabarina	*Smithiantha cinnabarina*	Temple bells
Smyrnium olusatrum	*Maceron cultivé*	Alexanders
Solandra maxima	*Solandra maxima*	Capa de oro / Golden chalice tree
Solanum	*Pomme de terre*	Potato
Solanum dulcamara	*Douce-amère*	Bittersweet
Solanum jasminoides	*Solanum jasminoides*	Potato vine
Solanum nigrum	*Morelle noire*	Black nightshade
Solanum physalifolium	*Morelle verte*	Green nightshade
Solanum pseudocapsicum	*Cerisier d'amour / Cerisier de Jérusalem*	
		Jerusalem cherry
Solanum pseudocapsicum	*Orangier de savetier / Pommier d'amour*	
		Jerusalem cherry
Solanum rantonnetii	*Solanum rantonnetii*	Blue potato bush
Solanum seaforthianum	*Solanum seaforthianum*	Potato creeper
Soldanella	*Soldanelle*	Snowbell
Soldanella alpina	*Soldanelle des Alpes*	Alpine snowbell
Soldanella minima	*Soldanella minima*	Least snowbell
Soldanella montana	*Soldanelle des montagnes*	Mountain tassel
Soleirolia	*Soleirolia*	
	Baby's tears / Mind your own business / Mother of thousands	
Solidago canadensis	*Verge d'or du Canada*	Canadian golden-rod
Solidago virgaurea	*Verge d'or*	Golden-rod
Sonchus	*Laiteron*	Sow-thistle
Sonchus arvensis	*Laiteron des champs*	Corn sow-thistle
Sonchus asper	*Laiteron rude*	Prickly sow-thistle
Sonchus oleraceus	*Laiteron potager*	Smooth sow-thistle
Sonchus palustris	*Laiteron des marais*	Marsh sow-thistle
Sophora tetraptera	*Sophora*	Kowhai
Sophora japonica	*Arbre des pagodes*	Pagoda tree
Sophora japonica	*Sophora du Japon*	Pagoda tree
Sorbus aucuparia	*Sorbier des oiseleurs*	Mountain ash / Rowan
Sorbus alnifolia	*Sorbier à feuilles d'aune*	Korean mountain ash
Sorbus americana	*Sorbier d'Amérique*	American mountain ash
Sorbus aria	*Alisier blanc / Allier / Allouchier*	White beam
Sorbus domestca	*Cormier / Sorbier domestique*	Service tree
Sorbus hupehensis	*Sorbus hupehensis*	Hupeh rowan
Sorbus intermedia	*Sorbus intermedia*	Swedish whitebeam
Sorbus latifolia	*Alisier de Fontainebleau*	
	French hales / Service tree of Fontainebleau	
Sorbus sargentiana	*Sorbus sargentiana*	Sargent's rowan
Sorbus torminalis	*Alisier torminal*	Wild service tree

Sparaxis	*Sparaxis*	Harlequin flower
Sparganium	*Rubanier*	Bur reed
Sparganium angustifolium	*Rubanie à feuilles étroites*	Floating bur-reed
Sparganium erectum	*Rubanier dressé*	Branched bur reed
Sparganium minimum	*Rubanier nain*	Least bur-reed
Sparmannia africana	*Sparmannia africana*	African hemp
Spartium junceum	*Genêt d'Espagne*	Spanish broom
Spathiphyllum wallisii	*Spathiphyllum wallisii*	Peace lily / White sails
Spathodea campanulata	*Spathodea campanulata*	
		African tulip tree / Flame-of-the-forest
Spergularia bocconi	*Spergulaire bocconei*	Greek sand spurrey
Spergularia marina	*Spergulaire marine*	Sea spurrey
Spergularia media	*Spergulaire marginée*	Greater sea spurrey
Spergularia rubra	*Spergulaire rouge*	Sand spurrey
Spergularia rupicola	*Spergulaire des rochers*	Cliff spurry
Spiraea 'Arguta/	*Spirée x arguta*	Bridal wreath / Foam of May
Spiraea x vanhouttei	*Spirée x vanhouttei*	Bridal wreath
Spiranthes romanzoffiana	*Spiranthe d'Irlande*	American lady's tresses
Spiranthes spiralis	*Spiranthe contourné*	Autumn lady's tresses
Sprekelia formosissima	*Amaryllis croix Saint-Jacqes*	
		Aztec lily / Jacobean lily
Stachys alpina	*Épiaire des Alpes*	Limestone woundwort
Stachys arvensis	*Épiaire des champs*	Field woundwort
Stachys byzantina	*Stachys byzantina*	Bunnies' ears
Stachys byzantina	*Oreille de chat*	Lamb's tongue
Stachys germanica	*Épiaire d'Allemagne*	Downy woundwort
Stachys officinalis	*Bétoine*	Betony
Stachys palustris	*Épiaire des marais*	Marsh woundwort
Stachys sylvatica	*Épiaire des bois*	Hedge woundwort
Stapelia variegata	*Stapelia variegata*	Star flower
Staphylea	*Faux pistachier*	Bladder nut
Stellaria graminea	*Stellaire graminé*	Lesser stitchwort
Stellaria holostea	*Stellaire holostée*	Greater stitchwort
Stellaria media	*Mouron des oiseaux*	Common chickweed
Stellaria neglecta	*Stellaire négligé*	Greater chickweed
Stellaria nemorum	*Stellaire des bois*	Wood chickweed
Stellaria pallida	*Stellaire pâle*	Lesser chickweed
Stellaria palustris	*Stellaire des marais*	Marsh stitchwort
Stenocarpus sinuatu	*Stenocarpus sinuatu*	Australian firewheel tree
Stenotaphrium secundatum	*Stenotaphrium secundatum*	St. Augustine's grass
Stephanotis floribunda	*Stephanotis floribunda*	
		Madagascar jasmine / Wax flower

Stipa arundinacea	*Stipa arundinacea*	Pheasant grass
Stipa gigantea	*Stipa gigantea*	Golden oats
Stratiotes aloides	*Stratiote faux-aloès*	Water soldier
Strelitzia	*Oiseau de Paradis*	Bird-of-paradise flower
Streptocarpus rexii	*Streptocarpus rexii*	Cape primrose
Streptosolen jamesonii	*Streptosolen jamesonii*	Marmalade bush
Strongylodon macrobotrys	*Strongylodon macrobotrys*	Jade vine
Stylidium graminifolium	*Stylidium graminifolium*	Trigger plant
Styrax obassia	*Styrax obassia*	Fragrant snowbel
Suaeda maritima	*Soude maritime*	Common seablite
Subularia aquatica	*Subulaire aquatique*	Awlwort
Succisa pratensis	*Succise des prés*	Devil's bit scabious
Sutherlandia frutescens	*Baguenaudier d'Éthiopie*	Sutherlandia frutescens
Swainsonia galegifolia	*Swainsonia galegifolia*	Darling pea
Symphoricarpus albus	*Symphorine*	Snowberry
Symphoricarpos orbiculata	*Symphorine orbiculata*	Indian currant
Symphytum	*Consoude*	Comfrey
Symphytum asperum	*Consoude hérissée*	Prickly comfrey
Symphytum officinale	*Grande consoude*	Common comfrey
Symphytum orientale	*Consoude d'Orient*	Soft comfrey
Symphytum tuberosum	*Consoude à tubercules*	Tuberous comfrey
Symphytum x uplandicum	*Consoude de Russia*	Russian comfrey
Symplocarpus	*Symplocarpe*	Skunk cabbage
Symplocos paniculata	*Symplocos paniculata*	Sapphira berry
Synadenium grantii	*Synadenium grantii*	African milkbush
Syngonium auritum	*Syngonium auritum*	Five fingers
Syringa	*Lilas*	Lilac
Syringa x chinensis	*Lilas varin*	Rouen lilac
Syringa emodi	*Lilas de l'Himalaya*	Himalayan lilac
Syringa persica	*Lilas de Perse*	Persian lilac
Eugenia myrtifolia	*Myrte d'Australie*	Australian brush cherry

T

Tabebuia chrysotricha	*Tabebuia chrysotricha*	Golden trumpet tree
Tabebuia rosea	*Tabebuia rosea*	Pink trumpet
Tacca chantrieri	*Tacca chantrieri*	Bat flower
Tacca leontopetaloides	*Tacca leontopetaloides*	South sea arrowroot
Tagetes erecta	*Rose d'Inde*	African marigold / Aztec marigold
Tagetes patula	*Œillet d'Inde*	French marigold
Tamarindus indica	*Tamarin / Tamarinier*	Tamarind
Tamarix	*Tamaris*	Tamarisk

Tamarix gallica	*Tamaris de France*	Tamarisk
Tamus communis	*Tamier commun*	Black bryony
Tanacetum coccineum	*Pyrèrthre*	Pyrethrum
Tanacetum parthenium	*Grande camomille*	Feverfew
Tanacetum vulgare	*Tanaisie commune*	Tansy
Taraxacum officinale	*Dent de lion / Pissenlit*	Dandelion
Taxodium distichum	*Cyprès chauve / Cyprès chauve*	Swamp cypress
Taxus baccata	*If*	Yew
Taxus baccata fastigiata	*If d'Irlande*	Irish yew
Taxus cuspidata	*If du Japon*	Japanese yew
Tecoma stans	*Tecoma stans*	Yellow bells / Yellow elder
Tecomaria capensis	*Chèvrefeuille du Cap*	Cape honeysuckle
Tecophilaea cyanocrocus	*Crocus du Chili*	Chilean blue crocus
Teesdalia nudicaulis	*Teesdalie à tige nue*	Shepherd's cress
Telopea speciosissima	*Telopea speciosissima*	Waratah
Telopea truncata	*Telopea truncata*	Tasmanian waratah
Templetonia retusa	*Templetonia retusa*	Coral bush
Terminalia catappa	*Badamier*	Indian almond / Tropical almond
Tetragonolobus maritimus	*Tétragonolobe siliqueeux*	Dragon's teeth
Tetranema roseum	*Tetranema roseum*	Mexican foxglove / Mexican violet
Tetrapanax papyriferus	*Tetrapanax papyriferus*	Rice-paper plant
Tetrastigma voinerianum	*Tetrastigma voinerianum*	Chestnut vine
Teucrium chamaedrys	*Germandrée petit-chêne*	Wall germander
Teucrium fruticans	*Germandrée fruticans*	Shrubby germander / Tree germander
Teucrium scordium	*Germandrée scordium*	Water germander
Teucrium scorodonia	*Germandrée / Sauge des bois*	Wood-sage
Thalictrum alpinum	*Rue des prés*	Alpine meadow rue
Thalictrum flavum	*Pigamon jaune*	Common meadow-rue
Thalictrum minus	*Petit pigamon*	Lesser meadow rue
Thamnocalamus spathaceus	*Thamnocalamus spathaceus*	Muriel bamboo
Thelypteris hexagonoptera	*Thelypteris hexagonoptera*	Broad beech fern
Thelypteris oreopteris	*Thelypteris oreopteris*	Mountain wood fern / Mountain fern
Thelypteris palustirs	*Thelypteris palustirs*	Marsh buckler fern
Thesium humifusum	*Thésium couché*	Bastard toadflax
Thespesia populnea	*Thespesia populnea*	Mahoe / Portia oil nut
Thevetia peruviana	*Laurier rose à fleurs jaune*	Yellow oleander
Thlaspi alpinum	*Thlaspi des Alpes*	Alpine penny-cress
Thlaspi arvense	*Tabouret des champs*	Common penny-cress
Thalictrum flavum	*Pigamon jaune*	Meadow rue
Thuja koraiensis	*Thuya de Corée*	Korean thuja

Thuja occidentalis	*Thuja du Canada*	American arbor-vitae / Eastern white cedar
Thuja orientalis	*Thuya d'Orient*	Biota / Chinese arbor-vitae / Chinese thuja
Thuja plicata	*Thuja plicata*	Western red cedar
Thujopsis dolabrata	*Tujopsis dolabrata*	Hiba
Thunbergia grandiflora	*Thunbergia grandiflora*	Blue trumpet vine
Thymus	*Thym*	Thyme
Thymus herba-barona	*Thym herba-barona*	Caraway thyme
Tiarella	*Tiarella*	Foamflower
Tibouchina urvelleana	*Tibouchina urvelleana*	Glory bush
Tigridia pavonia	*Œil de paon / Tigride*	Peacock flower / Tiger flower
Tilia	*Tilleul*	Lime / Linden
Tilia americana	*Tilleul d'Amérique*	American lime / Basswood
Tilia cordata	*Tilleul à petites feuilles*	Small leaved lime
Tilia x euchlora	*Tilleul de Crimée*	Caucasian lime / Crimean lime
Tilia mongolica	*Tilleul à feuille de vigne / Tilleul de Mongolie*	Mongolian Lime
Tilia petiolaris	*Tilleul petiolaris*	Pendent silver lime
Tilia platyphyllos	*Tilleul à grandes feuilles*	Broad-leaved lime / Large leafed lime
Tilia platyphylos	*Tilleul de Hollande*	Large leafed lime
Tilia tomentosa	*Tilleul de Hongrie*	European white lime
Tilia tomentosa	*Tilleul argenté*	European white lime / Silver lime
Tillandsia ionantha	*Tillandsia ionantha*	Sky plant
Tillandsia lindenii	*Tillandsia lindenii*	Blue flowered torch
Tillandsia usneoides	*Barbe de vieillard / Fille de l'air*	Spanish moss
Tillandsia usneoides	*Mousse espagnole*	Spanish moss
Tipuana tipu	*Tipuana tipu*	Tipa tree / Pride of Bolivia
Tithonia rotundiflora	*Soleil de Californie*	Mexican sunflower
Tofieldia pusilla	*Tofieldie fluette*	Scottish asphodel
Tolmiea menziesii	*Tolmiea menziesii*	Pick-a-back plant / Youth and age
Tordylium maximum	*Tordyle majeur*	Hartwort
Torenia fournieri	*Torenia fournieri*	Wish-bone flower
Torilis arvensis	*Torilis des champs*	Spreading bur parsley
Torilis japonica	*Torilis faux-cherfeuil*	Hedge parsley
Torilis japonica	*Grattau*	Hedge parsley
Torilis nodosa	*Torilis à feuilles glomérulées*	Knotted bur parsley
Torreya californica	*Torreya californica*	California buckeye
Trachelium caeruleum	*Trachélie*	Throatwort
Trachelospermum jasminoides	*Jasmin étoilé*	Confederate jasmine / Star jasmine
Trachycarpus fortunei	*Palmier de Chine*	Chusan palm / Windmill palm
Trachymene caerulea	*Trachymene caerulea*	Blue lace flower

Trachystemon orientalis	*Trachystème d'Orient*	Abraham, Isaac & Jacob
Tradescantia	*Tradescantia*	Spiderwort
Tradescantia fluminensis	*Tradescantia fluminensis*	Wandering Jew
Tradescantia spathacea	*Tradescantia spathacea*	Boat lily
Tradescantia zebrina	*Misère*	Silver inch plant
Tragopogon porrifolius	*Salsifis cultivé*	Salsify
Tragopogon pratensis	*Barbe-du-bouc*	Goat's beard / Jack-go-to-bed-at-noon
Tragopogon pratensis	*Salsifis des prés*	Goat's beard / Jack-go-to-bed-at-noon
Trapa natans	*Châtaigne d'eau / Macre*	Jesuit's nut / Water Chestnut
Trichocereus spachianus	*Trichocereus spachianus*	Torch cactus
Trichosanthes anguina	*Patole / Serpent végétal*	Snake gourd
Tricyrtis	*Tricyrtis*	Toad lily
Trientalis europaea	*Trientalis d'Europe*	Chickweed willow-herb
Trifolium	*Trèfle*	Clover
Trifolium arvense	*Trèfle des champs*	Hare's foot clover
Trifolium campestre	*Trèfle jaune*	Hop trefoil
Trifolium dubium	*Trèfle douteux*	Common yellow trefoil
Trifolium fraggiferum	*Trèfle fraisier*	Strawberry clover
Trifolium glomeratum	*Trèfle aggloméré*	Clustered clover
Trifolium hybridum	*Trèfle hybride*	Alsike clover
Trifolium incarnatum	*Farouche / Trèfle incarnat*	Crimson clover
Trifolium medium	*Trèfle flexueux*	Zigzag clover
Trifolium ochroleucon	*Trèfle jaunâtre*	Sulphur clover
Trifolium pratense	*Trèfle des prés*	Red clover
Trifolium repens	*Trèfle blanc / Trèfle rampant*	White clover
Trifolium squamosum	*Trèfle maritime*	Sea clover
Trifolium striatum	*Trèfle strié*	Soft clover
Trifolium suffocatum	*Trèfle touffé*	Suffocated clover
Triglochin maritima	*Troscart maritime*	Sea arrow-grass
Triglochin palustris	*Troscart des marais*	Marsh arrow-grass
Trigoella foenum-graecum	*Fénugrec*	Fenugreek
Trillium	*Trillie*	Trinity flower / Wood lily
Trillium erectum	*Trillie erectum*	Birthroot / Squawroot
Trillium grandiflorum	*Trillie grandiflorum*	Wake-robin
Trillium nivale	*Trillie nivale*	Dwarf white wood lily / Snow trillium
Trillium sessile	*Trillie sessile*	Toadshade / Wake-robin
Trillium undulatum	*Trillie undulatum*	Painted trillium / Painted wood lily
Trinia glauca	*Trinia glauque*	Honewort
Tristania conferta	*Tristania conferta*	Brush-box tree
Trollius europaeus	*Boule d'or / Trolle*	Globe flower
Tropaeolum	*Capucine*	Nasturtium
Tropaeolum majus	*Grande capucine*	Garden nasturtium

Tropaeolum peregrinum *Capucine des Canaris*   Canary creeper
Tropaeolum speciosum *Capucine élégante*   Flame creeper / Flame nasturtium
Tsuga canadensis   *Pruche / Tsuga du Canada*   Canada hemlock /
                                                        Eastern hemlock
Tsuga caroliniana   *Tsuga de Caroline*   Carolina hemlock
Tsuga diversifolia *Tsuga de Japon*   Japanese hemlock / Northern Japanese hemlock
Tsuga heterophylla   *Tsuga de Californie*   Western hemlock
Tsuga mertensiana   *Tsuga mertensiana*   Mountain hemlock
Tsuga sieboldii *Tsuga de Japon*   Japanese hemlock / Southern Japanese hemlock
Tuberaria guttata   *Hélianthème à gouttes*   Annual rock-rose
Tulipa   *Tulipe*   Tulip
Tulipa acuminata   *Tulipe cornue / Tulipe turque*   Horned tulip
Tulipa clusiana   *Tulipe de l'Écluse / Tulipe radis*   Lady tulip
Tulipa kaufmaniana   *Tulipa kaufmaniana*   Water lily tulip
Tulipa sylvestris   *Tulipe sauvage*   Wild tulip
Tussilago farfara   *Pas-d' âne*   Coltsfoot
Tylecodon paniculata   *Tylecodon paniculata*   Butter tree
Tylecodon reticulata   *Tylecodon reticulata*   Barbed wire plant
Typha angustifolia   *Massette à feuilles étroites*   Lesser bulrush
Typha latifolia   *Massette à larges feuilles*   False bulrush

U

Ulex europaeus   *Ajonc d'Europe*   Gorse
Ulmus   *Orme*   Elm
Ulmus americana   *Orme d'Amérique*   American white elm / White elm
Ulmus americana   *Orme à larges feuilles*   American white elm / White elm
Ulmus angustifolia   *Orme angustifolia*   Goodyer's elm
Ulmus angustifoliua cornubiensis *Orme de Cornouaillea*   Cornish elm
Ulmus carpinifolia   *Orme à feuilles de charme*   Smooth-leaved elm
Ulmus dicksonii   *Orme doré*   Cornish golden elm / Dickson's golden elm
Ulmus glabra   *Orme blanc*   Wych elm
Ulmus glabra Exoniensis *Orme de montagne fastigié*   Exeter elm
Ulmus x Hollandica   *Orme x Hollandica*   Dutch elm
Ulmus parvifolia *Orme de Chine /Orme à petites feuilles*   Chinese elm
Ulmus procera *Grand orme / Orme d'Angleterre*   English elm / Common elm
Ulmus pumila   *Orme de Sibérie*   Siberian elm
Ulmus "Sarniensis"   *Orme de Jersey*   Jersey elm / Wheatley elm
Ulmus "Vegeta"   *Orme 'Vegeta'*   Huntingdon elm
Umbellularia californica *Laurier de Californie* Californian laurel / Headache tree
Umbilicus rupestris   *Ombilic*   Wall pennywort
Urginea maritima   *Urginea maritima*   Crusaders' spears / Sea onion / Sea onion

Urtica dioica	*Grande ortie*	Stinging nettle
Urtica urens	*Ortie brûlante*	Small nettle
Utricularia intermedia	*Utricularia intermedia*	Irish bladderwort
Utricularia minor	*Utriculaire fluette*	Small bladderwort
Utricularis vulgaris	*Utriculaire commune*	Greater bladderwort
Uvularia grandiflora	*Uvularia grandiflora*	Bellwort / Merry-bells

V

Vaccinium angustifolium laevigatum	*Brimbelle*	Low bush blueberry
Vaccineum arctastaphylos	*Vaccineum arctastaphylos*	Caucasian whortleberry
Vaccinium corymbosum	*Airelle à corymbes*	Highbush blueberry
Vaccinium myrtillus	*Airelle / Myrtille*	Bilberry
Vaccinium myrtillus	*Myrtillier commun*	Whortleberry
Vaccinium oxycoccus	*Canneberge*	Cranberry
Vaccinium uliginosum	*Airelle des marais*	Northern bilberry
Vaccinium vitis-idaea	*Airelle rouge / Vigne du Mont Ida*	Cowberry
Valeriana	*Valériane*	Valerian
Valeriana dioica	*Valériane dioïque*	Marsh valerian
Valeriana officinalis	*Herbe aux chats / Valériane officinalis*	Cat's valerian / Common valerian
Vallisneria spiralis	*Vallisnérie spiralée*	Eel grass / Tape grass
Valerianella locusta	*Mâche doucette*	Cornsalad
Veratrum album	*Vératre blanc*	White false hellebore
Veratrum nigrum	*Vératre noir*	Black false hellebore
Verbascum	*Molène*	Mullein
Verbascum blattaria	*Herbe aux mites / Molène blattaire*	Moth mullein
Verbascum lychnitis	*Molène lychnide*	White mullein
Verbascum nigrum	*Molène noire*	Dark mullein
Verbascum phlomoides	*Molène faux-phlomide*	Orange mullein
Verbascum pulverolentum	*Molène pulvérulente*	Hoary mullein
Verbascum thapsus	*Bonhomme / Bouillon blanc*	Common mullein
Verbascum virgatum	*Molène fausse-blattaire*	Large flowered mullein
Verbena officinalis	*Verveine*	Vervain
Verbena rigida	*Verveine veineuse / Verveine ruguese*	Verbena rigida
Veronica	*Vérronique*	Speedwell
Veronica agrestis	*Véronique agreste*	Green field speedwell
Veronica anagallis-aquatica	*Mouron aquatique*	Water speedwell
Veronica arvensis	*Véronique des champs*	Wall speedwell
Veronica beccabunga	*Cresson de cheval*	Brooklime
Veronica catenata	*Véronique aquatique*	Pink water speedwell
Veronica fruticans	*Véronique des rochers*	Rock speedwell
Veronica hederifolia	*Véronique à feuilles de lierre*	Ivy speedwell

Veronica peregrina	*Véronique voyageuse*	American speedwell
Veronica perfoliata	*Véronique perfoliata*	Digger speedwell
Veronica persica	*Véronique de Perse*	Common field speedwell
Veronica polita	*Véronique luisante*	Grey field speedwell
Veronica praecox	*Véronique précoce*	Breck speedwell
Veronica prostrata	*Véronique couchée*	Prostrate speedwell
Veronica scutellata	*Véronique à Écusson*	Marsh speedwell
Veronica spicata	*Véronique en épi*	Spiked speedwell
Veronica triphyllos	*Véronique digitée*	Fingered speedwell
Veronica verna	*Véronique printanière*	Spring speedwell
Viburnum acerifolium	*Viorne à feuilles d'érable*	Viburnum acerifolium
Viburnum lantana	*Viorne cotoneuse /Viorne manciennne*	
		Wayfaring tree / Sheepberry
Viburnum odoratissimum	*Viorne odorante*	Sweet viburnum
Viburnum opulus	*Viorne obier*	Guelder rose
Viburnum plicatum	*Boule-de-neige*	Japanese snowball tree
Viburnum tinus	*Laurier-tin*	Laurustinus
Vicia	*Vesce*	Vetch
Vicia bithynica	*Vesce de Bithynie*	Bithynian vetch
Vicia cracca	*Vesce cracca*	Tufted vetch
Vicia hirsuta	*Vesce hérissée*	Hairy tare
Vicia lathyroides	*Vesce printanière*	Spring vetch
Vicia lutea	*Vesce jaune*	Yellow vetch
Vicia orobus	*Vesce orobe*	Upright vetch
Vicia sativa	*Vesce cultivée*	Common vetch
Vicia sepium	*Vesce des haies*	Bush vetch
Vicia sylvatica	*Vesce des forêts*	Wood vetch
Vicia tetrasperma	*Vesce à quatre graines*	Smooth tare
Vigna caracalla	*Vigna caracalla*	Snail flower
Vinca	*Pervenche*	Periwinkle
Vinca major	*Grande pervenche*	Greater periwinkle / Quater
Vinca minor	*Petite pervenche*	Lesser periwinkle
Vinca rosea	*Pervenche de Madagascar*	Madagascar periwinkle
Viola	*Violette*	Violet
Viola arvensis	*Pensée des champs*	Field pansy
Viola biflora	*Violette à deux fleurs*	Twin flowered violet
Viola canina	*Violette des chiens*	Heath dog violet
Viola cornuta	*Viola cornuta*	Horned violet
Viola hederacea	*Viola hederacea*	Australian violet / Ivy-leafed violet
Viola hirta	*Violette hérissée*	Hairy violet
Viola lactea	*Violette lactée*	Pale heath violet
Viola lutea	*Pensée des vosgess*	Mountain pansy

Viola odorata	*Violette odorante*	Sweet violet
Viola palustris	*Violette des marais*	Marsh violet
Viola pedata	*Violette pied d'oiseau*	Bird's foot violet
Viola reichenbachiana	*Violette des bois*	Wood dog violet
Viola riviniana	*Violette de rivin*	Common dog violet
Viola tricolor	*Pensée sauvage*	Heartsease / Wild pansy
Viola wittrockliana	*Pensée*	Pansy
Viscum album	*Gui*	Mistletoe
Vitex agnus castus	*Agneau chaste / Arbre au poivre/ Gattillier commun*	Chastity bush / Monk's pepper
Vitis	*Vigne*	Vine
Vitis amurensis	*Vigne de l'Amour*	Amur grape
Vitis coignetiae	*Vitis coignetiae*	Crimson glory vine
Vitis vinifera	*Vigne vrai*	Grape vine
Vriesea hieroglyphica	*Vriesea hieroglyphica*	King of the bromeliads
Vriesea splendens	*Vriesea splendens*	Flaming sword

W

Wahlenbergia albomarginata	*Wahlenbergia albomarginata*	New Zealand bluebell
Wahlenbergia hederacea	*Wahlenbergie à feuilles de lierre*	Ivy-leafed bellfower
Washingtonia filifera	*Washingtonia filifera*	Desert fan palm
Washingtonia robusta	*Washingtonia robusta*	Thread palm
Westringia fruticosa	*Westringia fruticosa*	Australian rosemary / Australian sassafras
Wigginsia vorwerkiana	*Wigginsia vorwerkiana*	Colombian ball cactus
Wistaria	*Glycine*	Wisteria
Wisteria floribunda	*Glycine du Japon*	Japanese wisteria
Wisteria sinensis	*Glycine de Chine*	Chinese wisteria
Wisteria venusta	*Wisteria venusta*	Silky wisteria
Wolffia arrhiza	*Wolfie sans racine*	Least duckweed
Woodsia alpina	*Woodsia des Alpes*	Alpine woodsia
Woodsia ilvensis	*Woodsia ilvensis*	Rusty woodsia
Woodwardia radicans	*Woodwardie radicans*	Chain fern
Woodwardia virginica	*Woodwardia virginica*	American chain fern / Virginia chain fern
Worsleya	*Worsleya*	Blue amaryllis

X

Xanthium spinosum	*Lampourde épineuse*	Spiny cocklebur
Xanthorhiza simplicissima	*Xanthorhiza simplicissima*	Yellow-root
Xanthorrhoea	*Xanthorrhoé*	Grass tree
Xeranthemum annuum	*Immortelle annuelle / Xanthème*	Immortelle

Y

Yucca aloifolia	*Yucca aloifolia*	Spanish bayonet
Yucca filamentosa	*Yucca filamentosa*	Adam's needle
Yucca gloriosa	*Yucca gloriosa*	Spanish dagger

Z

Zannichellia palustris	*Zanichellie des marais*	Horned pondweed
Zantedeschia aeothiopica	*Arum de Éthiopie*	Arum Lily
Zantedeschia elliotiana	*Zantedeschia elliotiana*	Golden arum lily
Zanthoxylum piperitum	*Clavalier / Poivrier du Japon*	Japan pepper
Zea	*Maïs*	Indian corn / Maize
Zea mays	*Maïs*	Ornamental maize / Sweet corn
Zelkova carpinifolia	*Faux orme de Sibérie*	Caucasian elm
Zephyranthes	*Zephyranthes*	Rain lily
Zephyranthes atamasco	*Zephyranthes atamasco*	Atamasco lily
Zostera angustifolia	*Zostère à feuilles étroites*	Narrow-leaved eel-grass
Zostera marina	*Zostère marine*	Common eel-grass